TAILIB

Digest of United Kingdom Energy Statistics 2004

Production team: Mike

James Achur (Production editor)
Rebecca Martyn
David Smithers
Clive Sarjantson
and chapter authors

A National Statistics publication

London: TSO

Digest of United Kingdom Energy Statistics

Enquiries about statistics in this publication should be made to the contact named at the end of the relevant chapter. Brief extracts from this publication may be reproduced provided that the source is fully acknowledged. General enquiries about the publication, and proposals for reproduction of larger extracts, should be addressed to the Production Editor, James Achur, at the address given in paragraph XXVIII of the Introduction.

The Department of Trade and Industry reserves the right to revise or discontinue the text or any table contained in this Digest without prior notice.

About TSO's Standing Order Service

The Standing Order Service, open to all TSO account holders, allows customers to automatically receive the publications they require in a specified subject area, thereby saving them the time, trouble and expense of placing individual orders, also without handling charges normally incurred when placing ad-hoc orders.

Customers may choose from over 4,000 classifications arranged in 250 sub groups under 30 major subject areas. These classifications enable customers to choose from a wide variety of subjects, those publications that are of special interest to them. This is a particularly valuable service for the specialist library or research body. All publications will be dispatched immediately after publication date. A Standing Orders Handbook describing the service in detail and a complete list of classifications may be obtained on request. Write to TSO, Standing Order Department, PO Box 29, St Crispins, Duke Street, Norwich, NR3 1GN, quoting reference 12.01.013. Alternatively telephone 0870 600 5522 and select the Standing Order Department (option 2); fax us on 0870 600 5533; or finally e-mail us at book.standing.orders@tso.co.uk.

National Statistics

National Statistics are produced to high professional standards set out in the National Statistics Code of Practice. They undergo regular quality assurance reviews to ensure that they meet customer needs. They are produced free from any political interference.

You can find a range of National Statistics on the Internet – www.statistics.gov.uk

---

Contents

Monthly and quarterly data are also available for Energy, Solid fuels and derived gases, Petroleum, Gas and Electricity at:

www.dti.gov.uk/energy/inform/energy_stats/

Information on Energy Prices is available at:

www.dti.gov.uk/ energy/inform/energy_prices/index.shtml

A list of tables

Chapter 7   Renewable sources of energy

Annex A   Energy, commodity balances, calorific values and conversion factors

Introduction

I   This issue of the Digest of United Kingdom Energy Statistics continues a series which commenced with the Ministry of Fuel and Power Statistical Digest for the years 1948 and 1949, published in 1950. The Ministry of Fuel and Power Statistical Digest was previously published as a Command Paper, the first being that for the years 1938 to 1943, published in July 1944 (Cmd. 6538).

II   The current issue updates the figures given in the Department of Trade and Industry's *Digest of United Kingdom Energy Statistics 2003*, published in July 2003.

III   This printed and bound issue consists of seven chapters and four annexes. The first chapter deals with overall energy. The other chapters cover the specific fuels, combined heat and power and renewable sources of energy. The annexes cover calorific values and conversion factors, a glossary of terms, further sources of information and major events in the energy industries,

IV   This Digest is also available on the Internet. Some additional information appears on the Internet only. The tables provided on the Internet are provided in Microsoft Excel format. Most Internet versions of the tables include data for earlier years which are not provided in the printed copy publication. For example commodity and energy balances (see VII and VIII, below) for 1998, 1999 and 2000 are included on the Internet, and tables that show five years in this printed version show 8 years in their Internet form because page sizes are not a limiting factor. In addition, the following appear on the Internet version only:

   Long term trends text and tables
   Major events from 1990 to 2001 - Annex D
   (only Major events for 2002 to 2004 appear in the printed and bound version)
   Energy and the environment – Annex E
   UK oil and gas resources - Annex F
   Foreign Trade – Annex G

V   Annual information on prices is included in the publication *Quarterly Energy Prices*. This is available together with *Energy Trends* on subscription from the DTI. Further information on these publications can be found in Annex C.

VI   Where necessary, data have been converted or adjusted to provide consistent series, however, in some cases changes in methods of data collection have affected the continuity of the series. The presence of remaining discontinuities is indicated in the chapter text or in footnotes to the tables.

VII   Chapters 2, 3, 4, 5 and 7 contain production and consumption of individual fuels and are presented using *commodity balances*. A commodity balance illustrates the flows of an individual fuel through from production to final consumption, showing its use in transformation (including heat generation) and energy industry own use. Further details of commodity balances and their use are given in Annex A, paragraphs A.7 to A.42.

VIII   The individual commodity balances are combined in an *energy balance,* presented in Chapter 1, *Energy*. The energy balance differs from a commodity balance in that it shows the interactions between different fuels in addition to illustrating their consumption. The energy balance thus gives a fuller picture of the production, transformation and use of energy showing all the flows. Expenditure on energy is also presented in energy balance format in Chapter 1. Further details of the energy balance and its use, including the methodology introduced two years ago for heat, are given in Annex A, paragraphs A.43 to A.58.

IX   Chapter 1 also covers general energy statistics and includes tables showing energy consumption by final users and an analysis of energy consumption by main industrial groups. Fuel production and consumption statistics are derived mainly from the records of fuel producers and suppliers.

X   Chapters 6 and 7 summarise the results of surveys conducted by Future Energy Solutions (part of AEA Technology) on behalf of the Department of Trade and Industry. These chapters estimate the contribution made by combined heat and power (CHP) and renewable energy sources to energy production and consumption in the United Kingdom.

XI   Some of the data shown in this Digest may contain unpublished revisions and estimates of trade from additional sources.

Definitions

XII   The text at the beginning of each chapter explains the main features of the tables. Technical notes and definitions, given at the end of this text, provide detailed explanations of the figures in the tables and how they are derived. Explanations of the logic behind an energy balance and for commodity balances are given in Annex A.

XIII   Most chapters contain some information on 'oil' or 'petroleum'; these terms are used in a general sense and vary according to usage in the field examined. In their widest sense they are used to include all mineral oil and related hydrocarbons (except methane) and any derived products.

XIV   An explanation of the terms used to describe electricity generating companies is given in Chapter 5, paragraphs 5.47 to 5.48.

XV   Data in this issue have been prepared on the basis of the Standard Industrial Classification (SIC 2003) as far as is practicable. For further details of classification of consumers see Chapter 1, paragraphs 1.54 to 1.58.

XVI   Where appropriate, further explanations and qualifications are given in footnotes to the tables.

Methodological changes

XVII   In Chapter 7, Renewable sources of energy, the international definition of total renewables has been adopted for all years. This excludes non-biodegradable wastes. Wastes are still shown in the tables of this chapter but as "below the line" items.

Geographical coverage

XVIII   The geographical coverage of the statistics is the United Kingdom. Shipments to the Channel Islands and the Isle of Man from the United Kingdom are not classed as exports, and supplies of solid fuel and petroleum to these islands are therefore included as part of United Kingdom inland consumption or deliveries.

Periods

XIX   Data in this Digest are for calendar years or periods of 52 weeks, depending on the reporting procedures within the fuel industry concerned. Actual periods covered are given in the notes to the individual fuel sections.

Revisions

XX   The tables contain revisions to some of the previously published figures, and where practicable the revised data have been indicated by an 'r'. The 'r' marker is used whenever the figure has been revised from that published in the printed copy of the 2003 Digest, even though some figures may have been amended on the Internet version of the tables. Statistics on energy in this Digest are classified as National Statistics. This means that they are produced to the professional standards set out in the National Statistics Code of Practice and relevant protocols. The National Statistics protocol on revisions requires that "Each organisation responsible for producing National Statistics will publish and maintain a general statement describing its practice on revisions". The following statement outlines the policy on revisions for energy statistics.

Revisions to data published in the *Digest of UK Energy Statistics*.
It is intended that any revisions should be made to previous years' data only at the time of the publication of the Digest (ie in July 2004 when this Digest is published, revisions can be made to 2002 and earlier years). In exceptional circumstances previous years' data can be amended between Digest publication dates, but this will only take place when quarterly *Energy Trends* is published. The reasons for substantial revisions will be explained in the 'Highlights' sheet of the Internet version of the table concerned. Valid reasons for revisions of Digest data include:
- revised and validated data received from a data supplier;
- the figure in the Digest was wrong because of a typographical or similar error.

Revisions to current years data published in *Energy Trends* but not in the *Digest of UK Energy Statistics*.
- All validated amendments from data suppliers will be updated when received and published in the next statistical release.
- All errors will be amended as soon as identified and published in the next statistical release.
- Data in energy and commodity balances format will be revised on a quarterly basis, to coincide with the publication of *Energy Trends*.

Further details on National Statistics Code of Practice and related protocols can be found at: www.statistics.gov.uk/about_ns/cop/default.asp

Energy data on the Internet
XXI   Energy data are held on the energy area of the DTI web site, under "information and statistics". The Digest is available at www.dti.gov.uk/energy/inform/dukes/ . Information on further DTI energy publications as in both printed copy and on the Internet is given in Annex C. The DTI web site is currently being redeveloped and the new site is expected to be available in the autumn. As a result the DTI web addresses used for the site in this publication may fail but mechanisms will be put in place to help customers locate the information they require.

XXII   Short term statistics are published:

- monthly, by the DTI on the Internet at www.dti.gov.uk/energy/inform/energy_stats/ .
- quarterly, by the DTI in paper and on the Internet in *Energy Trends,* and *Quarterly Energy Prices*: www.dti.gov.uk/energy/inform/energy_stats/ .

- quarterly, by the DTI in Statistical Press Release which provides a summary of information published in *Energy Trends* and *Quarterly Energy Prices* publications: www.gnn.gov.uk/gnn/national.nsf/TI/ .

- monthly, by the Office for National Statistics in the *Monthly Digest of Statistics (The Stationery Office)*.

To subscribe to *Energy Trends* and *Quarterly Energy Prices,* please contact Clive Sarjantson at the address given at paragraph XXVIII. Single copies available from the DTI Publications Orderline, as given in Annex C, priced £5 for Energy Trends and £7 for Quarterly Energy Prices.

Table numbering
XXIII   Page 10 contains a list showing the tables in the order in which they appear in this issue, and their corresponding numbers in previous issues.

Symbols used
XXIV   The following symbols are used in this Digest:

..	not available
-	nil or negligible (less than half the final digit shown)
r	Revised since the previous edition

Rounding convention

XXV   Individual entries in the tables are rounded independently and this can result in totals which are different from the sum of their constituent items.

Acknowledgements

XXVI   Acknowledgement is made to the main coal producing companies, the electricity companies, the oil companies, the gas pipeline operators, the gas suppliers, Transco, the Institute of Petroleum, the Coal Authority, the United Kingdom Iron and Steel Statistics Bureau, the National Environmental Technology Centre, Future Energy Solutions, the Department for Environment, Food and Rural Affairs, the Department for Transport, OFGEM, Building Research Establishment, HM Customs and Excise, the Office for National Statistics, and other contributors to the enquiries used in producing this publication.

Cover photograph

XXVII   The cover illustration used for this Digest and other 2004-2005 DTI energy statistics publications is from a photograph by Peter Askew. It was a winning entry in the DTI News Photographic Competition in 2002.

Contacts

XXVIII For general enquiries on energy statistics contact:

Clive Sarjantson on 020-7215 2698,   James Achur on 020-7215 2717
(E-mail:clive.sarjantson@dti.gsi.gov.uk)   **or**   (E-mail: james.achur@dti.gsi.gov.uk)

Department of Trade and Industry
Bay 232
1 Victoria Street
London SW1H 0ET
Fax: 020-7215 2723

Enquirers with hearing difficulties can contact the Department on the DTI Textphone: 020-7215 6740.

XXIX   For enquiries concerning particular data series or chapters contact those named on page 9 or at the end of the relevant chapter.

James Achur, Production Editor
July 2004

Contact List

The following people in the Department of Trade and Industry may be contacted for further information about the topics listed:

Chapter	Contact	Telephone 020 7215	E-mail
Total energy statistics	Julian Prime	6178	Julian.Prime@dti.gsi.gov.uk
Solid fuels and derived gases	Mike Janes	5186	Mike.Janes@dti.gsi.gov.uk
	James Achur	2717	James.Achur@dti.gsi.gov.uk
Oil and upstream gas resources	Clive Evans	5189	Clive.Evans@dti.gsi.gov.uk
	Martin Young	5184	Martin.Young@dti.gsi.gov.uk
North Sea profits, operating costs and investments	Suhail Siddiqui	5262	Suhail.Siddiqui@dti.gsi.gov.uk
	Philip Beckett	5260	Philip.Beckett@dti.gsi.gov.uk
Petroleum (downstream)	Ian Corrie	2714	Ian.Corrie@dti.gsi.gov.uk
	Martin Young	5184	Martin.Young@dti.gsi.gov.uk
Gas supply (downstream)	Mike Janes	5186	Mike.Janes@dti.gsi.gov.uk
	John Castle	2718	John.Castle@dti.gsi.gov.uk
Electricity	Mike Janes	5186	Mike.Janes@dti.gsi.gov.uk
	Joe Ewins	5190	Joe.Ewins@dti.gsi.gov.uk
Combined heat and power	Mike Janes	5186	Mike.Janes@dti.gsi.gov.uk
Prices and values Industrial, international and oil prices	Peter Matejic	2720	Peter.Matejic@dti.gsi.gov.uk
	Sara Atkins	6532	Sara.Atkins@dti.gsi.gov.uk
Renewable sources of energy	Mike Janes	5186	Mike.Janes@dti.gsi.gov.uk
Calorific values and conversion factors	Julian Prime	6178	Julian.Prime@dti.gsi.gov.uk
	Martin Young	5184	Martin.Young@dti.gsi.gov.uk
General enquiries (energy helpdesk)	Clive Sarjantson	2698	Clive.Sarjantson@dti.gsi.gov.uk

All the above can be contacted by fax on 020 7215 2723

Tables as they appear in this issue and their corresponding numbers in the previous three issues (1)

Chapter	2001	2002	2003	2004
ENERGY	-	-	-	1.1
	-	-	1.1	1.2
	-	1.1	1.2	1.3
	1.1	1.2	1.3	-
	1.2	1.3	-	-
	1.3	-	-	-
	-	-	-	1.4
	-	-	1.4	1.5
	-	1.4	1.5	1.6
	1.4	1.5	1.6	-
	1.5	1.6	-	-
	1.6	-	-	-
	1.8	1.8	1.8	1.8
	1.9	1.9	1.9	1.9
	1.10	1.1.1	1.1.1	1.1.1
	1.11	1.1.2	1.1.2	1.1.2
	1.12	1.1.3	1.1.3	1.1.3
	1.13	1.1.4	1.1.4	1.1.4
	1.14	1.1.5	1.1.5	1.1.5
	1.15	1.1.6	1.1.6	1.1.6
	1.16	1.1.7	1.1.7	1.1.7
	1.17	1.1.8	1.1.8	1.1.8
	1.7	1.7	1.7	1.7
	-	-	-	2.1
SOLID FUELS & DERIVED GASES	-	-	2.1	2.2
	-	2.1	2.2	2.3
	2.1	2.2	2.3	-
	2.2	2.3	-	-
	2.3	-	-	-
	-	-	-	2.4
	-	-	2.4	2.5
	-	2.4	2.5	2.6
	2.4	2.5	2.6	-
	2.5	2.6	-	-
	2.6	-	-	-
	2.7	2.7	2.7	2.7
	2.8	2.8	2.8	2.8
	2.9	2.9	2.9	2.9
	2.12	2.10	2.10	2.10
	2.13	2.11	2.11	2.11
	2.10	2.1.1	2.1.1	2.1.1
	2.11	2.1.2	2.1.2	2.1.2
	-	-	-	3.1
PETROLEUM	-	-	3.1	3.2
	-	3.1	3.2	3.3
	3.1	3.2	3.3	-
	3.2	3.3	-	-
	3.3	-	-	-
	-	-	-	3.4
	-	-	3.4	3.5
	-	3.4	3.5	3.6
	3.4	3.5	3.6	-
	3.5	3.6	-	-
	3.6	-	-	-
	-	-	-	-
	3.7	3.7	3.7	3.7
	-	-	-	-
	3.8	3.8	3.8	3.8
	3.9	3.9	3.9	3.9
	3.10	3.10	3.10	3.10
	3.11	3.1.1	3.1.1	3.1.1
	3.12	3.1.2	3.1.2	3.1.2

Chapter	2001	2002	2003	2004
NATURAL GAS	4.1	4.1	4.1	4.1
	4.2	4.2	4.2	4.2
	4.3	4.3	4.3	4.3
	4.4	4.1.1	4.1.1	4.1.1
	-	-	-	-
ELECTRICITY	5.1	5.1	5.1	5.1
	5.4	5.4	5.4	5.4
	5.2	5.2	5.2	5.2
	5.6	5.6	5.6	5.6
	5.3	5.3	5.3	5.3
	5.5	5.5	5.5	5.5
	5.7	5.7	5.7	5.7
	-	-	-	5.8
	5.8	5.8	5.8	5.9
	5.9	5.9	5.9	5.10
	5.10	5.1.1	5.1.1	5.1.1
	5.11	5.1.2	5.1.2	5.1.2
	5.12	5.1.3	5.1.3	5.1.3
	5.13	5.10	5.10	5.11
	-	-	-	-
COMBINED HEAT AND POWER	6.1	6.1	6.1	6.1
	6.2	6.2	6.2	6.2
	6.3	6.3	6.3	6.3
	6.4	6.4	6.4	6.4
	6.5	6.5	6.5	6.5
	6.6	6.6	6.6	6.6
	6.7	6.7	6.7	6.7
	6.8	6.8	6.8	6.8
	6.9	6.9	6.9	6.9
RENEWABLE SOURCES	-	-	-	7.1
	-	-	7.1	7.2
	-	7.1	7.2	7.3
	7.1	7.2	7.3	-
	7.2	7.3	-	-
	7.3	-	-	-
	7.4	7.4	7.4	7.4
	7.5	7.5	7.5	7.5
	7.6	7.6/7.1.1	7.6/7.1.1	7.6/7.1.1
ANNEX A CALORIFIC VALUES	A.1	A.1	A.1	A.1
	A.2	A.2	A.2	A.2

(1) Table numbers highlighted in blue appear on the DTI energy statisics web site only:
www.dti.gov.uk/energy/inform/energy_stats/

Chapter 1
Energy

Introduction

1.1   This chapter presents figures on overall energy production and consumption. Figures showing the flow of energy from production, transformation and energy industry use through to final consumption are presented in the format of an energy balance based on the individual commodity balances presented in Chapters 2 to 5 and 7.

1.2   The chapter begins with aggregate energy balances covering the last three years (Tables 1.1 to 1.3) starting with the latest year, 2003. Energy value balances then follow this for the same years (Tables 1.4 to 1.6) and Table 1.7 shows sales of electricity and gas by sector. Table 1.8 covers final energy consumption by the main industrial sectors over the last five years followed by Table 1.9, which shows the fuels used for electricity generation by these industrial sectors. The explanation of the principles behind the energy balance and commodity balance presentations is set out in Annex A. Long term trends commentary and Tables (1.1.1 to 1.1.8) for energy production, consumption and expenditure on energy, temperatures as well as analyses such as the relationship between energy consumption and the economy of the UK appear on DTI's energy statistics web site only at:

www.dti.gov.uk/energy/inform/dukes/dukes2004/01longterm.pdf

1.3   The amount of energy transformed into and sold for consumption as heat has been included in the annual energy balances since 1999. An explanation of the methodology that was used to derive the figures can be found in paragraph 1.33.

The energy industries

1.4   The energy industries in the UK play a central role in the economy by producing, transforming and supplying energy in its various forms to all sectors. They are also major contributors to the UK's Balance of Payments through the exports of crude oil and oil products. The box below summarises the energy industries' contribution to the economy:

- 3.3 per cent of GDP;

- 6.9 per cent of total investment;

- 34.1 per cent of industrial investment;

- 164,000 people directly employed (5 per cent of industrial employment);

- Many others indirectly employed (eg an estimated 320,000 in support of UK Continental Shelf activities);

- Trade surplus in fuels of £5.4 billion.

Aggregate energy balance (Tables 1.1, 1.2 and 1.3)

1.5   These tables show the flows of energy in the United Kingdom from production to final consumption through conversion into secondary fuels such as coke, petroleum products, secondary electricity and heat sold. The principles behind the presentation used in the Digest and how this links with the figures presented in other chapters are explained in Annex A. The figures are presented on an energy supplied basis, in tonnes of oil equivalent.

1.6   In 2003, the primary supply of fuels was 244.8 million tonnes of oil equivalent, a 1½ per cent increase compared to 2002. Indigenous production in 2003 was 4½ per cent lower than in 2002. Chart 1.1 illustrates the figures for the production and consumption of individual primary fuels in 2003. In 2003, as in the previous 10 years, overall primary fuel consumption was fully met by indigenous production, with the trade balances for petroleum and its products and gas offsetting net imports of coal, manufactured fuels and electricity.

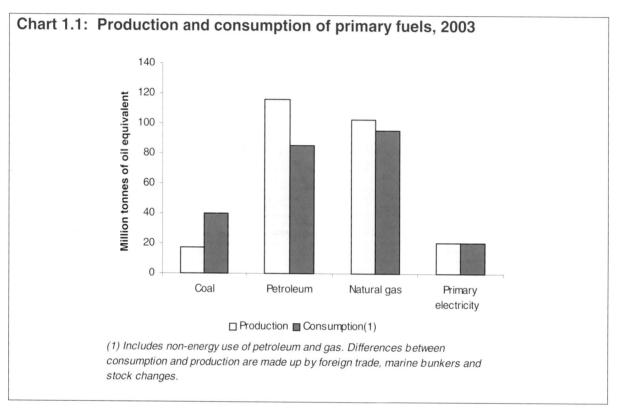

Chart 1.1: Production and consumption of primary fuels, 2003

□ Production ■ Consumption(1)

(1) Includes non-energy use of petroleum and gas. Differences between consumption and production are made up by foreign trade, marine bunkers and stock changes.

1.7   Total primary energy demand was 1½ per cent higher in 2003 than in 2002 at 245.1 million tonnes of oil equivalent. Chart 1.2 shows the composition of primary demand in 2003.

1.8   The transfers row in Tables 1.1 to 1.3 should ideally sum to zero with transfers from primary oils to petroleum products amounting to a net figure of zero. Similarly the manufactured gases and natural gas transfers should sum to zero.

1.9   The transformation section of the energy balance shows, for each fuel, the net inputs for transformation uses. For example, on Table 1.1, 4,293 thousand tonnes of oil equivalent of coal and 2 thousand tonnes of oil equivalent of petroleum products feeds into the production of 4,214 thousand tonnes of oil equivalent of coke, representing a loss of 80 thousand tonnes of oil equivalent in the manufacture of coke in 2003. In 2003, energy losses during the production of electricity and other secondary fuels amounted to 54,493 thousand tonnes of oil equivalent, shown in the transformation row in Table 1.1.

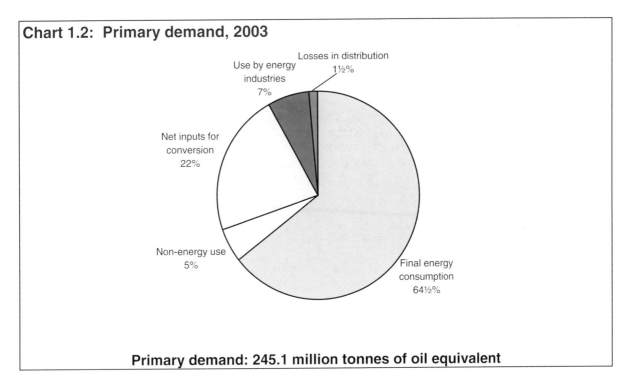

Chart 1.2: Primary demand, 2003

Losses in distribution 1½%

Use by energy industries 7%

Net inputs for conversion 22%

Non-energy use 5%

Final energy consumption 64½%

Primary demand: 245.1 million tonnes of oil equivalent

1.10   The next section of the table represents use of fuels by the energy industries themselves. This section also includes consumption by those parts of the iron and steel industry which behave like an energy industry ie are involved in transformation processes (see paragraph A.29 of Annex A). In 2003, energy industry use amounted to 16,834 thousand tonnes of oil equivalent of energy, a decrease of 1½ per cent on 2002 but a 1 per cent increase on 2001.

1.11   Losses presented in the energy balance include distribution and transmission losses in the supply of manufactured gases, natural gas, and electricity. Recorded losses fell between 2002 and 2003, which follows the trend of reducing loses since 2000. Losses in North Sea production of gas are no longer separately identified in a simplified Petroleum Product Reporting System which was introduced in January 2001 and has improved the quality of production data and reduced reported losses. Further details can be found in paragraph 4.30 in Chapter 4.

1.12   Total final consumption, which includes non-energy use of fuels, in 2003 was 170,381 thousand tonnes of oil equivalent, a 1 per cent increase on 2002, but still 1 per cent lower than in 2001. Final energy consumption in 2003 was mainly accounted for by the transport sector (33 per cent), the domestic sector (28 per cent), the industrial sector (20½ per cent), the commercial sector (6 per cent) and non-energy use (7½ per cent). These figures are illustrated in Chart 1.3. Recent trends in industrial consumption are shown in Table 1.8 and discussed in paragraphs 1.20 to 1.22.

1.13   The main fuels used by final consumers in 2003 were petroleum products (46½ per cent), natural gas (34 per cent) and electricity (17 per cent). Of the petroleum products consumed by final users 14½ per cent was for non-energy purposes; for natural gas 1½ per cent was consumed for non-energy purposes. The amount of heat that was bought for final consumption accounted for 1 per cent of the total.

1.14   Non-energy use of fuels includes use as chemical feedstocks and other uses such as lubricants. Non-energy use of fuels for 2003 are shown in Table 1A. Further details of non-energy use are given in Chapter 3, paragraphs 3.57 to 3.63 and Chapter 4, paragraphs 4.17.

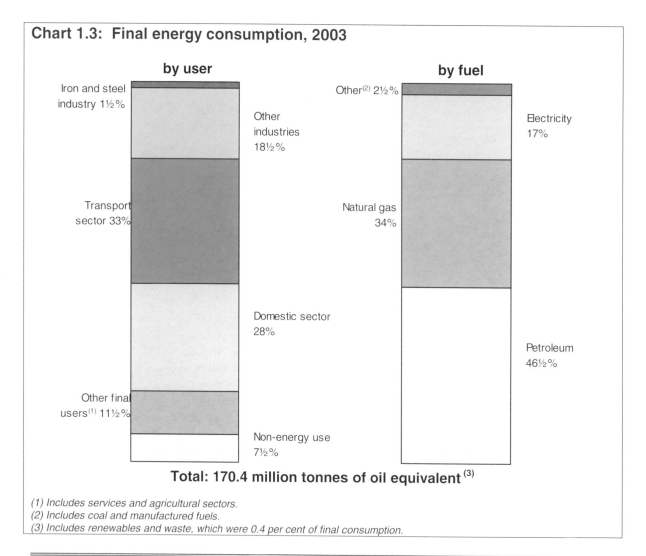

Chart 1.3: Final energy consumption, 2003

by user

Iron and steel industry 1½%

Other industries 18½%

Transport sector 33%

Domestic sector 28%

Other final users(1) 11½%

Non-energy use 7½%

by fuel

Other(2) 2½%

Electricity 17%

Natural gas 34%

Petroleum 46½%

Total: 170.4 million tonnes of oil equivalent (3)

(1) Includes services and agricultural sectors.
(2) Includes coal and manufactured fuels.
(3) Includes renewables and waste, which were 0.4 per cent of final consumption.

Table 1A: Non-energy use of fuels 2003

	Thousand tonnes of oil equivalent	
	Petroleum	Natural gas
Petrochemical feedstocks	6,730	917
Other	4,735	-
Total	**11,465**	**917**

Value balance of traded energy (Tables 1.4, 1.5 and 1.6)

1.15   Tables 1.4 to 1.6 present the value of traded energy in a similar format to the energy balances. The balance shows how the value of inland energy supply is made up from the value of indigenous production, trade, tax and margins (profit and distribution costs). The lower half of the table then shows how this value is generated from the final expenditure on energy through transformation processes and other energy sector users as well as from the industrial and domestic sectors. The balances only contain values of energy which is traded ie where a transparent market price is applicable. Further technical notes are given in paragraphs 1.24 to 1.59. In keeping with the energy balances, the value balances for 1999 onwards include data on heat generation and heat sold. Additionally, an estimate of the amount of Climate Change Levy paid is included in Tables 1.4, 1.5 and 1.6. This levy was introduced in April 2001 and is payable by non-domestic final consumers of gas, electricity, coal, coke and LPG.

1.16   Total expenditure by final consumers in 2003 is estimated at £64,490 million, (£64,270 million shown as actual final consumption and £195 million of coal consumed by the iron and steel sector in producing coke for their own consumption).

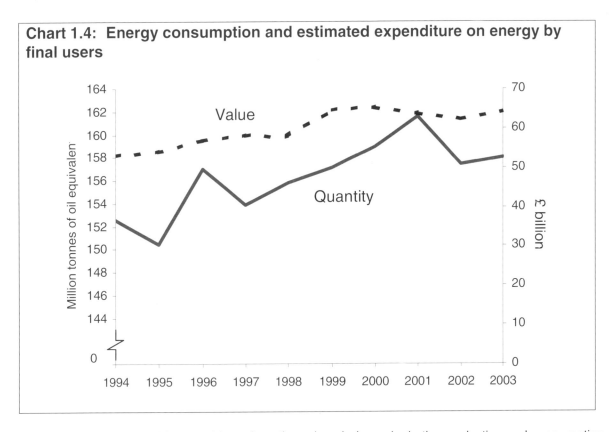

Chart 1.4: Energy consumption and estimated expenditure on energy by final users

1.17   This balance provides a guide on how the value chain works in the production and consumption of energy. For example in 2003, £14,315 million of crude oil were indigenously produced, of which £9,820 million were exported, and £6,495 million of crude oil were imported. Allowing for stock changes this provides a total value of inland crude oil supply of £11,055 million. This fuel was then completely consumed within the petroleum industry in the process of producing £15,645 million of petroleum products. Again some external trade and stock changes took place before arriving at a basic value of petroleum products of £14,000 million. In supplying the fuel to final consumers distribution costs were incurred and some profit was made amounting to £2,350 million, whilst duty and tax meant a further £25,990 million was added to the basic price to arrive at the final market value of £42,340 million. This was the value of petroleum products purchased of which industry purchased £1,425 million, domestic consumers for heating purposes purchased £705 million, with the vast majority purchased within the transportation sectors, £37,900 million.

1.18   Of the total final expenditure on energy in 2003 (£64,490 million) the biggest share, 59 per cent fell to the transport sector. Of the remaining 41 per cent, industry purchased around a quarter or £6,130 million, with the domestic sector purchasing over a half or £14,940 million.

Sales of electricity and gas by sector (Table 1.7)

1.19   Table 1.7 shows broad estimates for the total value of electricity and gas to final consumption. Net selling values provide some indication of typical prices paid in broad sectors and can be of use to supplement more detailed and accurate information contained in the rest of this chapter.

Energy consumption by main industrial groups (Table 1.8)

1.20   This table presents final energy consumption for the main industrial sub-sectors over the last 5 years.

1.21   So far as is practicable, the user categories have been grouped on the basis of the 2003 Standard Industrial Classification (see paragraphs 1.54 to 1.58). However, some data suppliers have difficulty in classifying consumers to this level of detail and the breakdown presented in these tables must therefore be treated with caution. The groupings used are consistent with those used in Table 1.9 which show industrial sectors' use of fuels for generation of electricity (autogeneration).

1.22   In 2003, 34.6 million tonnes of oil equivalent were consumed by the main industrial groups. The largest consuming groups were chemicals (20½ per cent), iron and steel and non-ferrous metals (12 per cent), metal products, machinery and equipment (12½ per cent), food, beverages and tobacco (11 per cent), and paper, printing and publishing (7½ per cent). The remaining groups accounted for 36½ per cent of total final energy consumption by industry. The figures are illustrated in Chart 1.5.

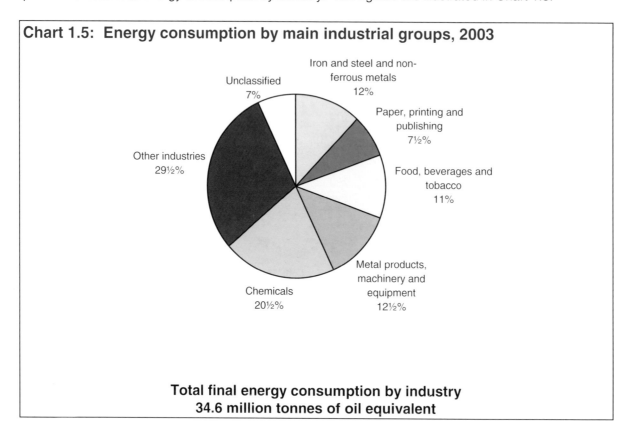

Chart 1.5: Energy consumption by main industrial groups, 2003

Iron and steel and non-ferrous metals
12%

Unclassified
7%

Paper, printing and publishing
7½%

Other industries
29½%

Food, beverages and tobacco
11%

Metal products, machinery and equipment
12½%

Chemicals
20½%

**Total final energy consumption by industry
34.6 million tonnes of oil equivalent**

Fuels consumed for electricity generation by main industrial groups (autogeneration) (Table 1.9)

1.23   This table gives details of the amount of each fuel consumed by industries in order to generate electricity for their own use. Fuel consumption is consistent with the figures given for "other generators" in Table 5.4 of Chapter 5. The term autogeneration is explained further in paragraphs 1.29 and 1.30. Electricity produced via autogeneration is included within the figures for electricity consumed by industrial sectors in Table 1.8. Table 1.9 has been produced using the information currently available and shows the same sector detail as Table 1.8, data cannot be given in as much detail as in the individual commodity balances and the energy balance because it could disclose information about individual companies. Table 1.9 allows users to allocate the fuel used for autogeneration to individual industry groups in place of the electricity consumed. Further information on the way Table 1.9 links with the other tables is given in paragraph 1.30.

Technical notes and definitions

I Units and measurement of energy

Units of measurement
1.24 The original units of measurement appropriate to each fuel are used in the individual fuel chapters. A common unit of measurement, the tonne of oil equivalent (toe), which enables different fuels to be compared and aggregated, is used in Chapter 1. For consistency with the International Energy Agency and with the Statistical Office of the European Communities, the tonne of oil equivalent is defined as follows:

1 tonne of oil equivalent $= 10^7$ kilocalories
$= 396.83$ therms
$= 41.868$ Gigajoules (GJ)
$= 11,630$ kWh

1.25 This unit should be regarded as a measure of energy content rather than a physical quantity. There is no intention to represent an actual physical tonne of oil, and indeed actual tonnes of oil will normally have measurements in tonnes of oil equivalent which differ from unity.

Thermal content - energy supplied basis of measurement
1.26 Tables 1.1 to 1.3, 1.8 and 1.1.1 to 1.1.5 (available on DTI's energy statistics site at www.dti.gov.uk/energy/inform/energy_stats/total_energy/) are compiled on an energy-supplied basis. Detailed data for individual fuels are converted from original units to tonnes of oil equivalent using gross calorific values and conversion factors appropriate to each category of fuel. The results are then aggregated according to the categories used in the tables. Gross calorific values represent the total energy content of the fuel, including the energy needed to evaporate the water present in the fuel (see also paragraph 1.52).

1.27 Estimated gross calorific values for 2003 are given on page 198. Calorific values are reviewed each year in collaboration with the fuel industries, and figures for earlier years can be found in Table A.2 on page 199. To construct energy balances on an energy supplied basis calorific values are required for production, trade, and stocks, as follows:

Coal The weighted average gross calorific value of all indigenous coal consumed is used to derive the thermal content of coal production and undistributed stocks. Thermal contents of imports and exports allow for the quality of coal. Thermal contents of changes in coal stocks at secondary fuel producers are the average calorific values of indigenous coal consumed.

Petroleum Work was carried out in 1997 to revise calorific values for petroleum products. It has not been possible to find any recent work on the subject.   In the absence of such work, the gross calorific values, included in Annex A, and used in the construction of these energy balances from 1990 onwards have been calculated using a formula derived by the US Bureau of Standards. This formula estimates the gross calorific value of products according to their density as follows:

$Gj = 51.83 - 8.78 \times d^2$, where d is the density of the product in terms of kilograms per litre.

For crude petroleum and refinery losses, the weighted average calorific value for all petroleum products from UK refineries is used. A notional figure of 42.7 GJ per tonne is used for non-energy petroleum products (industrial and white spirits, lubricants, bitumen, petroleum coke, waxes and miscellaneous products).

Gases Although the original unit for gases is the cubic metre, figures for gases are generally presented in the fuel sections of this Digest in gigawatt hours (GWh), having been converted from cubic metres using gross calorific values provided by the industries concerned. Conversion factors between units of energy are given on the flap inside the back cover.

Electricity and heat Unlike other fuels, the original unit used to measure electricity and heat is a measure of energy. The figures for electricity and heat can therefore be converted directly to toe using the conversion factors on the flap inside the back cover.

Primary electricity Hydro electricity and net imports of electricity are presented in terms of the energy content of the electricity produced (the energy supplied basis). This is consistent with international practice. Primary inputs for nuclear electricity assume the thermal efficiencies at nuclear stations given in Chapter 5, Table 5.10 (38 per cent in 2003). (See Chapter 5, paragraphs 5.25 and 5.55.)

Non-energy uses of fuel

1.28 Energy use of fuel mainly comprises use for lighting, heating, motive power and power for appliances. Non-energy use includes use as chemical feedstocks, solvents, lubricants and road making material. It should be noted that the estimated amounts of non-energy use of natural gas included in the Digest are very approximate. Non-energy uses of petroleum and gas are included in the figures for final energy consumption following the move over to the presentation of energy data in the format of commodity and energy balances. Further discussion of non-energy uses of lubricating oils and petroleum coke appears in Chapter 3, paragraphs 3.57 to 3.63.

Autogeneration of electricity

1.29 Autogeneration is defined as the generation of electricity by companies whose main business is not electricity generation, the electricity being produced mainly for that company's own use. Estimated amounts of fuel used for thermal generation of electricity by such companies, the output of electricity and the thermal losses incurred in generation are included within the Transformation sector in the energy balances shown in Tables 1.1 to 1.3. Electricity used in the power generation process by autogenerators is shown within the Energy Industry Use section. Electricity consumed by industry and commerce from its own generation is included as part of Final consumption. This treatment is in line with the practice in international energy statistics.

1.30 Figures on total amount of fuel used and electricity generated by autogenerators, and the amount of electricity for own consumption is shown in Tables 1.9, 5.1, 5.3 to 5.6. Table 1.9 summarises the figures by broad industrial groups. Much of the power generated is from combined heat and power (CHP) plants and data from Chapter 6 are included within Table 1.9. Differences will occur where CHP plants are classified to major power producers, and this mainly affects the chemicals sector. The method of allocating fuel used in CHP plants between electricity production and heat production is described in Chapter 6 paragraphs 6.35 to 6.37. This method can give rise to high implied conversion efficiencies in some sectors, most notably in the iron and steel sector.

Final consumption, deliveries, stock changes

1.31 Figures for final consumption relate to deliveries, if fuels can be stored by users and data on actual consumption are not available. Final consumption of petroleum and solid fuels is on deliveries basis throughout, except for the use of solid fuels by the iron and steel industry. Figures for domestic use of coal are based on deliveries to merchants. Figures for stock changes in Tables 1.1 to 1.3 cover stocks held by primary and secondary fuel producers, major distributors of petroleum products, and stocks of coke and breeze held by the iron and steel industry. Figures for stock changes in natural gas represent the net amount put into storage by gas companies operating pipelines.

1.32 Figures for final consumption of electricity include sales by the public distribution system and consumption of electricity produced by generators other than the major electricity producing companies. Thus electricity consumption includes that produced by industry and figures for deliveries of other fuels to industry exclude amounts used to generate electricity (except for years prior to 1987).

Heat sold

1.33 Heat sold is defined as heat that is produced and sold under the provision of a contract. The heat sold figures have been derived from two sources covering CHP plants and community heating schemes without CHP plants. Data for heat sold were supplied by CHP plants to the Combined Heat and Power Quality Assurance Programme and were processed by Future Energy Solutions (part of AEA Technology Environment). Data for heat consumption from community heating schemes were derived from the Building Research Establishment's (BRE) 'Nationwide Survey of Community Heating' that was carried out in 1997, a database of community heating schemes in social housing in 2000, and a Community Heating Sales Survey undertaken in early 2003 and repeated in 2004. The estimates from these sources have been used to derive heat sold figures since 1999. When information about where the heat was generated was not available from the BRE sources, it was assumed that domestic sector heat consumption was provided by the commercial sector, public sector heat consumption was provided by the public administration and industrial sectors (using proportions derived from CHP statistics) and that industrial sector heat consumption was provided by the industrial sector. The introduction of heat sold into the energy balances has not affected the individual fuel totals, since the energy used to generate the heat has been deducted from the final consumption section of the energy balance and transferred to the transformation section. The figures that are included in the balances should be treated as indicative of the amount of heat sold.

Valuation of energy purchases (Tables 1.4, 1.5, 1.6, 1.1.6)

1.34 In common with the rest of the chapter, these tables covering energy expenditure follow a balance format. Whilst a user may derive data on a similar basis as that previously published, the balance table allows for more varied use and interpretation of traded energy value data. That said the table continues to only show values for energy that has to be purchased and therefore does not include estimated values of a sector's internal consumption, such as coal used in the process of coal extraction.

The balance

1.35 The table balances around **market value of inland consumption** with the lower half of the table showing the total value of consumption by end users, sub divided into energy sector users and final users both for energy and non-energy use. The top half of the table shows the supply components that go to make up the final market value of inland consumption, namely upstream cost of production, imports, taxes and the margins and costs of delivering and packaging the fuel for the final consumer. The total final consumers value of energy consumption is represented by the lines 'total non energy sector use' and iron and steel sectors purchases of coal for use in solid fuel manufacture.

Fuel definitions in value balances

1.36 **Crude oil** includes NGLs and refinery feedstocks. **Natural gas** does not include colliery methane. **Electricity** only includes electricity delivered via the public distribution system and therefore does not value electricity produced and consumed by autogenerators, but the input fuels are included in transformation. **Manufactured solid fuels** includes coke, breeze and other solid manufactured fuels, mainly products from patent fuel and carbonisation plants. **Other fuels** includes all other fuels not listed, where they can be clearly considered as traded and some reasonable valuation can be made. Fuels mainly contributing to this year's values are wood, coke oven and colliery methane gases sold on to other industrial users and some use of waste products such as poultry litter.

Valuation

1.37 All figures are estimates and have been rounded to the nearest £5 million.

Energy end use

1.38 Values represent the cost to the final user including transportation of the fuel. They are derived, except where actual values are available, from the traded element of the volumes presented in aggregate energy balance and end user prices collected from information supplied by users or energy suppliers. The **energy sector** consists of those industries engaged in the production and sale of energy products, but values are not given for consumption of self-generated fuels eg coke oven gas used by coke producers. Many of the processes in the **iron and steel** industry are considered to be part of the energy sector in the energy balances, but for the purposes of this economic balance their genuine purchases are treated as those of final consumers, except for purchases of coal directly used in coke manufacture, which is shown separately as part of manufacture of solid fuel. Coal used directly in or to heat blast furnaces is shown as iron and steel final use. **Transformation** are those fuels used directly in producing other fuels eg crude oil in petroleum products. **Electricity generators** keep and use significant stocks of coal and the stocks used in consumption each year are shown separately. The value and margins for these being assumed to be the same as other coal purchased in the year. **Road transport** includes all motor spirit and DERV use. **Commercial and other users** includes public administration and miscellaneous uses not classified to the industrial sector.

Supply

1.39 The supply side money chain is derived using various methods. **Indigenous production** represents the estimated basic value of in year sales by the upstream producers. This value is gross of any taxes or cost they must meet. The valuation problems in attributing network losses in gas and electricity between upstream and downstream within this value chain, means any costs borne are included in the production value. **Imports and exports** are valued in accordance with Annex G (which can be found on the internet). However crude oil is treated differently where the value is formed from price data taken from a census survey of refiners and volume data taken from Tables 3.1 to 3.3. These values are considered to reflect the complete money chain more accurately than Tables G.1 to G.4. **Stock changes** are those for undistributed stocks except for coal where coke oven and generators stocks are included. A stock increase takes money out of the money chain and is therefore represented as a negative. **Distribution costs** are arrived at by removing an estimate of producers value along with any taxes from the end user values shown. For most fuel the estimate of producer value is derived from the consumption used for end use and the producer price taken from survey of producers. For electricity the Pool Purchase Price is used to value public distribution supply. No sector breakdown is given for gas and electricity margins because it is not possible to accurately measure delivery costs for each sector. **Taxes** include VAT where not refundable and duties paid on downstream sales. Excluded are the gas and fossil fuel levies, petroleum revenue tax and production royalties and licence fees. The proceeds from the fossil fuel levy are redistributed across the electricity industry, whilst the rest are treated as part of the production costs.

Sales of electricity and gas by sector (Table 1.7)

1.40 This table provides data on the total value of gas and electricity sold to final consumers. The data are collected from the energy supply companies. The data are useful in indicating relative total expenditure between sectors, but the quality of data provided in terms of industrial classification has been worsening in recent years. Net selling values provide some indication of typical prices paid in broad sectors.

II Energy balances (Tables 1.1, 1.2 and 1.3)

1.41 Tables 1.1, 1.2 and 1.3 show the energy flows as the primary fuels are processed (or used) and as the consequent secondary fuels are used. The net inputs to transformation are shown in the transformation rows and hence outputs from transformation processes into which primary fuels are input (such as electricity generation, heat generation or petroleum refining) appear as positive figures under the secondary product's heading in the tables. Similarly the net inputs are shown as negative figures under the primary fuel headings.

1.42 Readers should note that the energy and commodity balances presentation changed from the 1999 edition of the Digest following the consultation undertaken on the 1998 edition. Annex A explains in detail the principles behind the presentation.

1.43 The amount of heat sold in the UK was included in the energy balances from 1999. As discussed in paragraph 1.33 above, there are two main sources of heat data in the UK: from CHP plants and from district heating (community heating schemes).

III Measurement of energy consumption

Primary fuel input basis

1.44 Energy consumption is usually measured in one of three different ways. The first, known as the primary fuel input basis, assesses the total input of primary fuels and their equivalents. This measure includes energy used or lost in the conversion of primary fuels to secondary fuels (for example in power stations and oil refineries), energy lost in the distribution of fuels (for example in transmission lines) and energy conversion losses by final users. Primary demands as in Table 1.1, 1.2 and 1.3 are on this basis.

Final consumption - energy supplied basis

1.45 The second method, known as the energy supplied basis, measures the energy content of the fuels, both primary and secondary, supplied to final users. Thus it is net of fuel industry own use and conversion, transmission and distribution losses, but it includes conversion losses by final users. Table 1B presents shares of final consumption on this basis. The final consumption figures are presented on this basis throughout Chapter 1.

1.46 Although this is the usual and most direct way to measure final energy consumption, it is also possible to present final consumption on a primary fuel input basis. This can be done by allocating the conversion losses, distribution losses and energy industry use to final users. This approach can be used to compare the total primary fuel use which each sector of the economy accounts for. Table 1C presents shares of final consumption on this basis.

Final consumption - useful energy basis

1.47 Thirdly, final consumption may be expressed in the form of useful energy available after deduction of the losses incurred when final users convert energy supplied into space or process heat, motive power or light. Such losses depend on the type and quality of fuel and the equipment used and on the purpose, conditions, duration and intensity of use. Statistics on useful energy are not sufficiently reliable to be given in this Digest; there is a lack of data on utilisation efficiencies and on the purposes for which fuels are used.

Shares of each fuel in energy supply and demand

1.48 The relative importance of the energy consumption of each sector of the economy depends on the method used to measure consumption. Shares of final consumption on an energy supplied basis (that is in terms of the primary and secondary fuels directly consumed) in 2003 are presented in Table 1B. For comparison, Table 1C presents shares of final consumption on a primary fuel input basis.

Table 1B: Primary and secondary fuels consumed by final users in 2003 – energy supplied basis

	Percentage of each fuel						Percentage of each sector				
	Industry	Transport	Domestic	Others	Total		Solid fuels	Petrol-eum	Gas	Secondary electricity	Total
Solid fuels	55	-	44	1	100	Industry	4	22	44	30	100
Petroleum	11	82	5	2	100	Transport	-	99	-	1	100
Gas	26	-	58	15	100	Domestic	2	7	70	21	100
Secondary electricity	34	2	34	29	100	Others	-	7	47	46	100
All fuels	**21**	**36**	**31**	**12**	**100**	**All users**	**2**	**43**	**36**	**19**	**100**

Table 1C: Total primary fuel consumption by final users in 2003 - primary input basis

	Percentage of each fuel						Percentage of each sector				
	Industry	Transport	Domestic	Others	Total		Coal	Petrol-eum	Gas	Primary electricity	Total
Coal	35	2	35	27	100	Industry	24	15	47	13	100
Petroleum	11	81	5	2	100	Transport	1	97	1	1	100
Gas	29	1	51	20	100	Domestic	19	6	65	10	100
Primary electricity	34	2	34	29	100	Others	29	4	50	17	100
All fuels	**25**	**28**	**32**	**16**	**100**	**All users**	**17**	**33**	**41**	**10**	**100**

1.49 In 2003, every 1 toe of secondary electricity consumed by final users required, on average, 1.0 toe of coal, 0.9 toe of natural gas, 0.6 toe of primary electricity (nuclear, natural flow hydro and imports) and 0.1 toe of oil and renewables combined. The extent of this primary consumption is hidden in Table 1B, which presents final consumption only in terms of the fuels directly consumed. When all such primary consumption is allocated to final users, as in Table 1C, the relative importance of fuels and sectors changes; the transport sector, which uses very little electricity, declines in importance, whilst the true cost of final consumption in terms of coal use can now be seen.

1.50 Another view comes from shares of users' expenditure on each fuel (Table 1D based on Table 1.4). In this case the importance of fuels which require most handling by the user (solids and liquid fuels) is slightly understated, and the importance of uses taxed at higher rates (transport) is overstated in the All users line.

Table 1D: Value of fuels purchased by final users in 2003

	Solid fuels	Petroleum	Gas	Secondary electricity	Heat	Percentage of each sector Total
Industry	2	23	23	48	4	100
Transport	-	99	-	1	-	100
Domestic	2	5	42	51	-	100
Others	-	5	21	71	2	100
All users	**1**	**63**	**14**	**22**	**1**	**100**

Systems of measurement - international statistics

1.51 The systems of energy measurement used in various international statistics differ from the methods of the Digest as follows:

Net calorific values

1.52 Calorific values (thermal contents) used internationally are net rather than gross. The difference between the net and gross thermal content is the amount of energy necessary to evaporate the water present in the fuel or formed during the combustion process. The differences between gross and net values are taken to be 5 per cent for liquid and solid fuels (except for coke and coke breeze where there is no difference), 10 per cent for gases (except for blast furnace gas, 1 per cent), 15 per cent for straw, and 16 per cent for poultry litter. The calorific value of wood is highly dependent on its moisture content. In Annex A, the gross calorific value is given as 10 GJ per tonne at 50 per cent moisture content and this rises to 14.5 GJ at 25 per cent moisture content and 19 GJ for dry wood (equivalent to a net calorific value).

IV Definitions of fuels

1.53 The following paragraphs explain what is covered under the terms "primary" and "secondary" fuels.

Primary fuels

Coal - Production comprises all grades of coal, including slurry.

Primary oils - This includes crude oil, natural gas liquids (NGLs) and feedstock.

Natural gas liquids - Natural gas liquids (NGLs) consist of condensates (C_5 or heavier) and petroleum gases other than methane C_1, that is ethane C_2, propane C_3 and butane C_4, obtained from the onshore processing of associated and non-associated gas. These are treated as primary fuels when looking at primary supply but in the consumption data presented in this chapter these fuels are treated as secondary fuels, being transferred from the primary oils column in Tables 1.1, 1.2 and 1.3.

Natural gas - Production relates to associated or non-associated methane C_1 from land and the United Kingdom sector of the Continental Shelf. It includes that used for drilling production and pumping operations, but excludes gas flared or re-injected. It also includes colliery methane piped to the surface and consumed by collieries or others.

Nuclear electricity - Electricity generated by nuclear power stations belonging to the major power producers. See Chapter 5, paragraphs 5.47 and 5.48.

Natural flow hydro-electricity - Electricity generated by public supply and industrial natural flow hydroelectric power stations. Pumped storage stations are not included (see under secondary electricity below).

Renewable energy sources - In this chapter figures are presented for renewables and waste in total. Further details, including a detailed breakdown of the commodities covered are in Chapter 7.

Secondary fuels

Manufactured fuel - This heading includes manufactured solid fuels such as coke and breeze, other manufactured solid fuels, liquids such as benzole and tars and gases such as coke oven gas and blast furnace gas. Further details are given in Chapter 2, Tables 2.4, 2.5 and 2.6.

Coke and breeze - Coke oven coke and hard coke breeze (Chapter 2, Tables 2.4, 2.5 and 2.6).

Other manufactured solid fuels – Manufactured solid fuels produced at low temperature carbonisation plants and other manufactured fuel and briquetting plants (Chapter 2, Tables 2.4, 2.5 and 2.6).

Coke oven gas - Gas produced at coke ovens, excluding low temperature carbonisation plants. Gas bled or burnt to waste is included in production and losses (Chapter 2, Tables 2.4, 2.5 and 2.6).

Blast furnace gas - Blast furnace gas is mainly produced and consumed within the iron and steel industry (Chapter 2, Tables 2.4, 2.5 and 2.6).

Petroleum products - Petroleum products produced mainly at refineries, together with inland deliveries of natural gas liquids.

Secondary electricity - Secondary electricity is that generated by the combustion of another fuel, usually coal, natural gas or oil. The figure for outputs from transformation in the electricity column of Tables 1.1, 1.2 and 1.3 is the total of primary and secondary electricity, and the subsequent analysis of consumption is based on this total.

Heat sold – Heat sold is heat that is produced and sold under the provision of a contract.

V Classification of consumers

1.54   The Digest has been prepared, as far as is practicable, on the basis of the *Standard Industrial Classification (SIC) 2003* (www.statistics.gov.uk/methods_quality/classifications.asp).   SIC(2003) replaced SIC(1992) on 1 January 2003. SIC(1992) had been the basis of the industrial classification of energy statistics since 1995. Between 1986 and 1994 data in the Digest were prepared on the basis of the previous classification, SIC(1980).   The changes in classification between SIC(1992) and SIC(2003) are mainly in the very detailed classifications at the four or five digit level. As such the classifications used for energy statistics are unaffected by these changes.   However, not all consumption/disposals data are on this new basis, and where they are, there are sometimes constraints on the detail available. In particular the sectoral breakdown in the petroleum chapter is based on data that continue to be classified according to SIC (1968) by the oil industry. The main differences between the 1968 SIC (which was used as the basis for most data published for years prior to 1984) and the 1980 SIC were described in the 1986 and 1987 issues of the Digest. The differences between SIC 1980 and SIC 1992 are relatively minor. At the time of the change from the 1980 SIC to the 1992 SIC the main difference was that under the former showrooms belonging to the fuel supply industries were classified to the energy sector, whilst in the latter they are in the commercial sector. Since privatisation few gas, coal and electricity companies have retained showrooms and the difference is therefore minimal.

1.55   Table 1E shows the categories of consumers together with their codes in SIC 2003.   The coverage varies between tables (eg in some instances the 'other' category is split into major constituents, whereas elsewhere it may include transport). This is because the coverage is dictated by what data suppliers can provide. The table also shows the disaggregation available within industry. This disaggregation forms the basis of virtually all the tables that show a disaggregated industrial breakdown.

Table 1E: SIC 2003 classifications

Fuel producers	10-12, 23, 40

Final consumers:

Industrial

Unclassified	See paragraph 1.56 below
Iron and steel	27, *excluding 27.4*, 27.53, 27.54
Non-ferrous metals	27.4, 27.53, 27.54
Mineral products	14, 26
Chemicals	24
Mechanical engineering and metal products	28, 29
Electrical and instrument engineering	30-33
Vehicles	34, 35
Food, beverages & tobacco	15, 16
Textiles, clothing, leather, & footwear	17-19
Paper, printing & publishing	21, 22
Other industries	13, 20, 25, 36, 37, 41
Construction	45

Transport	60-63

Other final users

Domestic	Not covered by SIC 2003.
Public administration	75, 80, 85
Commercial	50-52, 55, 64-67, 70-74
Agriculture	01, 02, 05
Miscellaneous	90-93, 99

1.56   There is also an 'unclassified' category in the industry sector (see Table 1E). Wherever the data supplier is unable to allocate an amount between categories, but the Department of Trade and Industry has additional information, not readily available to readers, with which to allocate between categories, then this has been done. Where such additional information is not available the data are included in the 'unclassified' category, enabling the reader to decide whether to accept a residual, pro-rate, or otherwise adjust the figures. The 'miscellaneous' category also contains some unallocated figures for the services sector.

1.57   In Tables 6.8 and 6.9 of Chapter 6 the following abbreviated grouping of industries, based on SIC 2003, is used in order to prevent disclosure of information about individual companies:

Table 1F: Abbreviated grouping of Industry

Iron and steel and non-ferrous metal	27
Chemicals	24
Oil refineries	23.2
Paper, printing and publishing	21, 22
Food, beverages and tobacco	15, 16
Metal products, machinery and equipment	28, 29, 30, 31, 32, 34, 35
Mineral products, extraction, mining and agglomeration of solid fuels	10, 11, 14, 26
Sewage Treatment	(parts of 41 and 90)
Electricity supply	40.1
Other industrial branches	12, 13, 17, 18, 19, 20, 23.1, 23.3, 25, 33, 36, 37, 40.2, 41 (remainder) 45
Transport, commerce, and administration	1, 2, 5, 50 to 99 (except 90 and 92)
Other	40.3, 90 (remainder), 92

1.58 In Tables 1.8 and 1.9 the list above is further condensed and includes only manufacturing industry and construction as follows:

Table 1G: Abbreviated grouping of Industry for Tables 1.8 and 1.9

Iron and steel and non-ferrous metals	27
Chemicals	24
Paper, printing and publishing	21, 22
Food, beverages and tobacco	15, 16
Metal products, machinery and equipment	28, 29, 30, 31, 32, 34, 35
Other (including construction)	12, 13, 14, 17, 18, 19, 20, 23.1, 23.3, 25, 26, 33, 36, 37, 45

VI Monthly and quarterly data

1.59 Monthly and quarterly data on energy production and consumption (including on a seasonally adjusted and temperature corrected basis) split by fuel type are provided on the DTI website at www.dti.gov.uk/energy/inform/energy_stats/. Quarterly figures are also published in the DTI's quarterly statistical bulletin *Energy Trends and Quarterly Energy Prices*. See Annex C for more information about these bulletins.

Contact: *Julian Prime (Statistician)*   *Sara Atkins*
             julian.prime@dti.gsi.gov.uk   *Energy Prices*
             020-7215 6178   *sara.atkins@dti.gsi.gov.uk*
                                                020-7215 6532

             Chris Michaels
             chris.michaels@dti.gsi.gov.uk
             020-7215 2710

1.1 Aggregate energy balance 2003

Thousand tonnes of oil equivalent

	Coal	Manu-factured fuels (1)	Primary oils	Petroleum products	Natural gas (2)	Renewable & waste (3)	Primary electricity	Elect-ricity	Heat sold	Total
Supply										
Indigenous production	17,635	-	116,242	-	102,938	3,066	20,431	-	-	260,311
Imports	20,905	693	59,114	18,795	7,420	110	-	440	-	107,478
Exports	-396	-170	-81,927	-25,274	-15,223	-	-	-254	-	-123,245
Marine bunkers	-	-	-	-1,879	-	-	-	-	-	-1,879
Stock change (4)	+1,712	-92	+511	-294	+300	-	-	-	-	+2,138
Primary supply	**39,857**	**431**	**93,940**	**-8,653**	**95,436**	**3,177**	**20,431**	**186**		**244,804**
Statistical difference (5)	-70	-46	+210	-493	-11	-	-	+82	-	-327
Primary demand	**39,927**	**476**	**93,730**	**-8,159**	**95,447**	**3,177**	**20,431**	**103**	**-**	**245,131**
Transfers	-	-117	-1,367	+1,294	-7	-	-391	+391	-	-197
Transformation	**-38,706**	**1,856**	**-92,363**	**91,480**	**-29,657**	**-2,508**	**-20,040**	**33,649**	**1,796**	**-54,493**
Electricity generation	-33,092	-915	-	-649	-27,933	-2,449	-20,040	33,649	-	-51,429
Major power producers	-32,155	-	-	-104	-24,477	-950	-20,040	33,649	-	-51,429
Autogenerators	-938	-915	-	-544	-3,457	-1,499	-	2,927	-	-47,004
Heat generation	-379	-121	-	-164	-1,724	-59	-	-	1,796	-4,425
Petroleum refineries	-	-	-92,363	92,533	-	-	-	-	-	-650
Coke manufacture	-4,293	4,214	-	-2	-	-	-	-	-	170
Blast furnaces	-661	-1,614	-	-238	-	-	-	-	-	-80
Patent fuel manufacture	-282	291	-	-	-	-	-	-	-	-2,513
Other	-	-	-	-	-	-	-	-	-	10
Energy industry use	**4**	**892**	**-**	**5,756**	**7,619**	**-**	**-**	**2,561**	**2**	**16,834**
Electricity generation	-	-	-	-	-	-	-	1,568	2	1,571
Oil and gas extraction	-	-	-	-	6,607	-	-	47	-	6,654
Petroleum refineries	-	-	-	5,756	185	-	-	492	-	6,433
Coal extraction	4	-	-	-	16	-	-	107	-	127
Coke manufacture	-	419	-	-	-	-	-	-	-	419
Blast furnaces	-	470	-	-	42	-	-	72	-	584
Patent fuel manufacture	-	3	-	-	-	-	-	-	-	3
Pumped storage	-	-	-	-	-	-	-	70	-	70
Other	-	-	-	-	769	-	-	204	-	973
Losses	**-**	**158**	**-**	**-**	**499**	**-**	**-**	**2,568**	**-**	**3,226**
Final consumption	**1,216**	**1,165**	**-**	**78,859**	**57,664**	**669**	**-**	**29,015**	**1,794**	**170,381**
Industry	**462**	**840**	**-**	**7,324**	**14,803**	**226**	**-**	**9,843**	**1,136**	**34,634**
Unclassified	-	128	-	2,006	6	226	-	-	-	2,367
Iron and steel	-	695	-	19	1,644	-	-	563	-	2,921
Non-ferrous metals	54	17	-	63	437	-	-	621	-	1,192
Mineral products	203	-	-	263	1,146	-	-	648	-	2,260
Chemicals	36	-	-	380	3,883	-	-	1,732	1,118	7,148
Mechanical engineering etc.	7	-	-	270	745	-	-	752	12	1,786
Electrical engineering etc.	1	-	-	55	372	-	-	512	-	940
Vehicles	23	-	-	122	959	-	-	480	-	1,584
Food, beverages, etc.	82	-	-	326	2,383	-	-	1,016	5	3,814
Textiles, leather, etc.	9	-	-	225	651	-	-	294	-	1,178
Paper, printing etc.	24	-	-	124	1,340	-	-	1,164	-	2,652
Other industries	24	-	-	3,148	987	-	-	1,913	-	6,071
Construction	-	-	-	322	251	-	-	149	-	721
Transport	**-**	**-**	**-**	**55,334**	**-**	**-**	**-**	**686**	**-**	**56,020**
Air	-	-	-	11,936	-	-	-	-	-	11,936
Rail	-	-	-	342	-	-	-	-	-	342
Road	-	-	-	41,823	-	-	-	-	-	41,823
National navigation	-	-	-	1,233	-	-	-	-	-	1,233
Pipelines	-	-	-	-	-	-	-	-	-	-
Other	**753**	**325**	**-**	**4,736**	**41,944**	**443**	**-**	**18,486**	**658**	**67,346**
Domestic	733	325	-	3,436	33,189	247	-	9,954	11	47,895
Public administration	13	-	-	513	3,753	104	-	1,803	627	6,813
Commercial	-	-	-	367	3,128	-	-	6,383	-	9,878
Agriculture	3	-	-	328	128	72	-	346	-	878
Miscellaneous	4	-	-	91	1,746	20	-	-	20	1,881
Non energy use	**-**	**-**	**-**	**11,465**	**917**	**-**	**-**	**-**	**-**	**12,381**

(1) Includes all manufactured solid fuels, benzole, tars, coke oven gas and blast furnace gas.
(2) Includes colliery methane.
(3) Includes geothermal and solar heat.
(4) Stock fall (+), stock rise (-).
(5) Primary supply minus primary demand.

1.2 Aggregate energy balance 2002

Thousand tonnes of oil equivalent

	Coal	Manu-factured fuels (1)	Primary oils	Petroleum products	Natural gas (2)	Renewable & waste (3)	Primary electricity	Elect-ricity	Heat sold	Total
Supply										
Indigenous production	18,807r	-	127,037r	-	103,646r	2,790r	20,619r	-	-	272,899r
Imports	18,815r	181	62,152r	16,578r	5,201	-	-	790	-	103,718r
Exports	-395r	-272	-95,288r	-25,469r	-12,961	-	-	-66	-	-134,450r
Marine bunkers	-	-	-	-2,043r	-	-	-	-	-	-2,043r
Stock change (4)	+279	+190	+158r	+1,356r	-633	-	-	-	-	+1,352r
Primary supply	37,507r	99	94,060r	-9,577r	95,255r	2,790r	20,619r	723r	-	241,476r
Statistical difference (5)	-149r	-33	-556r	+443r	+169	-	-	+96r	-	-29r
Primary demand	37,656r	132	94,616r	-10,020r	95,085r	2,790r	20,619r	628r	-	241,505r
Transfers	-	-102	-2,017r	+1,970r	-9	-	-520r	+520r	-	-157r
Transformation	-35,504r	2,386	-92,599r	90,819r	-29,976r	-2,136r	-20,099r	32,572r	2,107r	-52,430r
Electricity generation	-29,683r	-592	-	-730r	-28,085r	-2,073r	-20,099r	32,572r	-	-48,690r
Major power producers	-28,706r	-	-	-124r	-25,044	-812r	-20,099r	29,872r	-	-44,912r
Autogenerators	-977r	-592	-	-606r	-3,041r	-1,261r	-	2,700r	2,107r	-892r
Heat generation	-615r	-170r	-	-260r	-1,891r	-63r	-	-	2,107r	-892r
Petroleum refineries	-	-	-92,599r	92,004r	-	-	-	-	-	-595r
Coke manufacture	-4,347r	4,192r	-	-1r	-	-	-	-	-	-156r
Blast furnaces	-543r	-1,362	-	-193r	-	-	-	-	-	-2,098r
Patent fuel manufacture	-316	317r	-	-	-	-	-	-	-	1r
Other	-	-	-	-	-	-	-	-	-	-
Energy industry use	6	829	-	5,960r	7,832	-	-	2,495r	6	17,128r
Electricity generation	-	-	-	-	-	-	-	1,477r	6	1,482r
Oil and gas extraction	-	-	-	-	6,818	-	-	46	-	6,865
Petroleum refineries	-	-	-	5,959r	279	-	-	566r	-	6,804r
Coal extraction	6	-	-	-	17	-	-	105	-	128
Coke manufacture	-	411	-	-	-	-	-	-	-	411
Blast furnaces	-	399	-	-r	19	-	-	70	-	488r
Patent fuel manufacture	-	20	-	-	-	-	-	-	-	20
Pumped storage	-	-	-	-	-	-	-	70	-	70
Other	-	-	-	-	699	-	-	162r	-	861
Losses	-	89	-	-	831	-	-	2,578	-	3,498
Final consumption	2,145r	1,497	-	76,809r	56,438r	654r	-	28,646r	2,101r	168,291r
Industry	724r	1,082r	-	6,350r	15,021r	222r	-	9,662r	1,338r	34,399r
Unclassified	-	191	-	1,650r	8	222r	-	-	-	2,071r
Iron and steel	-	849	-	82r	1,680	-	-	546	-	3,156r
Non-ferrous metals	87	42	-	85	425	-	-	541r	-	1,180r
Mineral products	322r	-	-	264	1,087	-	-	602	4r	2,280
Chemicals	44r	-	-	333r	4,117r	-	-	1,944r	1,327r	7,765r
Mechanical engineering etc.	10	-	-	281r	719	-	-	742r	-	1,753r
Electrical engineering etc.	3	-	-	54	357	-	-	498r	-	912r
Vehicles	37	-	-	203	924	-	-	473r	-	1,637r
Food, beverages, etc.	136	-	-	329	2,339	-	-	1,030r	7r	3,840r
Textiles, leather, etc.	14	-	-	192r	633	-	-	294	-	1,133r
Paper, printing etc.	40r	-	-	115	1,251	-	-	1,017r	-	2,423r
Other industries	31	-	-	2,287r	1,236r	-	-	1,835r	-	5,389r
Construction	-	-	-	476	245	-	-	139	-	860
Transport	-	-	-	54,637r	-	-	-	729	-	55,366r
Air	-	-	-	11,658r	-	-	-	-	-	11,658r
Rail	-	-	-	374r	-	-	-	-	-	374r
Road	-	-	-	41,946r	-	-	-	-	-	41,946r
National navigation	-	-	-	660r	-	-	-	-	-	660r
Pipelines	-	-	-	-	-	-	-	-	-	-
Other	1,421r	416r	-	5,328r	41,033r	432	-	18,256r	763	67,648r
Domestic	1,395r	416r	-	3,491r	32,358	243	-	9,848	33r	47,784r
Public administration	17r	-	-	769	3,692r	97	-	1,777r	730r	7,081r
Commercial	-	-	-	401r	3,104r	-	-	6,274	-	9,778r
Agriculture	4	-	-	563	130	72	-	356r	-	1,126
Miscellaneous	6	-	-	104r	1,749	20	-	-	-	1,878r
Non energy use	-	-	-	10,494r	384	-	-	-	-	10,878r

(1) Includes all manufactured solid fuels, benzole, tars, coke oven gas and blast furnace gas.
(2) Includes colliery methane.
(3) Includes geothermal and solar heat.
(4) Stock fall (+), stock rise (-).
(5) Primary supply minus primary demand.

1.3 Aggregate energy balance 2001

Thousand tonnes of oil equivalent

	Coal	Manu-factured fuels (1)	Primary oils	Petroleum products	Natural gas (2)	Renewable & waste (3)	Primary electricity	Elect-ricity	Heat sold	Total
Supply										
Indigenous production	19,967r	-	127,828	-	105,870r	2,576r	21,199r	-	-	277,439r
Imports	23,454r	111	58,425	19,051r	2,619	-	-	917	-	104,578r
Exports	-412	-268	-95,047r	-20,633	-11,894	-	-	-23	-	-128,277r
Marine bunkers				-2,433	-	-	-	-	-	-2,433
Stock change (4)	-1,867r	+115	-667r	-665	-57	-	-	-	-	-3,141
Primary supply	**41,142r**	**-42**	**90,538r**	**-4,680r**	**96,538r**	**2,576r**	**21,199r**	**894**	**-**	**248,166r**
Statistical difference (5)	-87r	-55	+109r	+382	+225r	-	-	+100r	-	+674r
Primary demand	**41,229r**	**14r**	**90,429r**	**-5,062r**	**96,313r**	**2,576r**	**21,199r**	**794r**	**-**	**247,491r**
Transfers	-	-112	+490r	-365r	-6	-	-432	+432	-	+8
Transformation	**-38,245r**	**2,880r**	**-90,919r**	**88,079r**	**-28,900r**	**-1,946r**	**-20,767r**	**32,445r**	**2,330**	**-55,043r**
Electricity generation	-31,485r	-600	-	-1,040r	-26,872r	-1,874r	-20,767r	32,445r	-	-50,194r
Major power producers	-30,490r	-	-	-380r	-23,797	-723r	-20,767r	29,873	-	-46,284r
Autogenerators	-996r	-600	-	-660	-3,075r	-1,151r	-	2,572r	-	-3,910r
Heat generation	-468r	-207r	-	-699r	-2,028r	-72r	-	-	2,330	-1,143r
Petroleum refineries	-	-	-90,919r	89,818r	-	-	-	-	-	-1,101r
Coke manufacture	-5,372	5,058	-	-	-	-	-	-	-	-314r
Blast furnaces	-575	-1,727	-	-	-	-	-	-	-	-2,302r
Patent fuel manufacture	-345r	356	-	-	-	-	-	-	-	11r
Other	-	-	-	-	-	-	-	-	-	-
Energy industry use	**7**	**957**	**-**	**5,422r**	**7,863r**	**-**	**-**	**2,405**	**3**	**16,657r**
Electricity generation	-	-	-	-	-	-	-	1,496r	3	1,498r
Oil and gas extraction	-	-	-	-	6,746	-	-	58	-	6,804
Petroleum refineries	-	-	-	5,421r	360	-	-	450	-	6,231r
Coal extraction	7	-	-	-	18	-	-	105	-	130
Coke manufacture	-	462	-	-	1	-	-	-	-	462
Blast furnaces	-	464	-	-r	32	-	-	76	-	572r
Patent fuel manufacture	-	32	-	-	-	-	-	-	-	32
Pumped storage	-	-	-	-	-	-	-	68r	-	68r
Other	-	-	-	-	706	-	-	152	-	858
Losses	**-**	**103**	**-**	**-**	**762r**	**-**	**-**	**2,657**	**-**	**3,522r**
Final consumption	**2,977r**	**1,722r**	**-**	**77,172r**	**58,782r**	**630r**	**-**	**28,609r**	**2,327**	**172,217r**
Industry	**1,109r**	**1,346r**	**-**	**7,179r**	**15,464r**	**213r**	**-**	**9,573r**	**1,001**	**35,884r**
Unclassified	-	241r	-	2,122r	9	213r	-	-	-	2,585r
Iron and steel	1	1,016r	-	305r	1,797r	-	-	725	-	3,843r
Non-ferrous metals	118r	89	-	81r	449	-	-	617	-	1,355r
Mineral products	322r	-	-	292r	1,186	-	-	601r	2	2,403r
Chemicals	266r	-	-	386r	4,080r	-	-	1,771r	988	7,491r
Mechanical engineering etc.	11r	-	-	272r	725r	-	-	707	-	1,715r
Electrical engineering etc.	3	-	-	62r	380	-	-	470	-	915r
Vehicles	48	-	-	186r	960r	-	-	481r	-	1,675r
Food, beverages, etc.	151r	-	-	370r	2,364r	-	-	961r	-	3,846r
Textiles, leather, etc.	34	-	-	221r	642	-	-	276	10	1,183r
Paper, printing etc.	112r	-	-	111r	1,345r	-	-	962r	-	2,531r
Other industries	45r	-	-	2,255r	1,273r	-	-	1,868	-	5,441r
Construction	-	-	-	514	253	-	-	134	-	901
Transport	**-**	**-**	**-**	**54,164r**	**-**	**-**	**-**	**759r**	**-**	**54,923r**
Air	-	-	-	11,774r	-	-	-	-	-	11,774r
Rail	-	-	-	451	-	-	-	-	-	451
Road	-	-	-	41,097r	-	-	-	-	-	41,097r
National navigation	-	-	-	843r	-	-	-	-	-	843r
Pipelines	-	-	-	-	-	-	-	-	-	-
Other	**1,868r**	**376**	**-**	**6,134r**	**42,351r**	**417**	**-**	**18,277r**	**1,326**	**70,748r**
Domestic	1,821	376	-	3,527r	32,625r	241	-	9,917	32	48,538r
Public administration	37r	-	-	884r	3,975r	93	-	1,815r	1,287	8,090r
Commercial	-	-	-	940r	3,190r	-	-	6,192	-	10,322r
Agriculture	3	-	-	650r	200r	72	-	353r	7	1,286r
Miscellaneous	7	-	-	133r	2,360r	11	-	-	-	2,511r
Non energy use	**-**	**-**	**-**	**9,754r**	**967r**	**-**	**-**	**-**	**-**	**10,722r**

(1) Includes all manufactured solid fuels, benzole, tars, coke oven gas and blast furnace gas.
(2) Includes colliery methane.
(3) Includes geothermal and solar heat.
(4) Stock fall (+), stock rise (-).
(5) Primary supply minus primary demand.

1.4 Value balance of traded energy in 2003[(1)]

£million

	Coal	Manufactured solid fuels	Crude oil	Petroleum products	Natural gas	Electricity	Heat sold	Other fuels	Total
Supply									
Indigenous production	710	115	14,315	15,645	7,255	7,250	345	55	45,685
Imports	925	70	6,495	3,525	135	170	-	-	11,320
Exports	-35	-15	-9,820	-4,865	-970	-	-	-	-15,705
Marine bunkers	-	-	-	-255	-	-	-	-	-255
Stock change	45	-5	65	-50	-	-	-	-	55
Basic value of inland consumption	**1,645**	**160**	**11,055**	**14,000**	**6,425**	**7,420**	**345**	**55**	**41,100**
Tax and margins									
Distribution costs and margins	260	20	-	2,350	4,185	6,175	-	-	12,990
Electricity generation	70	-	-	5	-	-	-	-	70
Solid fuel manufacture	55	-	-	-	-	-	-	-	55
of which iron & steel sector	45	-	-	-	-	-	-	-	45
Iron & steel final use	10	5	-	5	-	-	-	-	15
Other industry	5	5	-	300	-	-	-	-	310
Air transport	-	-	-	110	-	-	-	-	110
Rail and national navigation	-	-	-	15	-	-	-	-	15
Road transport	-	-	-	1,415	-	-	-	-	1,415
Domestic	130	5	-	90	-	-	-	-	225
Agriculture	-	-	-	15	-	-	-	-	15
Commercial and other services	-	-	-	20	-	-	-	-	20
Non energy use	-	-	-	380	85	-	-	-	465
VAT and duties	10	5	-	25,990	300	365	-	-	26,665
Electricity generation	-	-	-	15	-	-	-	-	15
Iron & steel final use	-	-	-	-	-	-	-	-	-
Other industry	-	-	-	225	-	-	-	-	225
Air transport	-	-	-	20	-	-	-	-	20
Rail and national navigation	-	-	-	70	-	-	-	-	70
Road transport	-	-	-	25,565	-	-	-	-	25,565
Domestic	10	5	-	40	300	365	-	-	720
Agriculture	-	-	-	10	-	-	-	-	10
Commercial and other services	-	-	-	40	-	-	-	-	40
Climate Change Levy	5	-	-	-	195	620	-	-	820
Total tax and margins	**275**	**20**	**-**	**28,340**	**4,680**	**7,160**	**-**	**-**	**40,475**
Market value of inland consumption	**1,920**	**185**	**11,055**	**42,340**	**11,105**	**14,580**	**340**	**55**	**81,575**
Energy end use									
Total energy sector	1,670	-	11,055	135	2,300	145	-	20	15,320
Transformation	1,670	-	11,055	135	2,225	-	-	20	15,100
Electricity generation	1,435	-	-	110	2,210	-	-	20	3,770
of which from stocks	35	-	-	-	-	-	-	-	35
Heat Generation	15	-	-	25	15	-	-	-	55
Petroleum refineries	-	-	11,055	-	-	-	-	-	11,055
Solid fuel manufacture	220	-	-	-	-	-	-	-	220
of which iron & steel sector	195	-	-	-	-	-	-	-	195
Other energy sector use	-	-	-	-	75	145	-	-	220
Oil & gas extraction	-	-	-	-	-	15	-	-	15
Petroleum refineries	-	-	-	-	15	90	-	-	105
Coal extraction	-	-	-	-	-	35	-	-	35
Other energy sector	-	-	-	-	60	-	-	-	60
Total non energy sector use	250	185	-	40,305	8,720	14,435	340	40	64,270
Industry	55	85	-	1,425	1,395	2,940	215	10	6,130
Iron & steel final use	30	70	-	35	150	130	-	-	415
Other industry	25	20	-	1,390	1,245	2,810	215	10	5,715
Transport	-	-	-	37,900	-	220	-	-	38,125
Air	-	-	-	2,510	-	-	-	-	2,510
Rail and national navigation	-	-	-	320	-	220	-	-	540
Road	-	-	-	35,075	-	-	-	-	35,075
Other final users	195	95	-	980	7,320	11,270	125	30	20,015
Domestic	190	95	-	705	6,255	7,660	-	30	14,940
Agriculture	-	-	-	70	20	195	-	-	285
Commercial and other services	-	-	-	205	1,050	3,420	125	-	4,795
Total value of energy end use	**1,920**	**185**	**11,055**	**40,440**	**11,015**	**14,580**	**340**	**55**	**79,590**
Value of non energy end use	**-**	**-**	**-**	**1,900**	**85**	**-**	**-**	**-**	**1,985**
Market value of inland consumption	**1,920**	**185**	**11,055**	**42,340**	**11,105**	**14,580**	**340**	**55**	**81,575**

(1) For further information see paragraphs 1.34 to 1.38.

1.5 Value balance of traded energy in 2002[1]

£million

	Coal	Manufactured solid fuels	Crude oil	Petroleum products	Natural gas	Electricity	Heat sold	Other fuels	Total
Supply									
Indigenous production	900	180	14,580r	12,745r	6,450r	7,535r	405r	50	42,845r
Imports	850	20	6,425r	3,080r	260r	190	-	-	10,820r
Exports	-30	-25	-10,510r	-4,125r	-850r	-	-	-	-15,540r
Marine bunkers	-	-	-	-245r	-	-	-	-	-245r
Stock change	-10	-	5	190	-5	-	-	-	180
Basic value of inland consumption	**1,710**	**175**	**10,495r**	**11,640r**	**5,860**	**7,725**	**405r**	**50**	**38,060r**
Tax and margins									
Distribution costs and margins	**320r**	**25**	**-**	**1,910r**	**4,225r**	**5,995**			**12,480r**
Electricity generation	50	-	-	5	-	-	-	-	55
Solid fuel manufacture	5	-	-	-	-	-	-	-	5
of which iron & steel sector	5	-	-	-	-	-	-	-	5
Iron & steel final use	-	5	-	10r	-	-	-	-	15r
Other industry	10	10	-	235r	-	-	-	-	255r
Air transport	-	-	-	50r	-	-	-	-	50r
Rail and national navigation	-	-	-	5	-	-	-	-	5
Road transport	-	-	-	1,190r	-	-	-	-	1,190r
Domestic	250	10	-	80r	-	-	-	-	345
Agriculture	-	-	-	15	-	-	-	-	15
Commercial and other services	-	-	-	30	-	-	-	-	35
Non energy use	-	-	-	290r	35	-	-	-	325r
VAT and duties	**15**	**5**	**-**	**26,125r**	**290**	**360**	**-**	**-**	**26,795r**
Electricity generation	-	-	-	15	-	-	-	-	15
Iron & steel final use	-	-	-	-r	-	-	-	-	-r
Other industry	-	-	-	185	-	-	-	-	185
Air transport	-	-	-	20	-	-	-	-	20
Rail and national navigation	-	-	-	45	-	-	-	-	45
Road transport	-	-	-	25,750r	-	-	-	-	25,750r
Domestic	15	5	-	40	290	360	-	-	710
Agriculture	-	-	-	20	-	-	-	-	20
Commercial and other services	-	-	-	50	-	-	-	-	50
Climate Change Levy	**5**	**-**	**-**	**-**	**205**	**625**	**-**	**-**	**835**
Total tax and margins	**340r**	**30**	**-**	**28,035r**	**4,720r**	**6,980**	**-**	**-**	**40,110r**
Market value of inland consumption	**2,050r**	**205**	**10,495r**	**39,675r**	**10,580r**	**14,705**	**405r**	**50r**	**78,165r**
Energy end use									
Total energy sector	**1,640r**	**-**	**10,495r**	**130**	**2,070**	**150**	**-**	**15**	**14,500r**
Transformation	**1,640r**	**-**	**10,495r**	**130**	**2,000**	**-**	**-**	**15**	**14,280r**
Electricity generation	1,365	-	-	100	1,985	-	-	15	3,465
of which from stocks	35	-	-	-	-	-	-	-	35
Heat Generation	30r	-	-	35r	15r	-	-	-	75r
Petroleum refineries	-	-	10,495r	-	-	-	-	-	10,495r
Solid fuel manufacture	245	-	-	-	-	-	-	-	245
of which iron & steel sector	210	-	-	-	-	-	-	-	210
Other energy sector use	**-**	**-**	**-**	**-**	**70**	**150**	**-**	**-**	**220**
Oil & gas extraction	-	-	-	-	-	15	-	-	15
Petroleum refineries	-	-	-	-	20	95	-	-	115
Coal extraction	-	-	-	-	-	40	-	-	40
Other energy sector	-	-	-	-	50	-	-	-	50
Total non energy sector use	**410r**	**205**	**-**	**38,050r**	**8,475r**	**14,550**	**400r**	**40**	**62,140r**
Industry	**65r**	**85**	**-**	**1,065r**	**1,365r**	**2,995**	**255r**	**10**	**5,840r**
Iron & steel final use	30	55	-	35r	145	120	-	-	385r
Other industry	40r	30	-	1,030r	1,220r	2,870	255r	10	5,455r
Transport	**-**	**-**	**-**	**36,010r**	**-**	**220**	**-**	**-**	**36,230r**
Air	-	-	-	1,790r	-	-	-	-	1,790r
Rail and national navigation	-	-	-	185r	-	220	-	-	400r
Road	-	-	-	34,035r	-	-	-	-	34,035r
Other final users	**345**	**120**	**-**	**975r**	**7,115r**	**11,340**	**145**	**30**	**20,070r**
Domestic	345	120	-	625r	6,085	7,510	5r	30	14,720r
Agriculture	-	-	-	105	20	215	-	-	340
Commercial and other services	-r	-	-	245	1,010r	3,615	140r	-	5,010r
Total value of energy end use	**2,050r**	**205**	**10,495r**	**38,180r**	**10,545r**	**14,705**	**405r**	**50r**	**76,640r**
Value of non energy end use	**-**	**-**	**-**	**1,495r**	**35**	**-**	**-**	**-**	**1,530r**
Market value of inland consumption	**2,050r**	**205**	**10,495r**	**39,675r**	**10,580r**	**14,705**	**405r**	**50r**	**78,165r**

(1) For further information see paragraphs 1.34 to 1.38.

1.6 Value balance of traded energy in 2001[1]

£million

	Coal	Manufactured solid fuels	Crude oil	Petroleum products	Natural gas	Electricity	Heat sold	Other fuels	Total
Supply									
Indigenous production	965	190	14,915r	13,200r	6,985	7,805	405	55	44,520r
Imports	1,180	10	6,235	3,555r	185	180	-	-	11,345r
Exports	-30	-25	-10,845r	-3,770r	-745	-	-	-	-15,415r
Marine bunkers	-	-	-	-325	-	-	-	-	-325
Stock change	-110	-	-130	-115	-	-	-	-	-355
Basic value of inland consumption	2,005	180	10,175	12,545r	6,425	7,980	405	55	39,770r
Tax and margins									
Distribution costs and margins	410	30	-	1,825r	3,755	6,450	-	-	12,475r
Electricity generation	85	-	-	5	-	-	-	-	90
Solid fuel manufacture	10	-	-	-	-	-	-	-	10
of which iron & steel sector	5	-	-	-	-	-	-	-	5
Iron & steel final use	-	5	-	5	-	-	-	-	10
Other industry	10	15	-	250r	-	-	-	-	275r
Air transport	-	-	-	125	-	-	-	-	125
Rail and national navigation	-	-	-	15	-	-	-	-	15
Road transport	-	-	-	935r	-	-	-	-	935r
Domestic	305	10	-	125	-	-	-	-	440
Agriculture	-	-	-	20	-	-	-	-	20
Commercial and other services	-	-	-	65r	-	-	-	-	65
Non energy use	-	-	-	280	90	-	-	-	375r
VAT and duties	20	5	-	26,365r	275	360	-	-	27,025r
Electricity generation	-	-	-	20	-	-	-	-	20
Iron & steel final use	-	-	-	10	-	-	-	-	10
Other industry	-	-	-	150r	-	-	-	-	150r
Air transport	-	-	-	20	-	-	-	-	20
Rail and national navigation	-	-	-	45	-	-	-	-	45
Road transport	-	-	-	26,010r	-	-	-	-	26,010r
Domestic	20	5	-	40	275	360	-	-	700
Agriculture	-	-	-	15	-	-	-	-	15
Commercial and other services	-	-	-	45	-	-	-	-	50r
Climate Change Levy	-	-	-	-	120	400	-	-	520
Total tax and margins	430	35	-	28,190r	4,150	7,210	-	-	40,015r
Market value of inland consumption	2,435	215	10,175	40,740r	10,575	15,195	405	55	79,790r
Energy end use									
Total energy sector	1,910	-	10,175	205r	2,170r	175	-	15	14,645r
Transformation	1,910	-	10,175	205r	2,090r	-	-	15	14,390r
Electricity generation	1,595	-	-	125r	2,070r	-	-	15	3,805r
of which from stocks	40	-	-	-	-	-	-	-	40
Heat Generation	25	-	-	80	15	-	-	-	120
Petroleum refineries	-	-	10,175	-	-	-	-	-	10,175
Solid fuel manufacture	290	-	-	-	-	-	-	-	290
of which iron & steel sector	245	-	-	-	-	-	-	-	245
Other energy sector use	-	-	-	-	80	175	-	-	255r
Oil & gas extraction	-	-	-	-	-	25	-	-	25
Petroleum refineries	-	-	-	-	30	110	-	-	140
Coal extraction	-	-	-	-	-	40	-	-	40
Other energy sector	-	-	-	-	55	-	-	-	55
Total non energy sector use	525	215	-	39,145r	8,310r	15,020	405	40	63,660r
Industry	95	105	-	1,235r	1,470r	3,145	175	15	6,235r
Iron & steel final use	30	65	-	50r	165	195	-	-	505r
Other industry	65	40	-	1,180r	1,300r	2,950	175	15	5,730r
Transport	-	-	-	36,700r	-	240	-	-	36,940r
Air	-	-	-	2,140r	-	-	-	-	2,140r
Rail and national navigation	-	-	-	240	-	240	-	-	485
Road	-	-	-	34,320r	-	-	-	-	34,320r
Other final users	430r	105	-	1,210r	6,845r	11,630	230	30	20,485r
Domestic	430	105	-	715r	5,735	7,540	5	30	14,560r
Agriculture	-	-	-	125r	25r	225	-	-	380r
Commercial and other services	5	-	-	370r	1,085	3,865	225	-	5,545r
Total value of energy end use	2,435	215	10,175	39,350r	10,485	15,195	405	55	78,305r
Value of non energy end use	-	-	-	1,390r	90	-	-	-	1,480r
Market value of inland consumption	2,435	215	10,175	40,740r	10,575	15,195	405	55	79,790r

(1) For further information see paragraphs 1.34 to 1.38.

1.7 Sales of electricity and gas by sector

United Kingdom

	1999	2000	2001	2002	2003
Total selling value (£ million)[1]					
Electricity generation - Gas	1,934	2,005	2,065	1,987	2,106
Industrial - Gas	1,131	1,243	1,749	1,592	1,661
- Electricity	3,872	3,601	3,319	3,146	3,085
of which:					
Fuel industries	141	166	175	152	144
Industrial sector	3,731	3,435	3,144	2,994	2,942
Domestic sector - Gas	5,343	5,222	5,460	5,797	5,956
- Electricity	7,240	7,120	7,182	7,154	7,295
Other - Gas	927	1,004	1,413	1,288	1,280
- Electricity	4,995	4,951	4,327	4,046	3,833
of which:					
Agricultural sector	222	228	227	213	193
Commercial sector	3,378	3,433	3,072	2,895	2,748
Transport sector	306	287	242	218	222
Public lighting	110	99	86	75	75
Public admin. and other services	979	901	706	645	595
Total, all consumers	**25,442**	**25,146**	**25,515**	**25,010**	**25,218**
of which gas	**9,335**	**9,474**	**10,687**	**10,664**	**11,004**
of which electricity	**16,107**	**15,672**	**14,828**	**14,346**	**14,214**
Average net selling value per kWh sold (pence)[1]					
Electricity generation - Gas	0.613	0.618	0.667	0.609	0.650
Industrial - Gas	0.548	0.583	0.838	0.819	0.850
- Electricity	3.902	3.530	3.247	3.096	2.971
of which:					
Fuel industries	3.429	3.524	3.362	3.194	2.974
Industrial sector	3.923	3.530	3.241	3.092	2.971
Domestic sector - Gas	1.492	1.412	1.440	1.540	1.543
- Electricity	6.564	6.366	6.227	6.246	6.302
Other - Gas	0.757	0.805	1.114	1.146	1.132
- Electricity	5.054	4.912	4.180	3.903	3.636
of which:					
Agricultural sector	5.788	6.033	5.537	5.149	4.804
Commercial sector	5.061	4.935	4.266	3.967	3.701
Transport sector	4.466	4.018	3.247	3.085	2.872
Public lighting	5.086	4.985	4.207	3.913	3.651
Public admin. and other services	5.092	4.918	3.945	3.669	3.423
Average, all consumers	**1.939**	**1.867**	**1.896**	**1.882**	**1.877**
of which gas	**0.928**	**0.918**	**1.043**	**1.057**	**1.080**
of which electricity	**5.223**	**4.981**	**4.618**	**4.486**	**4.373**

(1) Excludes VAT where payable - see paragraph 1.40 for a definition of average net selling value.

1.8 Final energy consumption by main industrial groups[1]

Thousand tonnes of oil equivalent

	1999	2000	2001	2002	2003
Iron and steel and non-ferrous metals					
Coal	216	50	119r	87	54
Manufactured solid fuels [2]	791	751	710	592	619
Blast furnace gas	139	96	272	227	27
Coke oven gas	199	199	123r	72	66
Natural gas	2,336	2,409	2,246r	2,105	2,082
Petroleum	105	191	386r	155r	82
Electricity	1,348	1,310	1,341	1,088r	1,183
Total iron and steel and non-ferrous metals	**5,134**	**5,006**	**5,198r**	**4,325r**	**4,113**
Chemicals					
Coal	297	57	266r	44r	36
Natural gas	4,023	4,003	4,080r	4,117r	3,883
Petroleum	168	216r	386r	333r	380
Electricity	1,864	1,998	1,771r	1,944r	1,732
Heat sold	1,074	1,087	988	1,327r	1,118
Total chemicals	**7,427**	**7,362r**	**7,491r**	**7,765r**	**7,148**
Metal products, machinery and equipment					
Coal	78	38	61	50r	31
Natural gas	2,126	2,175	2,064r	2,000	2,075
Petroleum	357	372r	521r	538r	447
Electricity	1,758	1,821	1,658r	1,713r	1,744
Heat sold	-	-	-	-	12
Total metal products, machinery and equipment	**4,319**	**4,405**	**4,304r**	**4,301r**	**4,310**
Food, beverages and tobacco					
Coal	151	77	151r	136	82
Natural gas	2,399	2,372	2,364r	2,339	2,383
Petroleum	281	224	370r	329	326
Electricity	1,077	974	961r	1,030r	1,016
Heat sold	-	-	-	7r	5
Total food, beverages and tobacco	**3,908**	**3,648r**	**3,846r**	**3,840r**	**3,814**

(1) Industrial categories used are described in Table 1G. Data excludes energy used to generate heat for all fuels except manufactured solid fuels and electricity.

(2) Includes tars, benzole, coke and breeze and other manufactured solid fuels.

1.8 Final energy consumption by main industrial groups[1] (continued)

	1999	2000	2001	2002	2003
Paper, printing and publishing					
Coal	83	37	112r	40r	24
Natural gas	1,078	1,383	1,345r	1,251	1,340
Petroleum	65	44r	111r	115	124
Electricity	945	958	962r	1,017r	1,164
Total paper, printing and publishing	**2,170**	**2,422r**	**2,531r**	**2,423r**	**2,652**
Other industries					
Coal	551	226	400r	367r	235
Natural gas	3,228	3,421	3,355r	3,202r	3,034
Petroleum	2,567	2,631	3,282r	3,219r	3,957
Electricity	2,551	2,751	2,879r	2,869r	3,004
Heat sold	12	12	13	4r	-
Total other industries	**8,909**	**9,040**	**9,929r**	**9,662r**	**10,230**
Unclassified					
Manufactured solid fuels (2)	244	231	209	189	124
Coke oven gas	6	17	32r	3	4
Natural gas	13	10	9	8	6
Petroleum	2,328	2,399	2,122r	1,650r	2,006
Renewables & waste	283	213	213r	222r	226
Total unclassified	**2,875**	**2,870**	**2,585r**	**2,071r**	**2,367**
Total					
Coal	1,375	485	1,109r	724r	462
Manufactured solid fuels (2)	1,035	982	919	781	743
Blast furnace gas	139	96	272	227	27
Coke oven gas	205	216	154r	74r	69
Natural gas	15,203	15,773	15,464r	15,021r	14,803
Petroleum	5,871	6,078r	7,179r	6,338r	7,324
Renewables & waste	283	213	213r	222r	226
Electricity	9,542	9,812	9,573r	9,662r	9,843
Heat sold	1,086	1,099	1,001	1,338r	1,136
Total	**34,741**	**34,754**	**35,884r**	**34,387r**	**34,634**

1.9 Fuels consumed for electricity generation (autogeneration) by main industrial groups[1]

Thousand tonnes of oil equivalent
(except where shown otherwise)

	1999	2000	2001	2002	2003
Iron and steel and non-ferrous metals					
Coal	726	703	769	750	770
Blast furnace gas	729	728	481r	466r	774
Coke oven gas	165	166	124r	123r	136
Natural gas	53	75	63	58r	52
Petroleum	57	34	20r	18	14
Other (including renewables) (2)	72	58	55	57	47
Total fuel input (3)	**1,801**	**1,764**	**1,512r**	**1,471r**	**1,794**
Electricity generated by iron & steel and non-ferrous	**545**	**459**	**504**	**417r**	**517**
metals (4) (in GWh)	6,338	5,338	5,863	4,844r	6,015
Electricity consumed by iron and steel and non-ferrous	**400**	**378**	**412**	**328r**	**366**
metals from own generation (5) (in GWh)	4,656	4,395	4,795	3,815r	4,251
Chemicals					
Coal	119	71	155	145	145
Natural gas	869	1,079	868r	763r	726
Petroleum	132	56	53r	30r	16
Other (including renewables) (2)	364	352	270r	302r	304
Total fuel input (3)	**1,485**	**1,558**	**1,346r**	**1,240r**	**1,190**
Electricity generated by chemicals (4)	**694**	**940**	**792r**	**759r**	**730**
(in GWh)	8,075	10,931	9,208r	8,830r	8,490
Electricity consumed by chemicals from own generation (5)	**585**	**687**	**532r**	**656r**	**555**
(in GWh)	6,803	7,993	6,188r	7,630r	6,450
Metal products, machinery and equipment					
Coal	0	0	-	-	-
Natural gas	23	137	48r	83r	87
Petroleum	11	11	6r	6	6
Other (including renewables) (2)	-	-	-	-	-
Total fuel input (3)	**34**	**147**	**54**	**89r**	**93**
Electricity generated by metal products, machinery	**15**	**66**	**24**	**38**	**44**
and equipment (4) (in GWh)	177	765	274	447r	515
Electricity consumed by metal products, machinery	**15**	**55**	**22**	**36r**	**42**
and equipment from own generation (5) (in GWh)	169	636	259	422r	485
Food, beverages and tobacco					
Coal	31	27	20	20	18
Natural gas	368	345	269	322r	323
Petroleum	10	5	5	4	5
Other (including renewables) (2)	-	-	-	-	-
Total fuel input (3)	**409**	**377**	**295r**	**347r**	**346**
Electricity generated by food, beverages and tobacco (4)	**191**	**183**	**144r**	**169r**	**171**
(in GWh)	2,220	2,122	1,679r	1,965r	1,986
Electricity consumed by food, beverages and tobacco	**172**	**86r**	**83**	**124**	**96**
from own generation (5) (in GWh)	2,005	1,005	966	1,438r	1,121

(1) Industrial categories used are described in Table 1G.
(2) Includes hydro electricity, solid and gaseous renewables and waste.
(3) Total fuels used for generation of electricity. Consistent with figures for fuels used by other generators in Table 5.4.

1.9 Fuels consumed for electricity generation (autogeneration) by main industrial groups[1] (continued)

Thousand tonnes of oil equivalent
(except where shown otherwise)

	1999	2000	2001	2002	2003
Paper, printing and publishing					
Coal	74	52	45r	40r	25
Natural gas	498	629	578	624r	834
Petroleum	15	12	12	9r	7
Other (including renewables) *(2)*	-	9	-	-	-
Total fuel input *(3)*	**586**	**701**	**636r**	**673r**	**866**
Electricity generated by paper, printing and publishing *(4)*	**267**	**337**	**296**	**319r**	**398**
(in GWh)	3,103	3,920	3,446	3,710r	4,634
Electricity consumed by paper, printing and publishing	**239**	**258**	**225**	**210r**	**262**
from own generation *(5)* *(in GWh)*	2,774	3,002	2,619r	2,439r	3,043
Other industries					
Coal	22	24	19r	14r	5
Coke oven gas	7	5	5	5	5
Natural gas	91	144	112r	162r	257
Petroleum	6	5	5	5	4
Other (including renewables) *(2)*	693	838	946r	1,006r	1,195
Total fuel input *(3)*	**819**	**1,016**	**1,087r**	**1,192r**	**1,467**
Electricity generated by other industries *(4)*	**102**	**131**	**96r**	**128r**	**140**
(in GWh)	1,189	1,528	1,115r	1,484r	1,628
Electricity consumed by other industries from own	**67**	**94**	**52r**	**80r**	**75**
generation *(5)* *(in GWh)*	776	1,090	609r	926r	873
Total					
Coal	972	877	1,008r	969r	963
Blast furnace gas	729	728	481r	466r	782
Coke oven gas	172	171	130r	128r	141
Natural gas	1,902	2,409	1,938r	2,013r	2,279
Petroleum	229	123	102r	72r	52
Other (including renewables) *(2)*	1,129	1,257	1,271r	1,365r	1,539
Total fuel input *(3)*	**5,133**	**5,564**	**4,929r**	**5,012r**	**5,756**
Electricity generated *(4)*	**1,814**	**2,116**	**1,856r**	**1,830r**	**2,001**
(in GWh)	21,102	24,604	21,586r	21,280r	23,269
Electricity consumed from own generation *(5)*	**1,478**	**1,558**	**1,327r**	**1,433r**	**1,395**
(in GWh)	17,183	18,121	15,436r	16,669r	16,223

(4) Combined heat and power (CHP) generation (i.e. electrical output from Table 6.8) plus non-chp generation, so that the total electricity generated is consistent with the "other generators" figures in Table 5.6.

(5) This is the electricity consumed by the industrial sector from its own generation and is consistent with the other generators final users figures used within the electricity balances (Tables 5.1 and 5.2). These figures are less than the total generated because some of the electricity is sold to the public distribution system and other users.

(6) The figures presented here are consistent with other figures presented elsewhere in this publication as detailed at (3), (4), and (5) above but are further dissaggregated. Overall totals covering all autogenerators can be derived by adding in figures for transport, services and the fuel industries. These can be summarised as follows:

Fuel input	1999	2000	2001	2002	2003
				Thousand tonnes of oil equivalent	
All industry	5,133	5,564	4,929r	5,012r	5,756
Fuel industries	897	1,159	1,281r	1,589r	1,656
Transport, Commerce and Administration	463	440	470r	430r	251
Services	841	859	808r	1,009r	1,099
Total fuel input	**7,334**	**8,023**	**7,488r**	**8,040r**	**8,761**
Electricity generated	**2,712**	**3,034**	**2,728r**	**2,882r**	**3,097**
Electricity consumed	**2,046**	**2,211**	**1,848r**	**2,109r**	**1,996**
					GWh
Electricity generated	31,544	35,285	31,720r	33,513r	36,019
Electricity consumed	23,979	25,714	21,495r	24,523r	23,211

Chapter 2
Solid fuels and derived gases

Introduction
2.1   This chapter presents figures on the supply and demand for coal and solid fuels derived from coal, and on the production and consumption of gases derived from the processing of solid fuels.

2.2   Balances for coal and manufactured fuels, covering each of the last three years, form the first six tables of this chapter (Tables 2.1 to 2.6). These are followed by a 5 year table showing the supply and consumption of coal as a time series (Table 2.7). Comparable 5 year tables bring together data for coke oven coke, coke breeze and manufactured solid fuels (Table 2.8) and coke oven gas, blast furnace gas, benzole and tars (Table 2.9). As in previous years, tables showing deep mines in production (Table 2.10) and opencast sites in production (Table 2.11) complete the chapter. The long term trends commentary and tables on coal production and stocks, and on coal consumption are on the DTI energy statistics web site at: www.dti.gov.uk/energy/inform/dukes/dukes2004/02longterm.pdf.

2.3   Detailed statistics of imports and exports of solid fuels are in Annex G, also available on the DTI energy statistics web site at: www.dti.gov.uk/energy/inform/dukes/dukes2004/annnexg.pdf.

2.4   Figures for actual consumption of coal are available for all fuel and power producers and for final use by the iron and steel industry. The remaining final users consumption figures are based on information on disposals by producers and on imports. For further details see the technical notes and definitions section which begins at paragraph 2.32 of this chapter.

Structure of the coal industry
2.5   When the coal industry was privatised at the end of 1994 there were four main coal producers: RJB Mining, Mining Scotland, Celtic Energy and Coal Investments. The last mentioned went into receivership in June 1996 and only two of their mines remained as going concerns under the company name of Midlands Mining. One of these two mines closed at the end of 1998 and the other at the beginning of 2000. The other four collieries reverted to the Coal Authority and were subsequently closed. RJB mining changed its name to UK Coal in 2001.

2.6   There are also a number of independent deep mines, which are listed in Table 2.10. Independent opencast coal producers are similarly listed in Table 2.11. Further coal and slurry are supplied from recovery operations.

Commodity balances for coal (Tables 2.1, 2.2 and 2.3)
2.7   These balance tables separately identify the three main types of coal, namely steam coal, coking coal, and anthracite, and show the variation both in the sources of supply and where the various types of coal are mainly used.

2.8   In 2003, 84½ per cent of coal demand was for steam coal, 10½ per cent was for coking coal and 5 per cent was for anthracite. Electricity generation accounted for 96½ per cent of demand for steam coal and 69 per cent of demand for anthracite. Coking coal was nearly all used in coke ovens (86½ per cent), but 13½ per cent was directly injected into blast furnaces.

2.9   Only 3 per cent of the total demand for coal was for final consumption, where it was used for steam raising, space or hot water heating or heat for processing. Steam coal accounted for 68 per cent of this final consumption, just over half of which was by industry, where mineral products (eg cement, glass and bricks) and food and beverages were the largest users. Domestic sector accounted for 57 per cent of the final demand for coal, with just over half of this demand being for steam coal and the remainder for anthracite.

2.10   Chart 2.1, below, compares the sources of coal supplies in the UK in 2003, along with a breakdown of consumption by user and serves to illustrate some of the features brought out below.

2.11   In 2003, 25 per cent of supply was met from deep-mined production, 20 per cent from opencast operations, 50 per cent from net imports and 1 per cent from other sources such as slurry. Supply from all these sources was not quite enough to meet demand and so 2.6 million tonnes (equivalent to under 1 per cent of total supply) were drawn down from coal stocks.

2.12   Recent trends in coal production and consumption are described in paragraphs 2.20 to 2.26.

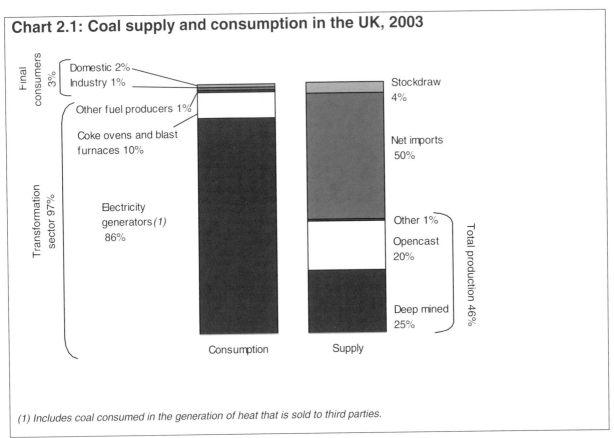

Chart 2.1: Coal supply and consumption in the UK, 2003

(1) Includes coal consumed in the generation of heat that is sold to third parties.

Commodity balances for manufactured fuels (Table 2.4, 2.5 and 2.6)

2.13   These tables cover fuels manufactured from coal, and gases produced when coal is used in coke ovens and blast furnaces.   Definitions of terms associated with coke, breeze and other manufactured solid fuels are set out in paragraphs 2.44 to 2.47.

2.14   The majority of **coke oven coke**, is home produced but in 2003 the volume of imports rose sharply and added some 21 per cent of the home produced volume.   About 4 per cent of home production was exported.   The amount screened out by producers as breeze and fines amounted to a fifth of production plus imports in 2003, and this appears as transfers in the coke breeze column of the balance. Transfers out of coke oven coke may not always be equal to transfers into coke oven breeze, due to differences arising from the timing, location of measurement and the practise adopted by the Iron and Steel works but since 2000, the Iron and Steel Statistics Bureau have been able to reconcile this data. In 2003, 94 per cent of the demand for coke was at blast furnaces (part of the transformation sector) with most of the remainder going into final consumption in the non-ferrous metals sector (eg foundry coke).

2.15   Most of the supply of **coke breeze** is from re-screened coke oven coke with direct production accounting for only 24 per cent of total supply. Some breeze is re-used in coke manufacture or in blast furnaces, but the majority is boiler fuel.

2.16   Patent fuels are manufactured smokeless fuels, produced mainly for the domestic market, as the balances show.   A small amount of these fuels (only 1½ per cent of total supply in 2003) is imported, but exports generally exceed imports.   Imports and exports of manufactured fuels can contain small quantities of non-smokeless fuels.

2.17   Chart 2.2 above shows the sources of coke, breeze and other manufactured solid fuels and a breakdown of their consumption.

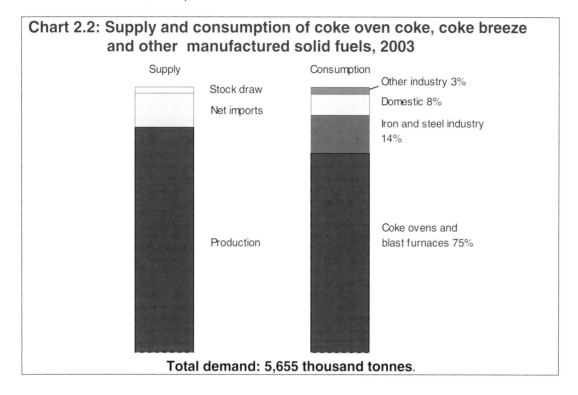

Chart 2.2: Supply and consumption of coke oven coke, coke breeze and other manufactured solid fuels, 2003

Supply

Consumption

Stock draw

Net imports

Production

Other industry 3%

Domestic 8%

Iron and steel industry 14%

Coke ovens and blast furnaces 75%

Total demand: 5,655 thousand tonnes.

2.18   The carbonisation and gasification of solid fuels at coke ovens produces **coke oven gas** as a by-product. Some of this (46 per cent in 2003) is used to fuel the coke ovens themselves while at steel works some is piped to blast furnaces and used in the production of steel (12 per cent in 2003). Elsewhere at steel works, the gas is used for electricity generation (17 per cent) or for heat production and for other iron and steel making processes (20 per cent) and the remaining 5 per cent is lost.

2.19   **Blast furnace gas** is a by-product of iron making in a blast furnace. A similar product is obtained when steel is made in basic oxygen steel converters, and "BOS" gas is included in this category. Most of this gas is used in other parts of integrated steel works with 57 per cent being used for electricity generation in 2003, 30 per cent being used in coke ovens and blast furnaces themselves, and 2 per cent being used for general heat production. The remaining 11 per cent is lost or burned as waste.

Supply and consumption of coal (Table 2.7)

2.20   **Production** - Figures for 2003 show that coal production (including slurry) fell by 6 per cent compared to production in 2002. Deep-mined production fell by 4½ per cent while opencast production fell by 7½ per cent. Overall demand for coal grew by 6½ per cent on 2002 and this resulted in an 11½ per cent rise in the volume of net imports. Longer term trends in production are illustrated in Chart 2.3 below.

2.21   Table 2A shows how production of coal is divided between England, Wales and Scotland. In 2003/04 68 per cent of coal output was in England, 26 per cent in Scotland, and 6 per cent in Wales.

2.22   Table 2A also shows how numbers employed in the production of coal have changed over the last three years. During 2003/04 total employment, including contractors, was lower by 10 per cent. At 31 March 2004, 79 per cent of the 8,365 people employed in UK coal mining worked in England, while 12 per cent were employed in Scotland and 9 per cent in Wales. The closure of Longannet mine in 2002 brought employment in deep mining for coal in Scotland to an end.

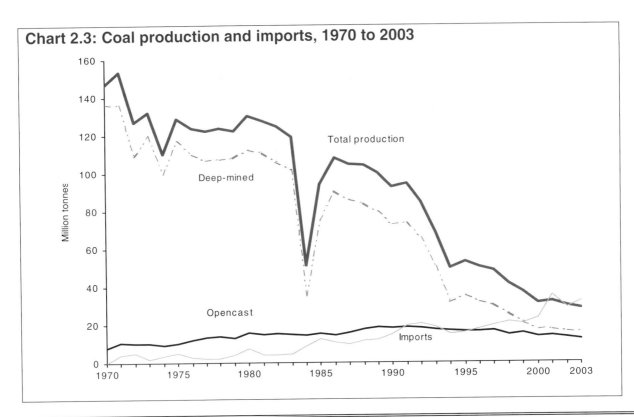

Chart 2.3: Coal production and imports, 1970 to 2003

Table 2A: Output from UK coal mines and employment in UK coal mines [1][2]

	Million tonnes				Number		
	Output				Employment		
	April 2001 to March 2002	April 2002 to March 2003	April 2003 to March 2004		end March 2002	end March 2003	end March 2004
Deep-mined							
England	16.6	15.0	14.1		7,605	6,100	5,867
Scotland	0.8	-	-		367	-	-
Wales	0.7	0.8	0.6		596	577	395
Total	18.1	15.8	14.7		8,568	6,677	6,262
Opencast							
England	4.9	5.0	3.7		1,117	1,113	724
Scotland	8.1	7.1	6.8		1,250	1,202	1,035
Wales	1.2	1.0	1.1		306	297	344
Total	14.2	13.1	11.6		2,673	2,612	2,103
Total							
England	21.5	20.0	17.8		8,722	7,213	6,591
Scotland	8.9	7.1	6.8		1,617	1,202	1,035
Wales	1.9	1.8	1.7		902	874	739
Total	32.3	28.9	26.3		11,241	9,289	8,365

Source: The Coal Authority
(1) Output is the tonnage declared by operators to the Coal Authority, including estimated tonnages. It excludes estimates of slurry recovered from dumps, ponds, rivers, etc.
(2) Employment includes contractors and is as declared by licensees to the Coal Authority at 31 March each year.

2.23   **Foreign trade -** Imports of coal and other solid fuel in 2003 amounted to 31.9 million tonnes, 11 per cent higher than in 2002 but still 10 per cent lower than 2001's record level. Within the total, imports of steam coal rose by 15 per cent – largely due to sharp increases in imports from Australia (up 45 per cent), South Africa (up 23½ per cent) and to a lesser extent Poland (up 21½ per cent). As Table 2B shows, in 2003, 70 per cent of the United Kingdom's imports of coal and other solid fuel came from just three countries: Australia, Russia and South Africa. A further 22 per cent of coal imports came from four additional countries, Colombia (steam coal), USA (mainly coking coal), Poland (mainly steam coal) and Canada (coking coal). Steam coal imports came mainly from South Africa (48 per cent), Russia (20 per cent) and Columbia (13½ per cent). All but 2 per cent of UK coking coal imports came from just three countries, Australia (68 per cent), the USA (17 per cent) and Canada (13 per cent). For more details of imports and exports of solid fuels by country of origin see Annex G on the DTI energy statistics web site at: www.dti.gov.uk/energy/inform/dukes/dukes2004/annnexg.pdf.

2.24   Major power producers have sourced an increasing proportion of their coal from imports over the last four years. In 1999 only 20.4 per cent of the coal they consumed was imported. This rose to a record level of 46.9 per cent (23.2 million tonnes) in 2001 but fell slightly to 43.0 per cent in 2003.

Table 2B: Imports of coal and other solid fuel in 2003[1]

					Thousand tonnes
	Steam coal	Coking coal	Anthracite	Other solid fuel	Total
European Union [2]	314	14	41	161	529
Australia	1,255	4,409	-	-	5,665
Canada	-	839	-	-	839
Colombia	3,398	-	-	8	3,405
Indonesia	402	-	-	-	402
Norway	145	-	-	1	146
People's Republic of China	170	-	40	470	679
Poland	1,896	-	6	-	1,902
Republic of South Africa	12,084	-	110	-	12,193
Russia	4,940	123	26	193	5,282
United States of America	20	1,089	45	-	1,154
Vietnam	-	-	45	-	45
Other countries	474	-	6	150	631
Total all countries	**25,098**	**6,474**	**319**	**983**	**32,874**

Source: H M Customs and Excise
(1) Country of origin basis.
(2) Includes extra-EU coal routed through the Netherlands.

2.25   **Transformation** - The 6½ per cent growth in coal consumption during 2003 compared to 2002 mainly results from an 11½ per cent rise in consumption by major power producers. This 5.4 million tonnes increase in coal consumption at power stations resulted from high gas prices leading to coal fired generation being used in preference to gas-fired generation. In addition, UK steel production especially in blast furnace use picked up in 2003 and this led to a rise of 1½ per cent in the use of coal for coke making and for injection at blast furnaces.

2.26   **Consumption** - Consumption by final consumers in 2003 showed a 43½ per cent fall compared to 2002, but this overstates the current rate of decline. Domestic sector consumption was 47½ per cent down as consumers may not have needed to replace high domestic stocks due to the very mild 2002/03 winter temperatures. Industrial consumption, at 0.7 million tonnes was 37 per cent lower than in 2002 but remained at the same level as in 2000.

2.27   Long term trends commentary and tables on the consumption of coal in the UK since 1970 onwards can be found on the DTI energy statistics web site www.dti.gov.uk/energy/inform/dukes/dukes2004/02longterm.pdf.

2.28   **Stocks** – Production and net imports together in 2003 were only 2½ per cent higher than in 2002, while demand for coal rose by 6½ per cent. Consequently a stock draw of 2.6 million tonnes was needed and this represents a 16 per cent fall in stock level. This contrasts with 0.4 million tonnes stock draw in 2002 and 2.9 million tonnes being added to stocks in 2001. Total stocks at the end of 2003 were therefore equivalent to 21½ per cent of the year's coal consumption, the lowest level in 7 years. Stocks held at collieries and opencast sites at the end of 2003 were 0.9 million tonnes lower than a year earlier but the high demand for coal fired generation in 2003 led to stocks held by the major power producers, at 10.8 million tonnes being 1.7 million tonnes lower than in 2002, the lowest level since 1996. The recent changes in coal stocks are illustrated in Chart 2.4 below.

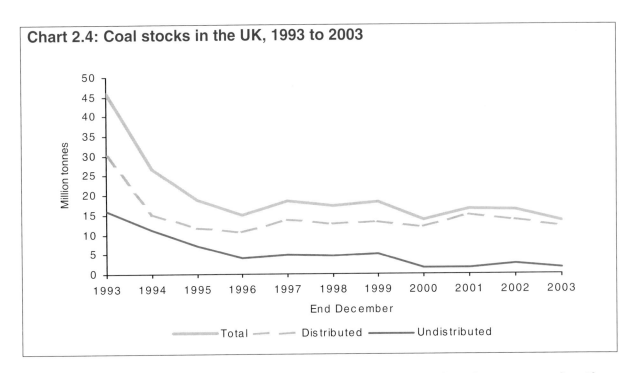

Chart 2.4: Coal stocks in the UK, 1993 to 2003

Total — — — Distributed ———— Undistributed

Supply and consumption of coke oven coke, coke breeze and other manufactured fuels (Table 2.8)

2.29   This table presents figures for the most recent five years on the same basis as the balance tables. Figures for stocks are also included. Coal used to produce these manufactured fuels is shown in Table 2.7. For **coke oven coke,** 2003 saw a reversal in the decline in UK steel making and demand rose by 8 per cent while production fell by only 1 per cent. This shortfall was more than met by imports which rose three fold to record levels in 2003, whilst exports fell by around 38 per cent. The surplus was added to stock and the net result of these changes was that stocks of coke at 230 thousand tonnes were 34½ per cent higher than at the end of 2002.

2.30   In 2003, the demand for **coke breeze** rose by 24½ per cent whilst production and re-screening grew by 40½ and 12 per cent respectively. The net effect was a 39 per cent increase in stock. There was a 14½ per cent decline in the demand for **other manufactured solid fuels,** mainly because of a 12½ per cent fall in domestic sector demand. UK production was down 9 per cent on 2002 levels.

Supply and consumption of coke oven gas, blast furnace gas, benzole and tars (Table 2.9)

2.31   This table presents figures for the most recent five years on the same basis as the balance tables. In 2003, production of and demand for **coke oven gas** grew by around ½ per cent each. Use in electricity generation, coke ovens and blast furnaces all grew but use for heat generation and for general heating purposes in the iron and steel industry fell. Both production and demand for **blast furnace gas** were higher in 2003 than in 2002 by around 19 per cent. This was driven largely by a strong surge in use for electricity generation and in blast furnaces.

Technical notes and definitions

2.32   These notes and definitions are in addition to the technical notes and definitions covering all fuels and energy as a whole in Chapter 1, paragraphs 1.24 to 1.59. For notes on the commodity balances and definitions of the terms used in the row headings see Annex A, paragraphs A.7 to A.42.

Steam coal, coking coal, and anthracite

2.33   **Steam coal** is coal classified as such by UK coal producers and by importers of coal. It tends to have calorific values at the lower end of the range.

2.34   **Coking coal** is coal sold by producers for use in coke ovens and similar carbonising processes. The definition is not therefore determined by the calorific value or caking qualities of each batch of coal sold, although calorific values tend to be higher than for steam coal.

2.35   **Anthracite** is coal classified as such by UK coal producers and importers of coal. Typically it has a high heat content making it particularly suitable for certain industrial processes and for use as a domestic fuel. Some UK anthracite producers have found a market for their lower calorific value output at power stations.

Coal production

2.36   **Deep-mined** - The statistics cover saleable output from deep mines including coal obtained from working on both revenue and capital accounts. All licensed collieries (and British Coal collieries prior to 1995) are included, even where coal is only a subsidiary product.

2.37   **Opencast** - The figures cover saleable output and include the output of sites worked by operators under agency agreements and licences, as well as the output of sites licensed for the production of coal as a subsidiary to the production of other minerals.

2.38   **Other** - Estimates of slurry etc recovered and disposed of from dumps, ponds, rivers, etc.

Imports and exports of coal and other solid fuels

2.39   Figures are derived from returns made to HM Customs and Excise and are broken down in greater detail in Annex G on the DTI energy statistics web site at: www.dti.gov.uk/energy/inform/dukes/dukes2004/annnexg.pdf.

2.40   However, in Tables 2.4, 2.5, 2.6 and 2.8, the export figures used for hard coke, coke breeze and other manufactured solid fuels for the years before 1998 (as reported on the DTI web site) are quantities of fuel exported as reported to DTI by the companies concerned, rather than quantities recorded by HM Customs and Excise in their Trade Statistics.

Allocation of imported coal

2.41   Although data are available on consumption of home produced coal, and also on consumption of imported coal by secondary fuel producers there is only very limited direct information on consumption of imported coal by final users. The DTI carries out surveys of the destination of steam coal imports (excluding those used by electricity generators) from time to time. The most recent was in 1998 and concluded that it was appropriate to allocate 60 per cent of such imports each year to industry, 15 per cent to the public administration sector, and 25 per cent to the domestic sector. This was revised in 2002 to 70, 25 and 5 per cent to industry, domestic and public administration respectively. These proportions remained unchanged in 2003. In addition, 10 per cent of anthracite imports, excluding cleaned smalls, are allocated to industry, with 90 per cent to the domestic sector in all years shown in the tables. All imports of coking coal and cleaned anthracite smalls are allocated to coke and other solid fuel producers.

Stocks of coal

2.42   Undistributed stocks are those held at collieries and opencast sites. It is not possible to distinguish these two locations in the stock figures. Distributed stocks are those held at power stations and stocking grounds of the major power producing companies (as defined in Chapter 5, paragraph 5.47), coke ovens and low temperature carbonisation plants, and patent fuel plants.

Transformation, energy industry use and consumption of solid fuels

2.43   Annex A of this Digest outlines the principles of energy and commodity balances and defines the activities that fall within these parts of the balances. However, the following additional notes relevant to solid fuels are given below:

Transformation: Blast furnaces - Coking coal injected into blast furnaces is shown separately within the balance tables.

Transformation: Low temperature carbonisation plants and patent fuel plants - Coal used at these plants for the manufacture of domestic coke such as Coalite and of briquetted fuels such as Phurnacite and Homefire.

Consumption: Industry - The statistics comprise sales of coal by the nine main coal producers to the iron and steel industry (excluding that used at coke ovens and blast furnaces) and to other industrial sectors and estimated proportions of anthracite and steam coal imports. The figures exclude coal used for industries' own generation of electricity, which appear separately under transformation.

Consumption: Domestic – Some coal is supplied free of charge or at reduced prices to current and retired miners, officials, etc in the coalfields. The concessionary fuel provided to miners in 2003 is estimated at 172 thousand tonnes. This estimate is included in the domestic steam coal and domestic anthracite figures.

Consumption of coke and other manufactured solid fuels - These are disposals from coke ovens to merchants. The figures also include estimated proportions of coke imports.

Coke oven coke (hard coke) and hard coke breeze

2.44   The statistics cover coke produced at coke ovens owned by Corus plc (formerly British Steel), Coal Products Ltd and other producers. Low temperature carbonisation plants are not included (see paragraph 2.47, below). Breeze (as defined in paragraph 2.45) is excluded from the figures for coke oven coke.

2.45   Breeze can generally be described as coke screened below 19 mm (¾ inch) with no fines removed, but the screen size may vary in different areas and to meet the requirements of particular markets. Coke that has been transported from one location to another is usually re-screened before use to remove smaller sizes, giving rise to further breeze.

2.46   In 1998, an assessment using industry data showed that on average over the last five years 91 per cent of imports have been coke and 9 per cent breeze and it is these proportions that have been used for 1998 and subsequent years in Tables 2.4, 2.5, 2.6 and 2.8.

2.47   Other manufactured solid fuels are mainly solid smokeless fuels for the domestic market for use in both open fires and in boilers. A smaller quantity is exported (although exports are largely offset by similar quantities of imports in most years). Manufacture takes place in patented fuel plants and low temperature carbonisation plants. The brand names used for these fuels include Homefire, Phurnacite, Ancit and Coalite.

Blast furnace gas, coke oven gas, benzole and tars

2.48   The following definitions are used in the tables that include these fuels:

Blast furnace gas - includes basic oxygen steel furnace (BOS) gas. Blast furnace gas is the gas produced during iron ore smelting when hot air passes over coke within the blast ovens. It contains carbon monoxide, carbon dioxide, hydrogen and nitrogen. In a basic oxygen steel furnace the aim is not to introduce nitrogen or hydrogen into the steel making process, so pure oxygen gas and suitable fluxes are used to remove the carbon and phosphorous from the molten pig iron and steel scrap. A similar fuel gas is thus produced.

Coke oven gas - is a gas produced during the carbonisation of coal to form coke at coke ovens.

Synthetic coke oven gas - is mainly natural gas that is mixed with smaller amounts of blast furnace and BOS gas to produce a gas with almost the same qualities as coke oven gas. The transfers row of

Tables 2.4, 2.5 and 2.6 show the quantities of blast furnace gas used for this purpose and the total input of gases to the synthetic coke oven gas process. There is a corresponding outward transfer from natural gas in Chapter 4, Table 4.1.

Benzole - a colourless, liquid, flammable, aromatic hydrocarbon by-product of the iron and steel making process. It is used as a solvent in the manufacture of styrenes and phenols but can also be used as a motor fuel.

Tars - viscous materials usually derived from the destructive distillation of coal, which are by-products of the coke and iron making processes.

Periods covered
2.49   Figures in this chapter (and figures for earlier years given in the tables on the DTI website) generally relate to periods of 52 weeks or 53 weeks as follows:

Year	52 weeks ended
1998	26 December 1998
1999	25 December 1999
	53 weeks ended
2000	30 December 2000
	52 weeks ended
2001	29 December 2001
2002	28 December 2002
2003	27 December 2003

The 53 week data for 2000 have been adjusted to 52 weeks by omitting data for an average week based on information provided by the largest companies for the first week in April 2000.

2.50   Data for coal used for electricity generation by major power producers follow the electricity industry calendar (see Chapter 5, paragraph 5.56) and coal use by other generators is for the 12 months ending 31 December each year. HM Customs and Excise data on imports and exports are also for the 12 months ended 31 December each year. Data for coal and coke use in the iron and steel industry, and for gases, benzole and tars produced by the iron and steel industry follow the iron and steel industry calendar (see Chapter 5, paragraph 5.57).

Data collection
2.51   In 2003, aggregate data on coal production were obtained from the Coal Authority. In addition the largest producers (Betws Anthracite, Celtic Energy, Energybuild, Goitre Tower Anthracite, H J Banks, Hall Construction Services Ltd (formerly known as Coal Contractors Limited), J D Flack & Sons Ltd, Scottish Coal Company Ltd and UK Coal plc) have provided data in response to an annual DTI inquiry covering production (deep-mined and opencast), trade, stocks, and disposals. The Iron and Steel Statistics Bureau (ISSB) provides DTI with an annual statement of coke and breeze production and use of coal, coke and breeze within that industry. The ISSB is also the source of data on gases produced by the iron and steel industry (coke oven gas, blast furnace gas and basic oxygen steel furnace gas). DTI directly surveys producers of manufactured fuels other than coke or breeze.

2.52   Trade in solid fuels is also covered by using data from HM Customs and Excise (see Annex G on DTI energy statistics web site). Consumption of coal for electricity generation is covered by data collected by DTI from electricity generators as described in Chapter 5, paragraphs 5.60 to 5.62.

Monthly and quarterly data
2.53   Monthly data on coal production, foreign trade, consumption and stocks are available on DTI's Energy Statistics web site www.dti.gov.uk/energy/inform/energy_stats/ in monthly Tables 2.4, 2.5, and 2.6. Quarterly commodity balances for coal; coke oven coke, coke breeze and other manufactured solid fuels; and coke oven gas, blast furnace gas, benzole and tars are published in DTI's quarterly statistical bulletin *Energy Trends* and these balances are also available on DTI's Energy Statistics web site. See Annex C for more information about *Energy Trends* and the DTI energy statistics web site.

Statistical differences

2.54   Tables 2.1 to 2.9 each contain a statistical difference term covering the difference between recorded supply and recorded demand. These statistical differences arise for a number of reasons. First, the data within each table are taken from varied sources, as described above, such as producers, intermediate consumers (such as electricity generators), final consumers (such as the iron and steel industry), and HM Customs and Excise. Second, some of these industries work to different statistical calendars (see paragraphs 2.49 and 2.50, above), and third, some of the figures are estimated either because data in the required detail are not readily available within the industry or because the methods of collecting the data do not cover the smallest members of the industry.

Contact: James Achur
Energy Markets Information and Analysis
james.achur@dti.gsi.gov.uk
020-7215 2717

John Castle
Energy Information Systems
john.castle@dti.gsi.gov.uk
020-7215 2718

2.1 Commodity balances 2003
Coal

Thousand tonnes

	Steam coal	Coking coal	Anthracite	Total
Supply				
Production	..	373	..	27,759
Other sources	..	-	..	500
Imports	25,098	6,474	319	31,891
Exports	-359	-2	-181	-542
Marine bunkers	-	-	-	-
Stock change (1)	..	-9	..	+2,613
Transfers	-	-	-	-
Total supply	..	**6,836**	..	**62,221**
Statistical difference (2)	..	+223	..	-148
Total demand	**52,759**	**6,613**	**2,997**	**62,369**
Transformation	**51,625**	**6,613**	**2,465**	**60,703**
Electricity generation	51,017	-	2,069	53,086
Major power producers	49,480	-	2,069	51,549
Autogenerators	1,537	-	-	1,537
Heat generation	608	-	-	608
Petroleum refineries	-	-	-	-
Coke manufacture	-	5,731	-	5,731
Blast furnaces	-	882	-	882
Patent fuel manufacture and low temperature carbonisation	-	-	396	396
Energy industry use	..	**-**	..	**6**
Electricity generation	-	-	-	-
Oil and gas extraction	-	-	-	-
Petroleum refineries	-	-	-	-
Coal extraction	..	-	..	6
Coke manufacture	-	-	-	-
Blast furnaces	-	-	-	-
Patent fuel manufacture	-	-	-	-
Pumped storage	-	-	-	-
Other	-	-	-	-
Losses	-	-	-	-
Final consumption	**1,129**	**-**	**531**	**1,660**
Industry	**674**	**-**	**13**	**687**
Unclassified	-	-	-	-
Iron and steel	-	-	-	-
Non-ferrous metals	..	-	..	89
Mineral products	..	-	..	304
Chemicals	..	-	..	54
Mechanical engineering etc	..	-	..	9
Electrical engineering etc	..	-	..	2
Vehicles	..	-	..	33
Food, beverages etc	..	-	..	113
Textiles, leather, etc	..	-	..	12
Paper, printing etc	..	-	..	35
Other industries	..	-	..	36
Construction	-	-	-	-
Transport	**-**	**-**	**-**	**-**
Air	-	-	-	-
Rail	-	-	-	-
Road	-	-	-	-
National navigation	-	-	-	-
Pipelines	-	-	-	-
Other	..	**-**	..	**973**
Domestic	426	-	518	944
Public administration	..	-	..	12
Commercial	-	-	-	6
Agriculture	..	-	..	5
Miscellaneous	..	-	..	6
Non energy use	**-**	**-**	**-**	**-**

(1) Stock fall (+), stock rise (-).
(2) Total supply minus total demand.

2.2 Commodity balances 2002
Coal

	Steam coal	Coking coal	Anthracite	Total
Supply				
Production	..	373	..	29,539
Other sources	..	-	..	450
Imports	21,895	6,315	477	28,687
Exports	-342	-3	-192	-537
Marine bunkers	-		-	-
Stock change *(1)*	..	+162	..	+351r
Transfers	-	-	-	-
Total supply	..	**6,847**	..	**58,490r**
Statistical difference *(2)*	..	+314	..	-154r
Total demand	**49,201r**	**6,533**	**2,910**	**58,644r**
Transformation	**47,090r**	**6,533**	**2,075**	**55,698r**
Electricity generation	46,102r	-	1,639	47,741r
Major power producers	44,506	-	1,639	46,145
Autogenerators	1,596r	-	-	1,596r
Heat generation	988r	-	-	988r
Petroleum refineries	-	-	-	-
Coke manufacture	-	5,807	-	5,807
Blast furnaces	-	726	-	726
Patent fuel manufacture and low temperature carbonisation	-	-	436	436
Energy industry use	..	-	..	**9**
Electricity generation	-	-	-	-
Oil and gas extraction	-	-	-	-
Petroleum refineries	-	-	-	-
Coal extraction	..	-	..	9
Coke manufacture	-	-	-	-
Blast furnaces	-	-	-	-
Patent fuel manufacture	-	-	-	-
Pumped storage	-	-	-	-
Other	-	-	-	-
Losses	-	-	-	-
Final consumption	**2,103r**	-	**834**	**2,937r**
Industry	**1,064r**	-	**31**	**1,095r**
Unclassified	-	-	-	-
Iron and steel	-	-	-	-
Non-ferrous metals	..	-	..	146
Mineral products	..	-	..	500
Chemicals	..	-	..	67r
Mechanical engineering etc	..	-	..	14
Electrical engineering etc	..	-	..	4
Vehicles	..	-	..	53
Food, beverages etc	..	-	..	189
Textiles, leather, etc	..	-	..	20
Paper, printing etc	..	-	..	58r
Other industries	..	-	..	44r
Construction	-	-	-	-
Transport	-	-	-	-
Air	-	-	-	-
Rail	-	-	-	-
Road	-	-	-	-
National navigation	-	-	-	-
Pipelines	-	-	-	-
Other	..	-	..	**1,842r**
Domestic	1,002r	-	803	1,805r
Public administration	..	-	..	18r
Commercial	-	-	-	5
Agriculture	..	-	..	6
Miscellaneous	..	-	..	8
Non energy use	-	-	-	-

(1) Stock fall (+), stock rise (-).

(2) Total supply minus total demand.

2.3 Commodity balances 2001
Coal

Thousand tonnes

	Steam coal	Coking coal	Anthracite	Total
Supply				
Production	..	312	..	31,513
Other sources	..	-	..	417
Imports	27,041	7,723	778	35,542
Exports	-301r	-4	-244	-549r
Marine bunkers	-	-	-	-
Stock change (1)	..	-366	..	-2,886
Transfers	-	-	-	-
Total supply	..	7,665	..	64,037
Statistical difference (2)	..	-231	..	-164r
Total demand	53,273r	7,896	3,032	64,201r
Transformation	50,304r	7,896	1,874	60,074r
Electricity generation	49,554r	-	1,378	50,932r
Major power producers	47,913	-	1,378	49,291
Autogenerators	1,641r	-	-	1,641r
Heat generation	750r	-	-	750r
Petroleum refineries	-	-	-	-
Coke manufacture	-	7,132	-	7,132
Blast furnaces	-	764	-	764
Patent fuel manufacture and low temperature carbonisation	-	-	496	496
Energy industry use	..	-	..	9r
Electricity generation	-	-	-	-
Oil and gas extraction	-	-	-	-
Petroleum refineries	-	-	-	-
Coal extraction	..	-	..	9r
Coke manufacture	-	-	-	-
Blast furnaces	-	-	-	-
Patent fuel manufacture	-	-	-	-
Pumped storage	-	-	-	-
Other	-	-	-	-
Losses	-	-	-	-
Final consumption	2,960r	-	1,158	4,118r
Industry	1,641r	-	48	1,689r
Unclassified	-	-	-	-
Iron and steel	1	-	-	1
Non-ferrous metals	..	-	..	199r
Mineral products	..	-	..	499r
Chemicals	..	-	..	411r
Mechanical engineering etc	..	-	..	14
Electrical engineering etc	..	-	..	4
Vehicles	..	-	..	70
Food, beverages etc	..	-	..	215r
Textiles, leather, etc	..	-	..	47r
Paper, printing etc	..	-	..	163r
Other industries	..	-	..	66r
Construction	-	-	-	-
Transport	-	-	-	-
Air	-	-	-	-
Rail	-	-	-	-
Road	-	-	-	-
National navigation	-	-	-	-
Pipelines	-	-	-	-
Other	..	-	..	2,429r
Domestic	1,251	-	1,110	2,361
Public administration	..	-	..	47r
Commercial	-	-	-	6
Agriculture	..	-	..	5
Miscellaneous	..	-	..	10
Non energy use	-	-	-	-

(1) Stock fall (+), stock rise (-).

(2) Total supply minus total demand.

2.4 Commodity balances 2003
Manufactured fuels

	Thousand tonnes				GWh		
	Coke oven coke	Coke breeze	Other manuf. solid fuel	Total manuf. solid fuel	Benzole and tars *(4)*	Coke oven gas	Blast furnace gas
Supply							
Production	4,286	315	392	4,993	1,773	9,588	15,635
Other sources	-	-	-	-	-	-	-
Imports	911	67	6	984	-	-	-
Exports	-170	-12	-55	-237	-	-	-
Marine bunkers	-	-	-	-	-	-	-
Stock change *(1)*	-60	-83	-	-143	-	-	-
Transfers *(2)*	-1,041	+1,041	-	-	-	+91	-4
Total supply	3,926	1,328	343	5,597	1,773	9,679	15,631
Statistical difference *(3)*	-26	-13	-19	-58	-	+73	-105
Total demand	3,952	1,341	362	5,655	1,773	9,606	15,736
Transformation	3,716	530	-	4,246	-	2,730	9,312
Electricity generation	-	-	-	-	-	1,638	9,002
Major power producers	-	-	-	-	-	-	-
Autogenerators	-	-	-	-	-	1,638	9,002
Heat generation	-	-	-	-	-	1,092	310
Petroleum refineries	-	-	-	-	-	-	-
Coke manufacture	-	-	-	-	-	-	-
Blast furnaces	3,716	530	-	4,246	-	-	-
Patent fuel manufacture	-	-	-	-	-	-	-
Low temperature carbonisation	-	-	-	-	-	-	-
Energy industry use	-	-	4	4	-	5,609	4,724
Electricity generation	-	-	-	-	-	-	-
Oil and gas extraction	-	-	-	-	-	-	-
Petroleum refineries	-	-	-	-	-	-	-
Coal extraction	-	-	-	-	-	-	-
Coke manufacture	-	-	-	-	-	4,441	428
Blast furnaces	-	-	-	-	-	1,168	4,296
Patent fuel manufacture	-	-	4	4	-	-	-
Pumped storage	-	-	-	-	-	-	-
Other	-	-	-	-	-	-	-
Losses	-	-	-	-	-	459	1,384
Final consumption	236	811	358	1,405	1,773	808	316
Industry	137	811	17	965	1,773	808	316
Unclassified	90	16	17	123	435	46	
Iron and steel	23	795	-	818	1,338	762	316
Non-ferrous metals	24	-	-	24	-	-	-
Mineral products	-	-	-	-	-	-	-
Chemicals	-	-	-	-	-	-	-
Mechanical engineering, etc	-	-	-	-	-	-	-
Electrical engineering, etc	-	-	-	-	-	-	-
Vehicles	-	-	-	-	-	-	-
Food, beverages, etc	-	-	-	-	-	-	-
Textiles, leather, etc	-	-	-	-	-	-	-
Paper, printing, etc	-	-	-	-	-	-	-
Other industries	-	-	-	-	-	-	-
Construction	-	-	-	-	-	-	-
Transport	-	-	-	-	-	-	-
Air	-	-	-	-	-	-	-
Rail	-	-	-	-	-	-	-
Road	-	-	-	-	-	-	-
National navigation	-	-	-	-	-	-	-
Pipelines	-	-	-	-	-	-	-
Other	99	-	341	440	-	-	-
Domestic	99	-	341	440	-	-	-
Public administration	-	-	-	-	-	-	-
Commercial	-	-	-	-	-	-	-
Agriculture	-	-	-	-	-	-	-
Miscellaneous	-	-	-	-	-	-	-
Non energy use	-	-	-	-	-	-	-

(1) Stock fall (+), stock rise (-).
(2) Coke oven gas and blast furnace gas transfers are for synthetic coke oven gas, see paragraph 2.48.
(3) Total supply minus total demand.
(4) Because of the small number of benzole suppliers, figures for benzole and tars cannot be given separately.

2.5 Commodity balances 2002
Manufactured fuels

	Thousand tonnes					GWh	
	Coke oven coke	Coke breeze	Other manuf. solid fuel	Total manuf. solid fuel	Benzole and tars (4)	Coke oven gas	Blast furnace gas
Supply							
Production	4,335	224	430	4,989	1,781r	9,549	13,130
Other sources	-	-	-	-	-	-	-
Imports	226	12	18	256	-	-	-
Exports	-272	-46	-67	-385	-	-	-
Marine bunkers	-	-	-	-	-	-	-
Stock change (1)	+261	-14	+14r	+261r	-	-	-
Transfers (2)	-927	+927	-	-	-	+104	-4
Total supply	**3,623r**	**1,103r**	**395r**	**5,121r**	**1,781r**	**9,653**	**13,126**
Statistical difference (3)	-35r	+28r	-28r	-35r	-	+62	-92r
Total demand	**3,658**	**1,075**	**423**	**5,156**	**1,781r**	**9,590r**	**13,218r**
Transformation	**3,224**	**331**	-	**3,555**	-	**3,018r**	**5,838r**
Electricity generation	-	-	-	-	-	1,480	5,402
Major power producers	-	-	-	-	-	-	-
Autogenerators	-	-	-	-	-	1,480	5,402
Heat generation	-	-	-	-	-	1,538r	436r
Petroleum refineries	-	-	-	-	-	-	-
Coke manufacture	-	-	-	-	-	-	-
Blast furnaces	3,224	331	-	3,555	-	-	-
Patent fuel manufacture	-	-	-	-	-	-	-
Low temperature carbonisation	-	-	-	-	-	-	-
Energy industry use	**17**	-	**10**	**27**	-	**5,321**	**4,095**
Electricity generation	-	-	-	-	-	-	-
Oil and gas extraction	-	-	-	-	-	-	-
Petroleum refineries	-	-	-	-	-	-	-
Coal extraction	-	-	-	-	-	-	-
Coke manufacture	-	-	-	-	-	4,270	510
Blast furnaces	-	-	-	-	-	1,051	3,585
Patent fuel manufacture	17	-	10	27	-	-	-
Pumped storage	-	-	-	-	-	-	-
Other	-	-	-	-	-	-	-
Losses	-	-	-	-	-	387	648
Final consumption	**417**	**744**	**413**	**1,574**	**1,781r**	**864r**	**2,637r**
Industry	**239**	**744**	**22**	**1,005**	**1,781r**	**864r**	**2,637r**
Unclassified	151	44	22	217	446r	30r	
Iron and steel	29	700	-	729	1,335r	834r	2,637r
Non-ferrous metals	59	-	-	59	-	-	-
Mineral products	-	-	-	-	-	-	-
Chemicals	-	-	-	-	-	-	-
Mechanical engineering, etc	-	-	-	-	-	-	-
Electrical engineering, etc	-	-	-	-	-	-	-
Vehicles	-	-	-	-	-	-	-
Food, beverages, etc	-	-	-	-	-	-	-
Textiles, leather, etc	-	-	-	-	-	-	-
Paper, printing, etc	-	-	-	-	-	-	-
Other industries	-	-	-	-	-	-	-
Construction	-	-	-	-	-	-	-
Transport	-	-	-	-	-	-	-
Air	-	-	-	-	-	-	-
Rail	-	-	-	-	-	-	-
Road	-	-	-	-	-	-	-
National navigation	-	-	-	-	-	-	-
Pipelines	-	-	-	-	-	-	-
Other	**178**	-	**391**	**569**	-	-	-
Domestic	178	-	391	569	-	-	-
Public administration	-	-	-	-	-	-	-
Commercial	-	-	-	-	-	-	-
Agriculture	-	-	-	-	-	-	-
Miscellaneous	-	-	-	-	-	-	-
Non energy use	-	-	-	-	-	-	-

(1) Stock fall (+), stock rise (-).
(2) Coke oven gas and blast furnace gas transfers are for synthetic coke oven gas, see paragraph 2.48.
(3) Total supply minus total demand.
(4) Because of the small number of benzole suppliers, figures for benzole and tars cannot be given separately.

2.6 Commodity balances 2001
Manufactured fuels

| | Thousand tonnes | | | | | GWh | |
	Coke oven coke	Coke breeze	Other manuf. solid fuel	Total manuf. solid fuel	Benzole and tars (4)	Coke oven gas	Blast furnace gas
Supply							
Production	5,306	210	487	6,003	2,115	11,516	14,767
Other sources	-	-	-	-	-	-	-
Imports	101	56	8	165	-	-	-
Exports	-176	-143	-75	-394	-	-	-
Marine bunkers	-	-	-	-	-	-	-
Stock change (1)	+116	+8	+37	+161	-	-	-
Transfers (2)	-982	+982	-	-	-	+68	-3
Total supply	**4,365**	**1,113r**	**457**	**5,935**	**2,115**	**11,584**	**14,764**
Statistical difference (3)	-29	-7	-38	-74	-	+141r	-100
Total demand	**4,394**	**1,120**	**495**	**6,009**	**2,115**	**11,443r**	**14,864**
Transformation	**3,957**	**313**	**-**	**4,270**	**-**	**3,365r**	**6,025r**
Electricity generation	-	-	-	-	-	1,490	5,493
Major power producers	-	-	-	-	-	-	-
Autogenerators	-	-	-	-	-	1,490	5,493
Heat generation	-	-	-	-	-	1,875r	532r
Petroleum refineries	-	-	-	-	-	-	-
Coke manufacture	-	9	-	9	-	-	-
Blast furnaces	3,957	304	-	4,261	-	-	-
Patent fuel manufacture	-	-	-	-	-	-	-
Low temperature carbonisation	-	-	-	-	-	-	-
Energy industry use	**32**	**-**	**12**	**44**	**-**	**6,053**	**4,709**
Electricity generation	-	-	-	-	-	-	-
Oil and gas extraction	-	-	-	-	-	-	-
Petroleum refineries	-	-	-	-	-	-	-
Coal extraction	-	-	-	-	-	-	-
Coke manufacture	-	-	-	-	-	4,720	649
Blast furnaces	-	-	-	-	-	1,333	4,060
Patent fuel manufacture	32	-	12	44	-	-	-
Pumped storage	-	-	-	-	-	-	-
Other	-	-	-	-	-	-	-
Losses	**-**	**-**	**-**	**-**	**-**	**231**	**965**
Final consumption	**405**	**807**	**483**	**1,695**	**2,115**	**1,794r**	**3,165r**
Industry	**338**	**807**	**37**	**1,182**	**2,115**	**1,794r**	**3,165r**
Unclassified	181	16	37	234	522	367r	-
Iron and steel	32	791	-	823	1,593	1,427r	3,165r
Non-ferrous metals	125	-	-	125	-	-	-
Mineral products	-	-	-	-	-	-	-
Chemicals	-	-	-	-	-	-	-
Mechanical engineering, etc	-	-	-	-	-	-	-
Electrical engineering, etc	-	-	-	-	-	-	-
Vehicles	-	-	-	-	-	-	-
Food, beverages, etc	-	-	-	-	-	-	-
Textiles, leather, etc	-	-	-	-	-	-	-
Paper, printing, etc	-	-	-	-	-	-	-
Other industries	-	-	-	-	-	-	-
Construction	-	-	-	-	-	-	-
Transport							
Air	-	-	-	-	-	-	-
Rail	-	-	-	-	-	-	-
Road	-	-	-	-	-	-	-
National navigation	-	-	-	-	-	-	-
Pipelines	-	-	-	-	-	-	-
Other	**67**	**-**	**446**	**513**	**-**	**-**	**-**
Domestic	67	-	446	513	-	-	-
Public administration	-	-	-	-	-	-	-
Commercial	-	-	-	-	-	-	-
Agriculture	-	-	-	-	-	-	-
Miscellaneous	-	-	-	-	-	-	-
Non energy use	**-**	**-**	**-**	**-**	**-**	**-**	**-**

(1) Stock fall (+), stock rise (-).
(2) Coke oven gas and blast furnace gas transfers are for synthetic coke oven gas, see paragraph 2.48.
(3) Total supply minus total demand.
(4) Because of the small number of benzole suppliers, figures for benzole and tars cannot be given separately.

2.7 Supply and consumption of coal

Thousand tonnes

	1999	2000	2001	2002	2003
Supply					
Production	36,163	30,600	31,513	29,539	27,759
Deep-mined	20,888	17,187	17,347	16,391	15,633
Opencast	15,275	13,412	14,166	13,148	12,126
Other sources (3)	914	598	417	450	500
Imports	20,293	23,446	35,542	28,687	31,891
Exports	-761	-661	-549r	-537	-542
Stock change (1)	-1,164	+4,681	-2,886	+351r	+2,613
Total supply	**55,445**	**58,663**	**64,037**	**58,490r**	**62,221**
Statistical difference (2)	-279	-199	-165r	-154r	-148
Total demand	**55,724**	**58,862**	**64,202r**	**58,644r**	**62,369**
Transformation	**50,886**	**56,136**	**60,074r**	**55,698r**	**60,703**
Electricity generation	41,178	46,198	50,932r	47,741r	53,086
Major power producers	39,583	44,762	49,291	46,145	51,549
Autogenerators	1,595	1,436	1,641r	1,596r	1,537
Heat generation	649	714	750r	988r	608
Coke manufacture	7,919	8,229	7,132	5,807	5,731
Blast furnaces	494	456	764	726	882
Patent fuel manufacture and low temperature carbonisation	646	540	496	436	396
Energy industry use	**10**	**12**	**10**	**9**	**6**
Coal extraction	10	12	10	9	6
Final consumption	**4,828**	**2,713**	**4,118r**	**2,937r**	**1,660**
Industry	**2,040**	**724**	**1,689r**	**1,095r**	**687**
Unclassified	-	-	-	-	-
Iron and steel	12	2	1	-	-
Non-ferrous metals	346	82	199r	146	89
Mineral products	586	202	499r	500	304
Chemicals	434	83	411r	67r	54
Mechanical engineering etc	25	8	14	14	9
Electrical engineering etc	7	2	4	4	2
Vehicles	79	44	70	53	33
Food, beverages etc	215	110	215r	189	113
Textiles, clothing, leather, etc	58	34	47r	20	12
Pulp, paper, printing etc	121	54	163r	58r	35
Other industries	157	103	66r	44r	36
Construction	-	-	-	-	-
Transport	-	-	-	-	-
Other	**2,788**	**1,990**	**2,429r**	**1,842r**	**973**
Domestic	2,517	1,908	2,361	1,805r	944
Public administration	229	60	47r	18r	13
Commercial	4	7	6	5	5
Agriculture	7	7	5	6	5
Miscellaneous	31	8	10	8	6
Non energy use	-	-	-	-	-
Stocks at end of year (4)					
Distributed stocks	13,174	12,005	14,954r	13,704	11,961
Of which:					
Major power producers	12,097	11,034	13,620	12,542	10,791
Coke ovens	1,054	943	1,309	1,148	1,157
Undistributed stocks	5,157	1,646	1,583	2,482	1,612
Total stocks	**18,331**	**13,651**	**16,537r**	**16,185r**	**13,572**

(1) Stock fall (+), stock rise (-).
(2) Total supply minus total demand.
(3) Estimates of slurry etc. recovered from ponds, dumps, rivers, etc.
(4) Excludes distributed stocks held in merchants' yards, etc., mainly for the domestic market, and stocks held by the industrial sector.

2.8 Supply and consumption of coke oven coke, coke breeze and other manufactured solid fuels

Thousand tonnes

	1999	2000	2001	2002	2003
Coke oven coke					
Supply					
Production	5,837	6,058	5,306	4,335	4,286
Imports	389	421	101	226	911
Exports	-79	-243	-176	-272	-170
Stock change *(1)*	+290	-216	+116	+261	-60
Transfers	-951	-827	-982	-927	-1,041
Total supply	**5,486**	**5,193**	**4,365**	**3,623r**	**3,926**
Statistical difference *(2)*	-154	-123	-29	-35r	-26
Total demand	**5,640**	**5,316**	**4,394**	**3,658**	**3,952**
Transformation	**5,113**	**4,764**	**3,957**	**3,224**	**3,716**
Blast furnaces	5,113	4,764	3,957	3,224	3,716
Energy industry use	**20**	**37**	**32**	**17**	**-**
Final consumption	**507**	**515**	**405**	**417**	**236**
Industry	**386**	**370**	**338**	**239**	**137**
Unclassified	226	191	181	151	90
Iron and steel	17	19	32	29	23
Non-ferrous metals	143	160	125	59	24
Other	**121**	**145**	**67**	**178**	**99**
Domestic	121	145	67	178	99
Stocks at end of year *(3)*	**333**	**548**	**432**	**171**	**230**
Coke breeze					
Supply					
Production	33	148	210	224	315
Imports	40	62	56	12	67
Exports	-165	-138	-143	-46	-12
Stock change *(1)*	-40	+22	+8	-14	-83
Transfers	+1,035	+827	+982	+927	+1,041
Total supply	**903**	**921**	**1,113r**	**1,103r**	**1,328**
Statistical difference *(2)*	-206	-115	-7	+28r	-13
Total demand	**1,109**	**1,036**	**1,120**	**1,075**	**1,341**
Transformation	**189**	**202**	**313**	**331**	**530**
Coke manufacture	24	14	9	-	-
Blast furnaces	165	188	304	331	530
Energy industry use	**-**	**-**	**-**	**-**	**-**
Final consumption	**920**	**834**	**807**	**744**	**811**
Industry	**920**	**834**	**807**	**744**	**811**
Unclassified	33	41	16	44	16
Iron and steel	887	793	791	700	795
Stocks at end of year *(3)*	**229**	**207**	**199**	**213**	**296**
Other manufactured solid fuels					
Supply					
Production	635	537	487	430	392
Imports	6	14	8	18	6
Exports	-54	-79	-75	-67	-55
Stock change *(1)*	-7	+38	+37	+14r	-
Total supply	**580**	**510**	**457**	**395r**	**343**
Statistical difference *(2)*	-5	-22	-38	-28r	-19
Total demand	**585**	**532**	**495**	**423**	**362**
Transformation	**-**	**-**	**-**	**-**	**-**
Energy industry use	**13**	**11**	**12**	**10**	**4**
Patent fuel manufacture	13	11	12	10	4
Final consumption	**572**	**521**	**483**	**413**	**358**
Industry	**18**	**25**	**37**	**22**	**17**
Unclassified	18	25	37	22	17
Other	**554**	**496**	**446**	**391**	**341**
Domestic	554	496	446	391	341
Stocks at end of year *(3)*	**141**	**103**	**66**	**52r**	**51**

(1) Stock fall (+), stock rise (-).
(2) Total supply minus total demand.
(3) Producers stocks and distributed stocks.

2.9 Supply and consumption of coke oven gas, blast furnace gas, benzole and tars

GWh

	1999	2000	2001	2002	2003
Coke oven gas					
Supply					
Production	12,090	12,661	11,516	9,549	9,588
Imports	-	-	-	-	-
Exports	-	-	-	-	-
Transfers (1)	+528	+460	+68	+104	+91
Total supply	**12,618**	**13,121**	**11,584**	**9,653**	**9,679**
Statistical difference (2)	-210	-264	+141r	+63r	+73
Total demand	**12,828**	**13,385**	**11,443r**	**9,590r**	**9,606**
Transformation	**3,748**	**3,797**	**3,365r**	**3,018r**	**2,730**
Electricity generation	1,999	1,987	1,490	1,480	1,638
Heat generation	1,749	1,810	1,875r	1,538r	1,092
Other	-	-	-	-	-
Energy industry use	**6,522**	**6,748**	**6,053**	**5,321**	**5,609**
Coke manufacture	5,283	5,555	4,720	4,270	4,441
Blast furnaces	1,239	1,193	1,333	1,051	1,168
Other	-	-	-	-	-
Losses	**173**	**325**	**231**	**387**	**459**
Final consumption	**2,385**	**2,515**	**1,794r**	**864r**	**808**
Industry	**2,385**	**2,515**	**1,794r**	**864r**	**808**
Unclassified	72	200	367r	30r	46
Iron and steel	2,313	2,315	1,427r	834r	762
Blast furnace gas					
Supply					
Production	19,023	17,743	14,767	13,130	15,635
Imports	-	-	-	-	-
Exports	-	-	-	-	-
Transfers (1)	-22	-17	-3	-4	-4
Total supply	**19,001**	**17,726**	**14,764**	**13,126**	**15,631**
Statistical difference (2)	-142	-103	-100	-92r	-105
Total demand	**19,143**	**17,829**	**14,864**	**13,218r**	**15,736**
Transformation	**9,585**	**9,089**	**6,025r**	**5,838r**	**9,312**
Electricity generation (4)	8,476	8,470	5,493	5,402	9,002
Heat generation	1,109	619	532r	436r	310
Other	-	-	-	-	-
Energy industry use	**6,219**	**6,034**	**4,709**	**4,095**	**4,724**
Coke manufacture	1,083	1,057	649	510	428
Blast furnaces	5,136	4,977	4,060	3,585	4,296
Other	-	-	-	-	-
Losses	**1,723**	**1,592**	**965**	**648**	**1,384**
Final consumption	**1,616**	**1,114**	**3,165r**	**2,637r**	**316**
Industry	**1,616**	**1,114**	**3,165r**	**2,637r**	**316**
Unclassified	-	-	-	-	-
Iron and steel (4)	1,616	1,114	3,165r	2,637r	316
Benzole and tars (3)					
Supply					
Production	2,343	2,393	2,115	1,781r	1,773
Final consumption	**2,343**	**2,393**	**2,115**	**1,781r**	**1,773**
Unclassified	580	597	522	446r	435
Iron and steel	1,763	1,796	1,593	1,335r	1,338

(1) To and from synthetic coke oven gas, see paragraph 2.48.
(2) Total supply minus total demand.
(3) Because of the small number of benzole suppliers, figures for benzole and tars cannot be given separately.
(4) For 2003, a new method of calculating fuel use for CHP in the iron and steel industry was agreed (see paragraph 6.33). As a result more blast furnace gas has been allocated to electricity generation and less to final consumption than in previous years. It has not been possible to recalculate CHP use for previous years on this new basis.

2.10 Major deep mines in production at 29 March 2004 [1]

Licensee	Site	Location
Energybuild	Aberpergwm Colliery	Glyn Neath
J Flack & Sons Ltd	Hay Royds Colliery	Huddersfield
Tower Colliery Ltd	Tower Colliery	Rhondda, Cynon Taff
UK Coal plc	Daw Mill Colliery	Warwickshire
	Ellington Colliery	Northumberland
	Harworth Colliery	Nottinghamshire
	Kellingley Colliery	Yorkshire
	Maltby Colliery	Yorkshire
	Riccall Colliery (Selby Complex)	Yorkshire
	Rossington Colliery	Yorkshire
	Stillingfleet Colliery (Selby Complex)	Yorkshire
	Thoresby Colliery	Nottinghamshire
	Welbeck Colliery	Nottinghamshire
	Wistow Colliery (Selby Complex)	Yorkshire

(1) In addition there were 6 smaller deep mines in production at 29 March 2004, viz:

Ayle Colliery, owned by Ayle Colliery Co Ltd, in Northumberland
Blaentillery Colliery, owned by Blaentillery Mining Ltd, in Torfaen
Eckington Colliery, owned by Eckington Colliery Partnerships, in Derbyshire
Nanthir Colliery, owned by M & W A Anthracite Ltd, in Neath, Port Talbot
Monument Colliery, owned by M Bradley, M Bradley and R Ashly, in Gloucestershire
Geison Colliery, owned by S & T Fuels (Partnership), in Rhondda, Cynon Taff

Notes:
Hatfield Colliery, owned by Coalpower Ltd, went into administration on 3 December 2003 and is not currently producing coal.
The Selby Complex, consisting of Riccall and Stillingfleet mines, owned by UK Coal plc, is due to close during summer 2004; Wistow colliery closed on 13 May 2004.

Source: The Coal Authority

2.11 Opencast sites in production at 29 March 2004[1]

Licensee	Site Name	Location
Aardvark TMC (trading as ATH Resources)	Skares Road	Cumnock, East Ayrshire
ATH Garleffan Ltd	Garleffan Extension	New Cumnock, East Ayrshire
Brymbo Developments Ltd	Brymbo Steelworks	Wrexham
Bryn Bach Coal Ltd	Cwm Yr Onen Colliery Reclamation *	Neath, Port Talbot
Celtic Energy Ltd	Margam Opencast	Bridgend
	Nant Helen Extension	Powys
	Selar	Neath & Port Talbot
Dynant Fach Colliery Company Ltd	Dynant Fawr	Carmarthenshire, South Wales
G M Mining	Drumshangie	North Lanarkshire
	Kingslaw Site	Kirkcaldy, Fife
H J Banks & Company Ltd	Delhi Site	Stannington, Northumberland
	Moss Carr Site	Leeds, Yorkshire
	Woodhead Site	Barnsley, Yorkshire
Hall Construction Services Ltd	Earlseat OCCS	East Wemys, Fife
	New Albion Revised	Moira, Leicestershire
I & H Brown Ltd	Begg Farm	Kirkcaldy, Fife
	Colton Remainder	Dunfermline, Fife
J Fenton & Sons (Contractors) Ltd	Meadowhill Farm Gartknowie Extension	Forest Mill, Clackmannanshire
Kier Minerals Ltd	Greenburn Project *	New Cumnock, East Ayrshire
LEM Resources Ltd	Crock Hey Site	St Helens, Merseyside
Minerals (UK) Ltd	Bwlch Ffos Mining Site	Neath, Port Talbot
Newscheme Ltd	Ynys Dawley Farm	Neath, Port Talbot
Patrick Gillooly Ltd	Wilsontown *	Rootpark, South Lanarkshire
S & H Plant Hire Ltd	Park Level Opencast Site *	Neath, Port Talbot
Scottish Coal Company Ltd	Broken Cross & Extension	Lanark, South Lanarkshire
	Glentaggart	Lanark, South Lanarkshire
	Greenbank (St Ninians)	Nr Kelty, Fife
	House of Water	New Cumnock, East Ayrshire
	Pennyvenie	Dalmellington, East Ayrshire
	Rigghead Farm Prospect Extension	New Cumnock, East Ayrshire
	Spireslack Revised	Cumnock, East Ayrshire
UK Coal Mining Ltd	Arkwright Extension	Chesterfield, Derbyshire
	Ashby Woulds (Hicks Lodge)	Donisthorpe, Leicestershire
	Forge & Monument Restoration	Codnor Park, Derbyshire
	Hilltop Group-Southfield Site	Shildon, Durham
	Maiden's Hall	Morpeth, Northumberland
	Moorehouse (Anglers East)	Wakefield, Yorkshire
	Orgreave Reclamation	Treeton, Rotherham, Yorkshire
	Stobswood	Stobswood, Northumberland

(1) There were 39 opencast sites as at 29 March 2004. 35 sites were in production and 4 sites were developing.

Source: The Coal Authority

Note: The sites marked * are currently developing and not yet in production.

Chapter 3
Petroleum

Introduction

3.1   This chapter contains commodity balances covering the supply and disposal of primary oils (crude oil and natural gas liquids), feedstocks (including partly processed oils) and petroleum products in the UK in the period 2001 to 2003. These balances are given in Tables 3.1 to 3.6. Additional data have been included in supplementary tables on areas not covered by the format of the balances. This extra information includes details on refinery capacities and aggregates for refinery operations, and extra detail on deliveries into consumption, including breakdowns by country, sector and industry.

3.2   Statistics of imports and exports of crude oil, other refinery feedstocks and petroleum products, refinery receipts, refinery throughput and output and deliveries of petroleum products are obtained from the United Kingdom oil industry and the Department of Trade and Industry's Petroleum Production Reporting System.

3.3   The annual figures relate to calendar years or the ends of calendar years. In the majority of tables the data cover the United Kingdom.

3.4   Information on long-term trends (Tables 3.1.1 and 3.1.2) and the annex on the oil and gas resources of the UK (Annex F) are now only available on DTI's energy statistics web site www.dti.gov.uk/energy/inform/dukes/dukes2004/03longterm.pdf and www.dti.gov.uk/energy/inform/dukes/dukes2004/annexf.pdf. This information is included to provide a more complete picture of the UK oil and gas production sector.

Commodity balances for primary oil (Tables 3.1, 3.2 and 3.3)

3.5   These tables show details of the production, supply and disposals of primary oils (crude oil and natural gas liquids (NGLs)) and feedstocks in 2003, 2002 and 2001. The upper half of the table (Supply) equates to the upstream oil industry, covering the supply chain from the production of oil and NGLs, recorded by individual oil terminals and oil fields, to their disposal to export or to UK refineries (see Annex F, Table F.2 on DTI's energy statistics web site). The lower half of the table covers the use of these primary oils, including the amount used as a fuel during the extraction process (ie burned to provide power for drilling and pumping operations) and as inputs into refineries, as recorded by the refineries. The statistical difference in the tables thus represents the differences between data reported by these different sources and the sites of production and consumption.

3.6   Gross production of crude oil and NGLs in 2003 was 106 million tonnes, a decline of 8½ per cent on 2002 and 23 per cent lower than the peak production level of 137 million tonnes in 1999. Almost three-quarters of the United Kingdom's primary oil production in 2003 was exported, and imported crude oil accounted for 64 per cent of UK requirements. Feedstocks (including partly processed oils) made up 10 per cent of total imports of oil in 2003. Total oil imports in 2003 were 5 per cent lower than in 2002. Exports of primary oils and feedstocks in 2003 were 75 million tonnes or 14 per cent lower than those recorded in 2002. Exports in 2003 were 38 per cent higher than imports and made a significant contribution to the UK economy (see Annex G on DTI's energy statistics web site). This is down from previous years where exports were 53 per cent higher than imports in 2002 and 62 per cent higher in 2001. Further declines in exports and increases in imports will be seen as indigenous production continues to decline. Chart 3.1 illustrates recent trends in production, imports and exports of crude oil, NGLs and feedstocks.

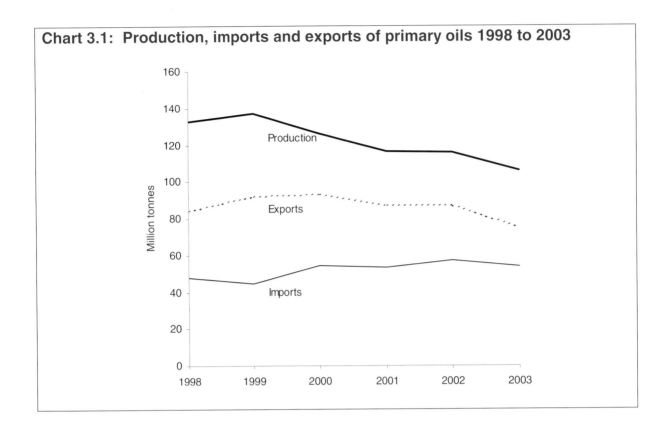

Chart 3.1: Production, imports and exports of primary oils 1998 to 2003

3.7   Although the UK currently produces enough crude oil to meet its own needs, it still imports crude oil. There are various reasons why this makes commercial sense. Primarily refineries consider the type of crude oil rather than its source origin. Most UK refineries use North Sea 'type' crude and do not differentiate between the UK and Norwegian sectors of the North Sea. Indeed, some UK refiners have production interests in both UK and Norwegian waters so the company may own the imported crude at the point of production. The close proximity of some UK and Norwegian oil fields mean that they may use the same pipeline infrastructure, for example the Norpipe oil terminal in Teesside receives both UK and Norwegian crude from the North Sea. Some crude oils are specifically imported for the heavier hydrocarbons which they contain as these are needed for the manufacture of various petroleum products such as bitumen and lubricating oils. This is in contrast to most North Sea type crude which contains a higher proportion of the lighter hydrocarbon fuels resulting in higher yields of products such as motor spirit and other transport fuels.

3.8   Chart 3.2 compares the level of imports and exports of crude oil, NGLs and feedstocks with those for petroleum products over the period 1998 to 2003. Production from the United Kingdom Continental Shelf peaked in 1999 and has subsequently gradually declined in recent years. As would expected, crude oil exports have followed a similar path to production albeit that they initially levelled off between 1999 and 2000 before slowly declining. Crude oil imports have steadily increased to substantially narrow the gap with exports although the UK remains a net exporter of crude. Exports of petroleum products declined from 1998 to 2001 but have subsequently increased while imports of products have followed a similar pattern to that of crude imports by steadily increasing. The UK is still a net exporter of petroleum products and the significant refinery infrastructure suggests that it will continue to do so for sometime. In 2001 the reduction in net product exports resulted from refinery upgrading work for the introduction of low sulphur fuels (discussed below). Additional analysis of the exports and imports of oil products is given in paragraphs 3.14 to 3.18 and the long term trend internet section (3.1.2-3.1.9) and additional details about trends in UK oil production are given in Annex F on DTI's energy statistics web site.

Chart 3.2: Imports and exports of crude oil and petroleum products 1998 to 2003

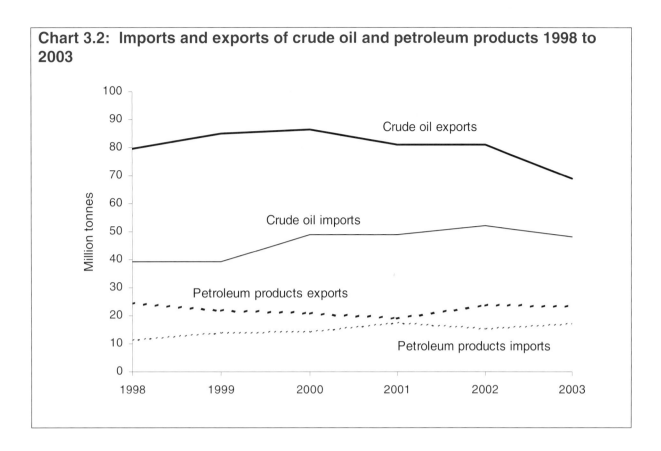

3.9   It will be seen from the balances in Table 3.1 that the overall statistical difference in the primary oil balance for 2003 is plus 229 thousand tonnes. This means that the total quantities of crude oil and NGLs reported as being produced by the individual UK production fields are 229 thousand tonnes more than the totals reported by UK oil companies as being received by refineries or going for export. The reasons for this are discussed later in paragraphs 3.35 to 3.39.

Commodity balances - Petroleum products (Tables 3.4 to 3.6)

3.10   These tables show details of the production, supply and disposals of petroleum products into the UK market in 2003, 2002 and 2001. The upper half of the table (Supply) covers details of the overall availability of these products in the UK as calculated by observing production at refineries, and adding in the impact of trade (imports and exports), stock changes, product transfers and deliveries to international marine bunkers. The lower half of the table covers the uses made of these products, including the uses made within refineries as fuels in the refining process, and details of the amounts reported by oil companies within the UK as delivered for final consumption.

Supply of petroleum products

3.11   Total petroleum products output from UK refineries in 2003 was 84½ million tonnes, which was ½ per cent higher than the level in 2002 (itself 2½ per cent higher than 2001). The first half of 2001 saw the closure of, or slowdowns at, a number of refineries for upgrade work for the introduction of ultra low sulphur petrol. Whilst these refineries were shut down or running slowly for this upgrade work the opportunity was taken to carry out major maintenance overhauls, which in some cases resulted in prolonged shutdowns. The fall in refinery output in 2001 was due to the extended shutdowns in this period while the increase in 2002 reflects the refineries operating normally following the upgrade work in the previous year.

3.12   In terms of output of individual products, production of aviation turbine fuel decreased by 1½ per cent in 2003 compared to 2002 and production of motor spirit and gas/diesel oil both decreased (by 1½ and 3 per cent respectively). These decreases were offset by an apparent increase in fuel oil production of some 9 per cent. This may reflect continued upgrading work at refineries although the benefits of increased production are not yet apparent in the overall production figures.

3.13 The decrease in production of aviation turbine fuel over the last few years is primarily due to the fact that aviation turbine fuel and gas diesel oil are extracted from the same fraction of crude oil (middle distillates), though to different quality criteria. Therefore, as the demand for gas/diesel oil and other middle distillates has increased, there is less of this fraction of the crude oil processed at refineries available for production of aviation turbine fuel. More information on refinery capacity in the UK and refinery capacity utilisation is given in paragraphs 3.40 and 3.41.

3.14 The UK has been a net exporter of oil products every year since 1974, with the exception of 1984 due to the effects of the industrial action in the coal-mining sector. Exports of petroleum products were 23 million tonnes in 2003, ½ per cent lower than in 2002 and 22 per cent higher than in 2001. Imports of oil products into the UK were 17 million tonnes in 2003, which were 13 per cent higher than in 2002 but 1 per cent lower than in 2001. Overall, the UK net exports decreased to 6 million tonnes in 2003, down from the high level of 8 million tonnes reported in 2002 and higher than the 1½ million tonnes in 2001.

3.15 The United States remains one of the key markets for UK exports of oil products, with 4 million tonnes being exported there in 2003. These exports made up 16½ per cent of total UK exports of oil products in 2003, with the other main countries receiving UK exports of petroleum products being Belgium, France, Ireland, the Netherlands, and Spain. The main sources of the UK's imports of petroleum products in 2003 were France, Germany, Kuwait, the Netherlands, Saudi Arabia and the UAE.

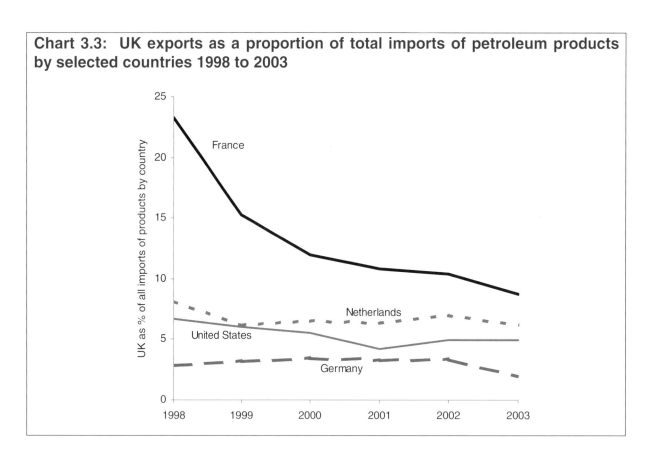

Chart 3.3: UK exports as a proportion of total imports of petroleum products by selected countries 1998 to 2003

3.16 Chart 3.3 shows how the UK has penetrated selected overseas markets for its petroleum products. UK supplied 5 per cent of the total volume of US imports of petroleum products in 2003 (mostly in the form of motor spirit) and 9, 6 and 2 per cent respectively of the total imports of petroleum products into France, the Netherlands and Germany (mostly as gas oil for heating, motor spirit and fuel oil). The UK regularly supplies the vast majority of total oil products imported into Ireland (mostly motor spirit and DERV fuel for transport and gas/diesel oil and burning oil for heating).

3.17 Differences in product types explain why the UK imports petroleum products when it has a surplus available for export. Exports in 2003 were mainly made up of motor spirit (5½ million tonnes), gas/diesel oil (5½ million tonnes) and fuel oil (6½ million tonnes). Imports were made up of aviation turbine fuel (7½ million tonnes), motor spirit (2 million tonnes) and gas/diesel oil (3½ million tonnes). The make up of refinery structure in the UK is such that it contains a surplus of capacity for some petroleum products such as motor spirit, leading to a surplus availability within the UK for export. Imports take place to cover specific periods of heavy demand within the UK, such as around the time of the Budget or during the summer, or cover production shortfalls in the refinery shutdowns for maintenance.

3.18 Similarly for gas/diesel oil, exports from the UK tend to be of lower grades of gas/diesel oil for use as heating fuels, while imports tend to be of higher-grade gas/diesel oil with a low sulphur content. With the introduction of low sulphur DERV fuel and motor spirit into the UK market (see paragraph 3.51 below) and the required increased production capacity at UK refineries for these fuels, UK imports of these products increased to meet the shortfall. Aviation turbine fuel is imported simply because the UK cannot make enough of it to meet demand. It is derived from the same sort of hydrocarbons as gas/diesel oil, and as such there is a physical limit to how much can be made from the amount of oil processed in the UK.

3.19 More information on the structure of refineries in the UK and trends in imports and exports of crude oil and oil products is given in the long-term trends section on DTI's energy statistics web site (Table 3.1.1).

3.20 In 2003, 7½ per cent of UK production of fuel oil and 3 per cent of gas/diesel oil production went into international marine bunkers, totalling 1¾ million tonnes of products, 2 per cent of total UK refinery production in the year. These are sales of fuels that are destined for consumption on ocean going vessels. As such the products cannot be classified as being consumed within the UK, and these quantities are thus treated in a similar way to exports in the commodity balances. It should be noted that these quantities do not include deliveries of fuels for use in UK coastal waters, which are counted as UK consumption and the figures given in the transport section of the commodity balances.

3.21 Details are given in the balances of stocks of products held within the UK either at refineries or oil distribution centres such as coastal oil terminals (undistributed stocks). In addition, some information is available on stocks of oil products held by major electricity generators (distributed stocks). However, these figures exclude any details of stocks held by distributors of fuels or stocks held at retail sites, such as petrol stations. The figures for stocks in the balances also solely relate to those stocks currently present in the UK and as such exclude any stocks that might be held by UK oil companies in other countries under bilateral agreements.

3.22 In order for the UK to be prepared for any oil emergency, the UK Government places an obligation on companies supplying oil products into final consumption in the UK to maintain a certain level of stocks of oil products used as fuels. As part of this, oil companies are allowed to hold stocks abroad under official governmental bilateral agreements that can count towards their stocking obligations. The stocks figures in Table 3.10 take account of these bilateral stocks (see paragraphs 3.65 to 3.68) to give a true picture of the amount of stocks available to the UK.

Consumption of petroleum products

3.23 To help users gain the maximum information from the commodity balances, the text in the following section examines the data given on the consumption of oil products in the period 2001 to 2003. The main sectors of consumers will be looked at first (going down the tables) and then the data for individual products will be looked at (going across the tables).

3.24 Table 3.4 shows how overall deliveries of petroleum products into consumption in the UK in 2003, including those used by the UK refining industry as fuels within the refining process and all other uses, totalled 77½ million tonnes. This was 1 per cent higher than in 2002 and ¾ per cent higher than in 2001. Deliveries had been on a declining trend since 1990, barring a slight increase in 1996, and now appear to have levelled.

3.25   From the tables, one of the most significant changes in deliveries of products in recent years has been the decline in use for electricity generation. In 2003 only 597 million tonnes of oil products were used for electricity generation by major power producers and autogenerators of electricity, compared with 671 million tonnes in 2002 and much higher levels in earlier years (see long term trends, Table 3.1.2 on DTI's energy statistics web site). This change is primarily a result of the move by major electricity producers away from oil-based fuels towards using natural gas as their fuel of choice for electricity generation. This trend is also reflected in the declining level of usage by auto-producers of electricity over the period, despite the growth in auto-generation of electricity by industry as a whole, and in the significant declining use in heat generation.

3.26   The data included under the blast furnaces heading of the Transformation sector represents fuel oil used in the manufacture of iron and steel which is directly injected into blast furnaces, as opposed to being used as a fuel to heat the blast furnaces. The fuel used for the latter (mostly gas/diesel oil) is included under the blast furnaces heading of the Energy Industry Use sector.

3.27   Other figures in the Energy Industry Use sector relate to uses within the UK refining industry in the manufacture of oil products. These are products either used as fuels during refining processes or products used by the refineries themselves as opposed to being sold to other consumers, but excluding any fuels used for the generation of electricity. These amounts are included in the Transformation sector totals. Given the interest in the total amounts of fuels used within refineries, Table 3.7 includes data on total refinery fuel usage (ie including that used in the generation of electricity) over the period 1999 to 2003. The data under the other headings of the Energy Industry Use sector represent fuels used by the gas supply industry.

3.28   Final consumption of oil products in 2003, ie excluding any uses by the energy industries themselves or for transformation purposes, amounted to 71½ million tonnes, 2 million tonnes higher than in 2002 and 1½ million tonnes higher than in 2001.   Chart 3.4 shows the breakdown of consumption for energy uses by each sector in 2003.

3.29   The total amount of oil products used by industry was in decline in the middle-1990s due to industry moving away from the use of oil products as an energy source. In the three-year period 1998 to 2000 oil use by industry was fairly constant. In 2001 industrial use of oil products increased by 1 million tonnes to 6½ million tonnes and fell back ½ million tonnes to 6 million tonnes in 2002. Industrial usage increased in 2003 by almost 1 million tonnes to 7 million tonnes.

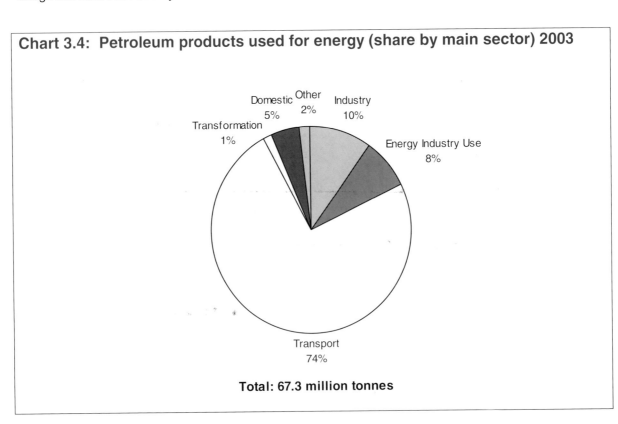

Chart 3.4: Petroleum products used for energy (share by main sector) 2003

Domestic 5%

Other 2%

Industry 10%

Transformation 1%

Energy Industry Use 8%

Transport 74%

Total: 67.3 million tonnes

3.30 Transport sector consumption in 2003 was 1½ per cent higher than in 2002 and 2 per cent higher than in 2001. Higher usage for air transport in 2003 compared to 2002 (up 2½ per cent) with lower consumption of road fuels (down ¼ per cent). Motor spirit declined by just over 4 per cent but this was partly offset by an increase in use of DERV fuel (up 4½ per cent). In 2003, transport usage totalled 50 million tonnes and accounted for 70 per cent of total final consumption of oil products. Consumption by other sectors decreased by 12 per cent in 2003 compared with 2002.

3.31 Consumption of non-energy products increased to 10½ million tonnes in 2003, up by 9 per cent when compared to 2002. In 2003, non-energy products made up 14½ per cent of final consumption of oil products, compared with 14 per cent in 2002. More detail on the non-energy uses of oil products, by product and by type of use where such information is available, is given in Table 3D and paragraphs 3.57 to 3.63 later in this text.

3.32 Looking at the final consumption of individual products, 76 per cent of total final consumption in 2003 was made up of consumption of just three products; aviation turbine fuel, motor spirit and gas/diesel oil, ie predominantly transport products (some gas/diesel oil is used for power generation). Consumption of aviation turbine fuel increased by 2½ per cent in 2003 to 11 million tonnes due to the gradual recovery in air travel following the 11th September 2001 terrorist attacks. Changes in the consumption of aviation fuel are discussed in more detail in paragraphs 3.54 to 3.56 below. For motor spirit, consumption decreased by 4 per cent in 2003. Total final consumption of gas/diesel oil increased by 4 per cent in 2003 and, within this, that part of the total consumed as road fuel (ie as DERV) increased by 4½ per cent. More detailed information on consumption of motor spirit and gas/diesel oil over the period 1999 to 2003 is given in Table 3.8 and discussed in paragraphs 3.42 to 3.53.

3.33 As mentioned above, fuel oil consumption by electricity generators in the UK has decreased between 2002 and 2003. In 2003 total final consumption of fuel oil was 1½ million tonnes, up by 29 per cent on 2002. This is due to an increase in industrial usage of 22 per cent. The increase was partially offset by decreased use by major power producers (down by 23 per cent) and heat generation (down by 39 per cent). Further detail on the consumption of fuel oil broken down by grade is given in Table 3.8.

3.34 Tables 3.4 to 3.6 include estimates for the use of gas for road vehicles. These estimates were based on information on the amounts of duty received by HM Customs and Excise from the tax on gas used as a road fuel. It is estimated that some 104 thousand tonnes of gas (mostly butane or propane) was used in road vehicles in the UK in 2003. While a very small use when compared to overall consumption of these fuels and the consumption of fuels for road transport as a whole, the consumption of these gases for road transport in 2003 has risen five-fold since 2000.

Supply and disposal of products (Table 3.7)

3.35 This table brings together the commodity balances for primary oils and for petroleum products into a single overall balance table.

3.36 The statistical difference for primary oils in the table includes own use in onshore terminals and gas separation plants, losses, platform and other field stock changes. Another factor is the time lag that can exist between production and loading onto tankers being reported at an offshore field and the arrival of these tankers at onshore refineries and oil terminals. This gap is usually minimal and works such that any effect of this at the start of a month is balanced by a similar counterpart effect at the end of a month. However, there can be instances where the length of this interval can be significant and, if it happens at the end of a year, significant effects on the statistical differences seen for the years involved can result.

3.37 With the downstream sector, the statistical differences can similarly be used to assess the validity and consistency of the data. From the tables, these differences are generally a very small proportion of the totals involved.

3.38 Paragraphs 3.72 to 3.83 provide details on the reasons why statistical differences occur for the upstream and downstream sectors.

3.39 The downstream oil data reporting system was reviewed in late 2001 and early 2002 after some discrepancies in the reporting of refinery production data were identified. It was noticed that potential losses within the refining system could be incorrectly reported elsewhere. Given the impact of these factors on the statistical differences, corrections were incorporated in the "Losses in refining process" line in Table 3.7 for the years affected, ie 1999 to 2002. Further work has been done on this and more work is planned to improve the quality of the downstream oil data over the next year.

Refinery capacity

3.40 Data for refinery capacity as at the end of 2003 are presented in Table 3A, with the location of these refineries illustrated in Map 3A. These figures are collected annually by the Department of Trade and Industry from individual oil companies. Capacity per annum for each refinery is derived by applying the rated capacity of the plant per day when on-stream by the number of days the plant was on stream during the year. Fluctuations in the number of days the refinery is active are usually the main reasons for annual changes in the level of capacity. Reforming capacity covers catalytic reforming, and cracking/conversion capacity covers processes for upgrading residual oils to lighter products, eg catalytic, thermal or hydro-cracking, visbreaking and coking.

Table 3A: UK refinery processing capacity as at end 2003 [1]

| | Million tonnes per annum | | |
(Symbols relate to Map 3A)	Distillation	Reforming	Cracking and Conversion
Shell UK Ltd			
❶ Stanlow	11	1	3.8
ExxonMobil Co. Ltd			
❷ Fawley	16	2	4.5
BP Ltd			
❸ Coryton	8	1	2.3
❹ Grangemouth	10	1	3.4
Total (BP)	18	3	5.7
TotalFinaElf Ltd.			
❺ Lindsey Oil Refinery Ltd South Killingholme	10	1	4.1
Texaco Refining Co. Ltd			
❻ Pembroke	10	1	6.1
Conoco Ltd			
❼ Killingholme	10	2	10.0
TotalFinaElf / Murco Pet. Ltd			
❽ Milford Haven	5	0	1.9
Petroplus International Ltd			
❾ North Tees	5	-	-
Petrochem Carless Ltd			
① Harwich	0	-	-
Eastham Refinery Ltd			
② Eastham	1	-	-
Nynas UK AB			
③ Dundee (Camperdown)	0	-	-
Total all refineries	90	13	36.2

(1) Rated design capacity per day on stream multiplied by the average number of days on stream.

Map 3A: Distribution of UK refineries active as at end 2003
Symbols relate to refinery details given in Table 3A

3.41 At the end of 2003 the UK had 9 major refineries operating, with three minor refineries in existence. Distillation capacity in the UK at the end of 2003 was 90.3 million tonnes, 1.4 million tonnes higher than at the end of 2002. Total UK reforming capacity at the end of 2003 was unchanged at 13.8 million tonnes and cracking and conversion capacity was 1.3 million tonnes lower at 36.2 million tonnes.

Additional information on inland deliveries of selected products (Table 3.8)

3.42 This table gives details for consumption of motor spirit, gas/diesel oil and fuel oils given in the main commodity balance tables for the period 1999 to 2003. It includes information on retail and commercial deliveries of motor spirit and DERV fuel that cannot be accommodated within the structure of the commodity balances, but which are of interest. The table also includes additional details of the quantities of motor spirit and DERV fuel sold collectively by hypermarket and supermarket companies in the UK.

3.43 Motor spirit deliveries in 2003 were 4 per cent down compared to 2002, and 5 per cent lower than in 2001. In contrast, deliveries of DERV fuel were 4½ per cent higher in 2003 compared to 2002 which in turn was 5 per cent higher than in 2001.

3.44 Several factors are behind the differing trends seen for motor spirit and DERV fuel. For a number of years, there has been a sustained year-on-year increase in the number of diesel-engined vehicles in use in the UK. Diesel vehicles are more fuel-efficient than their petrol equivalents. In the National Travel Survey carried out by the Department for Transport, diesel-engined cars averaged 39 miles per gallon of fuel, compared with 30 miles per gallon for petrol-engined cars. Traditionally the greater fuel-efficiency of diesel vehicles had been at the expense of higher purchase prices and a performance deficit when compared to petrol-engined equivalents. More recently, the purchase prices for diesel and petrol engined vehicles have become more similar and improved technology has substantially reduced the performance deficit.

3.45 The price differential between DERV fuel and motor spirit has affected the relative demands for the two road fuels. In the early 1990s there was a significant price differential that worked in favour of using DERV fuel. For example, the average retail price for a litre of 4-star petrol in 1990 was 44.87 pence compared to 40.48 pence for a litre of DERV fuel, representing a 10 per cent saving. By December 2003, average retail prices for a litre of the most common grade of motor spirit purchased (ultra low sulphur petrol (ULSP)) and DERV fuel were 75.88 and 77.56 pence per litre respectively. In the mid 1990s, the policy on DERV taxation was changed for environmental reasons and the level of tax was increased to remove the favourable price differential. It is thought that the removal of the favourable differential significantly reduced the rate of transfer from petrol to diesel engine vehicles in recent years compared to what would have otherwise occurred.

3.46 Chart 3.5 shows how the share of total motor spirit deliveries accounted for by unleaded fuel has increased from 72 per cent in 1997 to effectively 100 per cent in 2003. It should be noted that, since 1st January 2000, retails sales of leaded petrol ceased as a result of the implementation of a European strategy to reduce pollution from road traffic (known as the Auto-Oil Directive). Since 2000 effectively all petrol sold has been unleaded. Prior to 2002, super premium unleaded accounted for about 2 per cent of total motor spirit deliveries but this has since grown to over 4 per cent in 2003. It is suspected that the recent increase in the use of this fuel is due to the declining availability of lead replacement petrol (LRP) but there has also been recent growth in the marketing of super premium unleaded as a high performance product that will have increased sales.

3.47 Since 1990 there has been an overall trend of a reduction in the consumption of motor spirit in the UK. Consumption in 2003 was 17 per cent lower than the peak of 24 million tonnes of motor spirit in 1990. Chart 3.5 shows the drop in the level of consumption of leaded fuel caused by motorists switching to using unleaded petrol in their vehicles.

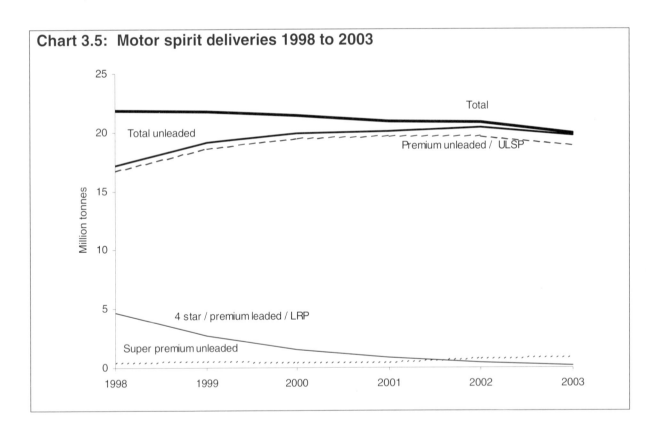

Chart 3.5: Motor spirit deliveries 1998 to 2003

3.48 As mentioned above and as illustrated in Chart 3.6, the large differential between the price of a litre of leaded and unleaded motor spirit helped encourage motorists to switch from leaded to unleaded petrol. In addition, the implementation of the Auto-Oil Directive banned the general sale of leaded petrol (4-star) from 1st January 2000 giving a final push for motorists to switch to unleaded fuels.

3.49 The switch to unleaded petrol provided an impetus for people to change their vehicles to either new ones or those of more recent manufacture. The resultant reduction in the age of the vehicle stock has probably further reduced overall motor spirit consumption, as newer vehicles tend to be more fuel efficient due to improved technology.

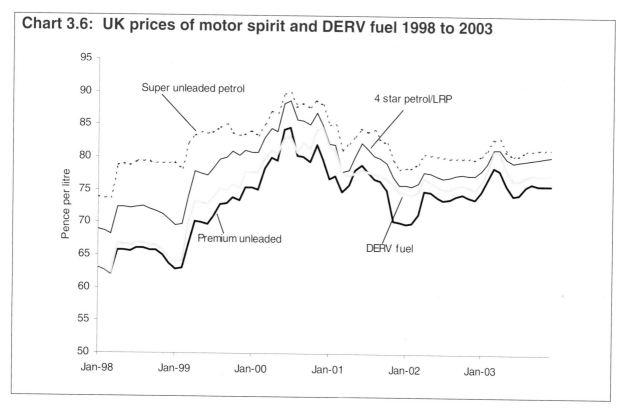

Chart 3.6: UK prices of motor spirit and DERV fuel 1998 to 2003

3.50 Chart 3.6 illustrates the large differential that existed between the price of 4-star leaded petrol and DERV fuel, with the latter being priced at similar levels to premium grade unleaded petrol. As with the differential between leaded and unleaded petrol, this price differential also worked to encourage motorists to convert to diesel-engined vehicles. Chart 3.7 contains details of vehicle licence registrations for private cars during each year for the period 1993 to 2003, broken down by type of engine. Whilst the number of petrol-engined vehicles licensed only grew by 9½ per cent, the number of diesel-engined vehicles licensed has increased more than 250 percent in the same period.

3.51 Although not specifically covered by the statistics included in this Digest, differential duty rates have been used to encourage the switch to low sulphur road fuels, specifically Ultra Low Sulphur Diesel fuel (ULSD) and Ultra Low Sulphur Petrol (ULSP). This extra differential has mostly been used to allow producers to cover the additional costs of providing the ULSD and ULSP, initially through covering the extra cost of importing these low sulphur products and then latterly through funding changes in refinery processes. By mid 2002, 100 per cent of UK refinery capacity for the production of premium grade unleaded petrol (the grade replaced by ULSP) had been converted over to produce ULSP. The introduction of duty differentials has had a significant effect on moving consumers over to what are regarded as more environmentally friendly fuels. Duty differential are now being used to encourage the uptake of sulphur free fuels. Sulphur free diesel will be appearing in late 2004 with sulphur free petrol following in early 2005.

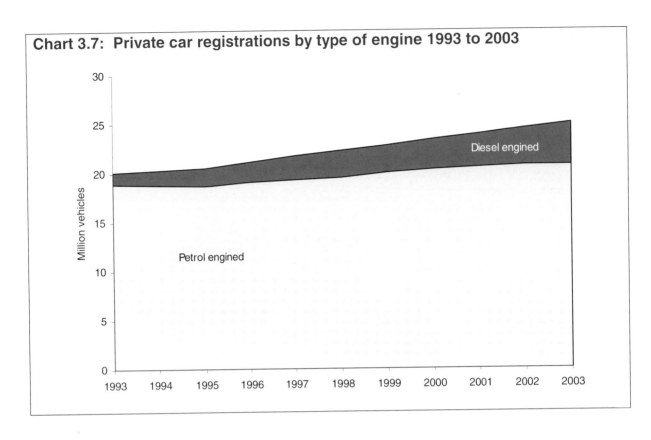

Chart 3.7: Private car registrations by type of engine 1993 to 2003

Diesel engined

Petrol engined

Million vehicles

1993 1994 1995 1996 1997 1998 1999 2000 2001 2002 2003

3.52   Sales by super/hypermarkets have taken an increasing share of retail deliveries (ie deliveries to dealers) of motor spirit and DERV fuel in recent years as Table 3B shows. These figures have been derived from a survey of super/hypermarket companies to collect details of their sales of motor spirit and DERV fuel. The share of total deliveries (ie including deliveries direct to commercial consumers) is shown in brackets.

Table 3B: Super/hypermarkets share of retail deliveries, 1999 to 2003

per cent

	Motor spirit		DERV fuel	
1999	25.4	(25)	18.3	(8)
2000	26.9	(26)	19.6	(9)
2001	28.2	(27)	20.8	(10)
2002	29.3	(29)	22.7	(11)
2003	30.7	(30)	23.6	(12)

Figures in brackets are shares of total deliveries.

3.53 The increases seen in recent years represent an increase in sales by super/hypermarket companies although the percentage shares are also affected by the decline in the overall deliveries of motor spirit in the UK seen in these years as mentioned earlier. Hypermarket deliveries of motor spirit in 2003 remained at the same level as in 2002 while their DERV deliveries increased by 15 per cent. For motor spirit in particular, the hypermarkets are being noticeably successful at increasing or at least maintaining their sales as overall consumption declines.

Aviation fuel

3.54 Data in Tables 3.4 to 3.6 show the changing amounts of aviation turbine fuel (ATF) kerosene being consumed in the UK between 2001 and 2003. The long-term trends section on the Internet discusses the trend seen since 1970 in the use of ATF kerosene in the UK. Overall, deliveries in the UK in 2003 were 2½ per cent higher than in 2002.

3.55 Chart 3.8 shows annual deliveries of ATF kerosene in the UK over the last decade. ATF consumption increased steadily until 1997 and then rapidly until 2000. The September 11th terrorist attacks on the United States had a significant impact on the global aviation industry and reversed the trend for a period lasting more than twelve months. The increase in ATF deliveries between 2002 and 2003 illustrates the subsequent recovery the global aviation industry.

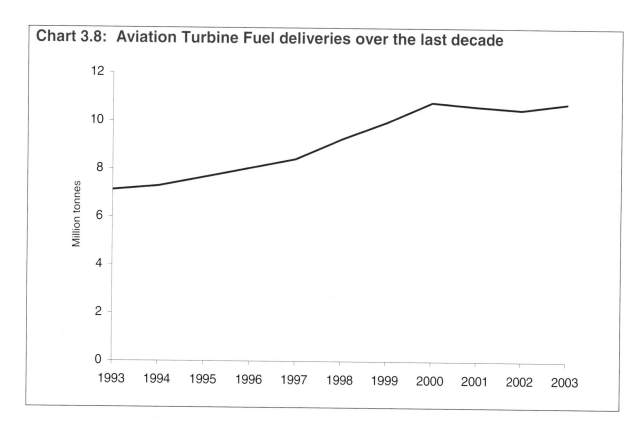

Chart 3.8: Aviation Turbine Fuel deliveries over the last decade

3.56 Chart 3.9 shows the aviation industry's activities over the last ten years split by the domestic and international passenger uplifts and cargo delivery categories. It is clear to see that the events of September 11th 2001 had varied effects on the different sections of the industry. International air passenger movements suffered a fall in the rate of growth, while domestic flights appear to be largely unaffected. The most significant effect however is clearly visible within the cargo division of the industry, which saw a fall of 21 per cent in 2001. Growth of 3.6 and 3.7 per cent in 2002 and 2003 respectively suggest that the segment is returning to its previous levels. The differing ways in which the demand for the industry's separate services reacted to the terrorist attack implies that rather than causing a reluctance of passengers in the UK to fly, the negative effect of the economy, causing cargo demand to fall, had the greatest impact.

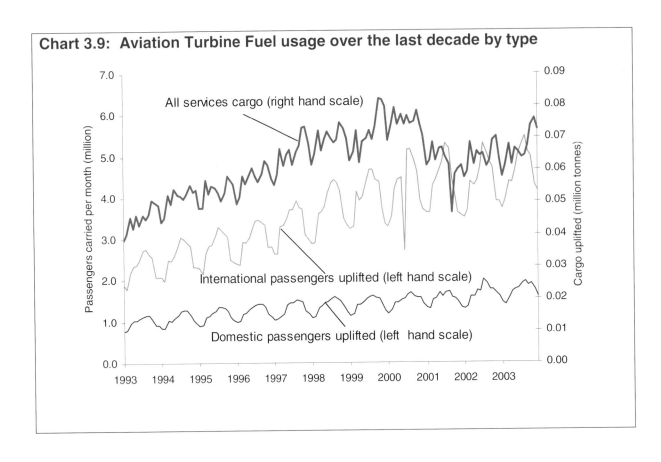

Chart 3.9: Aviation Turbine Fuel usage over the last decade by type

Additional information on inland deliveries for non-energy uses

3.57   Table 3C below summarises additional data on the non–energy uses made of the total deliveries of oil products included as the bottom line in the commodity balances in Tables 3.4 to 3.6. It provides extra information on the uses of lubricating oils and greases by use, and details of products used as petro-chemical feedstocks.

3.58   All inland deliveries of lubricating oils and petroleum coke have been classified as going for non-energy uses only.   However, some deliveries are used for energy purposes though it is difficult to estimate energy use figures for these products with any degree of accuracy, hence no such estimates appear in the commodity balance tables.

3.59   For lubricating oils, about 50 per cent of inland deliveries each year are lost as a film on manufactured goods, lost due to evaporation, consumed during use (ie burnt within engines) or for products like process oils and white oils, the oil becomes part of the product. Work done by the Department for Environment, Food and Rural Affairs (DEFRA) suggests that each year about 50 per cent of inland deliveries become available as waste or used lubricating oil. Some 85 per cent of the waste/used lubricating oil (ie some 360 thousand tonnes) is centrally collected and processed for reuse as Recovered Fuel Oil. The remaining 15 per cent of the waste is probably burnt locally in small space heaters. Studies have shown that the UK's 85 per cent collection rate of used lubricating oils is one of the highest in Europe.

3.60   For petroleum coke, more information is available allowing more accurate estimates to be made. It has been possible to analyse the data available for the imports of petroleum coke to identify which type of company is importing the product.   This work has shown that a significant proportion of petroleum coke imports each year are made by energy companies, such as power generators or fuels merchants, with another substantial proportion being imported by cement manufacturers.   Whilst it cannot be certain that these imports are being used as a fuel, information on the use of petroleum coke in cement manufacture does suggest that it is being used as a fuel.

Table 3C: Additional information on inland deliveries for non-energy uses, 2001 to 2003

Thousand tonnes

	2001	2002	2003
Feedstock for petroleum chemical plants:			
Propane	670	808	781
Butane	259	544	714
Other gases	1,816	1,757	1,810
Total gases	2,742	3,109	3,305
Naphtha (LDF)	1,592	1,480	2,215
Middle Distillate Feedstock (MDF)	411	403	287
Other products	-	-	-
Total feedstock	4,745	4,794	5,807
Lubricating oils and grease:			
Aviation	3	3	3
Industrial	541	545	522
Marine	32	31	40
Motors	260	240	288
Agricultural	10	11	15
Fuel oil sold as lubricant	-	-	-
Total lubricating oils and grease	846	829	868
Other non-energy products:			
Industrial spirit	83	32	33
White spirit	97	125	114
Bitumen	1,934	2,385	2,320
Petroleum wax	33	51	57
Petroleum coke	702	774	830
Miscellaneous products	475	596	449
Total non-energy use	8,886	9,586	10,478

3.61 Using imports data, estimates have been constructed which show that around 830 thousand tonnes of petroleum coke were imported for inland deliveries in 2003 compared to around 840 thousand tonnes in 2002. Around 260 thousand tonnes of petroleum coke were estimated to have been imported in 2001 for energy uses (for electricity generation, use as a fuel in the manufacture of cement, sold as a solid fuel or to be used in the manufacture of other solid fuels). In 2002, the level for energy use was 320 thousand tonnes. Estimates of imports for energy uses fell in 2003 to 263 thousand tonnes or 32 per cent of total supplies.

3.62 Analysis of the data on the quantity and value of imports of petroleum coke into the UK from HM Customs and Excise provides some estimates for the cost of imports and gives some indication of the prices being paid. These are only indicative of the prices being paid in the port of importation, and do not include the extra transport costs from the port to the final destination that would be part of more rigorous price estimate. Details of these estimates are included in Annex G on trade in fuels, as part of Table G.3 on the DTI energy statistics website. A breakdown has been made by grade of petroleum coke and type of use for imports into the UK, which is given in Table 3D below. Calcined petroleum coke is virtually pure carbon, and as such is more valuable than non-calcined (otherwise known as "green") petroleum coke, as shown by the higher price per tonne it commands and the fact that it is not used simply as a fuel.

Table 3D: Estimated £ per tonne for imports of petroleum coke into the UK

	Non-calcined ("green") petroleum coke			Calcined petroleum coke
	Energy	Non-energy	Total	Non-energy
2001	32.9	50.1	41.3	122.4
2002	18.0	37.9	26.2	131.0
2003	22.2	28.9	25.9	122.7

3.63   Petroleum coke is a relatively low energy content fuel, having a calorific value of 35.8 GJ per tonne, compared with an average for petroleum products of 45.9 GJ per tonne, and 43.4 GJ per tonne for fuel oil. It is however higher than coal (27.6 GJ per tonne) and in certain areas is competing with coal as a fuel. It has the advantage of being a very cheap fuel, since it is often regarded as a waste product rather than a specific output from the refining process. Compared to imports of coal, prices of petroleum coke per GJ were about 60 per cent lower in 2003.

Inland deliveries by country (Table 3.9)

3.64   This table shows deliveries in England and Wales, Scotland, and Northern Ireland for 2001 to 2003. The figures for deliveries for energy use show decreases in use for Scotland and England and Wales. The 11 per cent increase in energy use in Northern Ireland between 2001 and 2003 reflect increases in deliveries of road fuels with motor spirit up by 4 per cent and DERV up by 41½ per cent. These increases probably reflect success in tackling illegal cross-border smuggling from the Republic of Ireland into Northern Ireland. Despite a 10½ per cent increase in DERV deliveries, energy deliveries in England and Wales fell slightly between 2001 and 2003, with motor spirit down by 5 per cent. The 4 per cent fall in Scotland largely resulted from a 6½ per cent decrease in motor spirit deliveries. Scotland and Northern Ireland also experienced significant increases in deliveries of burning oil, up by 28½ per cent and 16 per cent respectively.   Non-energy use deliveries in England and Wales increased by 19 per cent and increased by 15 per cent in Scotland with these changes being driven by demand for feedstock for the petrochemical industry.   Non-energy use in Northern Ireland is substantially lower than other parts of the UK since there are no refineries there.

Stocks of oil (Table 3.10)

3.65   This table shows stocks of crude oil, feedstocks (including partly processed oils) and products (in detail) at the end of each year. Stocks of crude oil and feedstocks decreased in 2003, with decreases in stocks held at offshore facilities and oil terminals offsetting an increase in stocks held at refineries.

3.66   The UK holds emergency stocks of oil to help reduce the adverse impact on the UK of any disruptions of supplies of oil arising from domestic or international incidents.   EU legislation (EU Directive 93/98) requires EU member states to hold strategic oil stocks equivalent to 90 days worth of average daily consumption calculated from the previous calendar year. These stocks are held purely to deal with oil supply emergencies, not to manage or affect prices. Since the UK is currently self-sufficient in oil supplies, it receives a derogation of 25 per cent on its obligation and is only required to hold stocks equivalent to 67½ days of consumption.

3.67   To meet this obligation the UK government requires companies supplying oil products into final consumption in the UK to maintain a certain level of emergency stocks of oil products as fuels. As part of this, oil companies are allowed to hold stocks abroad under official government bilateral agreements. The stock figures in Table 3.10 take account of these stocks to give a true picture of the amount of stocks available to the UK.

3.68   Stocks of petroleum products at the end of 2003 were 10 per cent higher than a year earlier. The total stocks of crude oil and products held by UK companies at the end of 2003 were equivalent to approximately 78.6 days of UK consumption.

Technical notes and definitions

Indigenous production

3.69   The term indigenous is used throughout this chapter and includes oil from the UK Continental Shelf both offshore and onshore.

Deliveries

3.70   These are deliveries into consumption, as opposed to being estimates of actual consumption or use. They are split between inland deliveries and deliveries to marine bunkers. Inland deliveries will not necessarily be consumed in the United Kingdom (eg aviation fuels).

Sources of data

3.71   The majority of the data included in the text and tables of this chapter are derived from the UK Petroleum Industry Association (UKPIA) data collection system. Data relating to the inland operations of the UK oil industry (ie information on the supply, refining and distribution of oil in the UK) are collected from companies. The data format and coverage have been designed to meet most of the needs of both government and the industry itself. Each member of UKPIA provides returns on its refining activities and deliveries of various products to the internal UK market. This information is supplemented whenever necessary to allow for complete coverage within the statistics, with separate exercises carried out on special topics (for example, the work on super/hypermarkets referred to in paragraph 3.52).

Statistical differences

3.72   In Tables 3.1 to 3.7, there are headings titled "statistical differences". These are differences between the separately observed figures for production and delivery of crude oil and products during the path of their movement from the point of production to the point of consumption.

3.73   These headings listed in the primary oil commodity balances (Tables 3.1 to 3.3) are differences between the separately observed and reported figures for production from onshore or offshore fields and supply to the UK market that cannot be accounted for by any specific factors. Primarily they result from inaccuracies in the meters at various points along offshore pipelines. These meters vary slightly in their accuracy within accepted tolerances, giving rise to both losses and gains when the volumes of oil flowing are measured. Errors may also occur when non-standard conditions are used to meter the oil flow.

3.74   Another technical factor that can contribute to the statistical differences relates to the recording of quantities at the producing field (which is the input for the production data) and at oil terminals and refineries, since they are in effect measuring different types of oil. Terminals and refineries are able to measure a standardised, stabilised crude oil, ie with its water content and content of NGLs at a standard level and with the amounts being measured at standard conditions. However, at the producing field they are dealing with a "live" crude oil that can have a varying level of water and NGLs within it. While offshore companies report live crude at field, the disposals from oil terminals and offshore loading fields are reported as stabilised crude oil. This effectively assumes that terminal disposals are stabilised crude production figures. These changes were introduced in the 2002 edition of this Digest.

3.75   Part of the overall statistical difference may also be due to problems with the correct reporting of individual NGLs at the production site and at terminals and refineries. It is known that there is some mixing of condensate and other NGLs in with what might otherwise be stabilised crude oil before it enters the pipeline. This mixing occurs as it removes the need for separate pipeline systems for transporting the NGLs and it also allows the viscosity of the oil passing down the pipeline to be varied as necessary. While the quantity figures recorded by terminals are in terms of stabilised crude oil, with the NGL component removed, there may be situations where what is being reported does not comply with this requirement.

3.76   Refinery data are collated from details of individual shipments received and made by each refinery and terminal operating company. Each year there are thousands of such shipments, which may be reported separately by two or three different companies involved in the movement. Whilst intensive work is carried out to check these returns, it is possible that some double counting of receipts might be occurring.

3.77 Temperature, pressure and natural leakage also contribute to the statistical differences. In addition, small discrepancies can occur between the estimated calorific values used at the field and the more accurate values measured at the onshore terminal where data are shown on an energy basis. The statistical differences can also be affected by rounding or clerical errors or unrecorded losses, such as leakage. Other contributory factors are inaccuracies in the reporting of the amounts being disposed of to the various activities listed, including differences between the quantities reported as going to refineries and the actual amounts passing through refineries.

3.78 Similarly, the data under these headings in Tables 3.4 to 3.6 are the differences between the deliveries of petroleum products to the inland UK market reported by the supplying companies and estimates for such deliveries. These estimates are calculated by taking the output of products reported by refineries and then adjusting it by the relevant factors (such as imports and exports of the products, changes in the levels of stocks etc.).

3.79 It may be thought that such differences should not exist as the data underlying both the observed deliveries into the UK market and the individual components of the estimates (ie production, imports, exports, stocks) come from the same source (the oil companies). While it is true that each oil company provides data on its own activities in each area, there are separate areas of operation within the companies that report their own part of the overall data. Table 3E below illustrates this.

Table 3E: Sources of data within oil companies

Area covered	Source
Refinery production	Refinery
Imports and exports	Refinery, logistics departments, oil traders
Stocks	Refinery, crude and product terminals, major storage and distribution sites
Final deliveries	Sales, marketing and accounts departments

3.80 Each individual reporting source will have direct knowledge of its own data. For example, refineries will know what they produce and how much leaves the refinery gate as part of routine monitoring of the refinery operations. Similarly other such data as sales to final consumers or imports and exports will be closely monitored. Companies will ensure that each component set of data reported is as accurate as possible but their reporting systems may not be integrated, meaning that internal consistency checks across all reported data cannot be made. Each part of a company may also work to different timings as well, which may further add to the degree of differences seen. The main area where there is known to be a problem is with the "Transfers" heading in the commodity balances.

3.81 The data reported under this heading have two components. Firstly there is an allowance for reclassification of products within the refining process. For example, butane can be added to motor spirit to improve the octane rating, aviation turbine fuel could be reclassified as gas diesel oil if its quality deteriorates, and much of the fuel oil imported into the UK is further refined into other petroleum products. Secondly and in addition to these inter-product transfers, the data also include an allowance to cover the receipt of backflows of products from petrochemical plants. Such plants are often very closely integrated with refineries (for example, BP's refinery at Grangemouth is right next to the petrochemical plant). A deduction for these backflows thus needs to be included under the "Transfers" heading so that calculated estimates reflect net output and are thus more comparable with the basis of the observed deliveries data.

3.82 However, there is scope for error in the recording of these two components. With inter-product transfers, the data are recorded within the refinery during the refining and blending processes where the usual units used to record the changes are volume rather than masses. Different factors apply for each product when converting from a volume to mass basis, as shown by the conversion factors given in Annex A of this Digest. Thus, a balanced transfer in volume terms may not be equivalent when converted to a mass basis. This is thought to be the main source of error within the individual product balances.

3.83   With the backflows data, as the observed deliveries data are derived from sales data on a "net" basis and will therefore exclude the element of backflows, it is thought that there is significant scope for error in the recording of the backflows when received at a refinery.   For example, these could be seen simply as an input of fuel oils to be used as a feedstock, and thus recorded as an input without their precise nature being recorded – in effect a form of double-counting. It is this relationship between the petrochemical sector and refineries that is thought to be the main source of error in the overall oil commodity balances. As mentioned in paragraph 3.39, work is planned over the next year to review the downstream oil reporting system.

Imports and exports

3.84   The information given under the headings "imports" and "exports" in this chapter are the figures recorded by importers and exporters of oil. They thus differ in some cases from the import and export figures provided by HM Customs and Excise that are given in Annex G on the Internet.   These differences may arise since whilst the trader's figures are a record of actual movements in the period, for non-EU trade, HM Customs and Excise figures show the trade as declared by exporters on documents received during the period stated. The Customs figures also include re-exports. These are products that may have originally entered the UK as imports from another country and been stored in the UK prior to being exported back out of the UK, as opposed to having been actually produced in the UK.

Marine bunkers

3.85   This covers deliveries to ocean going and coastal vessels under international bunker contracts. Other deliveries to fishing, coastal and inland vessels are excluded.

Crude and process oils

3.86   These are all feedstocks, other than distillation benzene, for refining at refinery plants. Gasoline feedstock is any process oil whether clean or dirty which is used as a refinery feedstock for the manufacture of gasoline or naphtha.   Other refinery feedstock is any process oil used for the manufacture of any other petroleum products.

Refineries

3.87   Refineries distilling crude and process oils to obtain petroleum products.   This excludes petrochemical plants, plants only engaged in re-distilling products to obtain better grades, crude oil stabilisation plants and gas separation plants.

Products used as fuel (energy use)

3.88   The following paragraphs define the product headings used in the text and tables of this chapter, which are used for energy in some way, either directly as a fuel or as an input into electricity generation.

Refinery fuel - Petroleum products used as fuel at refineries.

Ethane - An ethane (C_2H_6) rich gas in natural gas and refinery gas streams. Primarily used, or intended to be used, as a chemical feedstock.

Propane - Hydrocarbon containing three carbon atoms, gaseous at normal temperature but generally stored and transported under pressure as a liquid. Used mainly for industrial purposes and some domestic heating and cooking.

Butane - Hydrocarbon containing four carbon atoms, otherwise as for propane. Additionally used as a constituent of motor spirit to increase vapour pressure and as a chemical feedstock.

Naphtha (Light distillate feedstock) - Petroleum distillate boiling predominantly below 200°C.

Aviation spirit - All light hydrocarbon oils intended for use in aviation piston-engine power units, whether in the air, on land, or on water, including bench testing of aircraft engines.

Motor spirit - Blended light petroleum components used as fuel for spark-ignition internal-combustion engines other than aircraft engines:

(i)   4 star grade - all finished motor spirit with an octane number (research method) not less than 97. This can include leaded petrol or unleaded petrol containing an alternative to lead as an anti-wear additive (lead replacement petrol – LRP).

(ii)   Premium unleaded grade - all finished motor spirit, with an octane number (research method) not less than 95.

(iii)   Ultra Low Sulphur Petrol - this is finished motor spirit with a specification similar to that for Premium unleaded grade, but with a sulphur content of less that 50 parts per million (ppm).

(iv)   Super premium unleaded grade - all finished motor spirit, with an octane number (research method) not less than 97.

Aviation turbine fuel (ATF) - All other turbine fuel intended for use in aviation gas-turbine power units, whether in the air, on land or on water, including bench testing of aircraft engines.

Burning oil (kerosene) - Refined petroleum fuel, intermediate in volatility between motor spirit and gas oil, used for lighting and heating. White spirit and kerosene used for lubricant blends are excluded.

Gas oil/automotive diesel - Petroleum fuel having a distillation range immediately between kerosene and light-lubricating oil:

(i)   **DERV (Diesel Engined Road Vehicle) fuel** - automotive diesel fuel for use in high speed, compression ignition engines in vehicles subject to Vehicle Excise Duty.

(ii)   **Ultra Low Sulphur Diesel** – A grade of DERV fuel with less than 50 ppm sulphur (below 0.005 per cent).

(iii)   **Gas oil** - used as a burner fuel in heating installations, for industrial gas turbines and as for DERV (but in vehicles not subject to Vehicle Excise Duty eg Agriculture vehicles, fishing vessels, construction equipment).

(iv)   **Marine diesel oil** - heavier type of gas oil suitable for heavy industrial and marine compression-ignition engines.

Fuel oil - Heavy petroleum residue blends used in atomising burners and for heavy duty marine diesel engines (marine bunkers, etc.) normally requiring pre-heating before combustion, but excluding fuel oil for grease making or lubricating oil and fuel oil sold as such for road making.

Orimulsion - An emulsion of bitumen in water used as a fuel primarily in power stations. In the tables Orimulsion is normally excluded from fuel oil, but where it is not shown separately it will be designated as part of fuel oils. From May 1996 Orimulsion has been classified as a type of bitumen for overseas trade purposes (see below). It was last imported in February 1997. Since that time the sole power station in the UK that was using it as a fuel has ceased to generate.

Products not used as fuel (non-energy use)
3.89   The following paragraphs define the product headings used in the text and tables of this chapter, which are used for non-energy purposes.

Feedstock for petroleum chemical plants - All petroleum products intended for use in the manufacture of petroleum chemicals. This includes middle distillate feedstock of which there are several grades depending on viscosity. The boiling point ranges between 200°C and 400°C. (A deduction has been made from these figures equal to the quantity of feedstock used in making the conventional petroleum products that are produced during the processing of the feedstock. The output and deliveries of these conventional petroleum products are included elsewhere as appropriate.)

White spirit - A highly refined distillate with a boiling range of about $150\,^{\circ}C$ to $200\,^{\circ}C$ used as a paint solvent and for dry cleaning purposes etc.

Industrial spirit - Refined petroleum fractions with boiling ranges up to $200\,^{\circ}C$ dependent on the use to which they are put - eg seed extraction, rubber solvents, perfume etc.

Lubricating oils (and grease) - Refined heavy distillates obtained from the vacuum distillation of petroleum residues. Includes liquid and solid hydrocarbons sold by the lubricating oil trade, either alone or blended with fixed oils, metallic soaps and other organic and/or inorganic bodies. A certain percentage of inland deliveries are re-used as a fuel (see paragraphs 3.57 to 3.63).

Bitumen - The residue left after the production of lubricating oil distillates and vacuum gas oil for upgrading plant feedstock. Used mainly for road making and building construction purposes. Includes other petroleum products, creosote and tar mixed with bitumen for these purposes and fuel oil sold as such for road making.

Petroleum wax - Includes paraffin wax, which is a white crystalline hydrocarbon material of low oil content normally obtained during the refining of lubricating oil distillate, paraffin scale, slack wax, microcrystalline wax and wax emulsions. Used for candle manufacture, polishes, food containers, wrappings etc.

Petroleum cokes - Carbonaceous material derived from hydrocarbon oils, uses for which include metallurgical electrode manufacture. Quantities of imports of this product are used as a fuel, primarily in the manufacture of cement (see paragraphs 3.57 to 3.63).

Miscellaneous products - Includes aromatic extracts, defoament solvents and other minor miscellaneous products.

Main classes of consumer

3.90 The following are definitions of the main groupings of users of petroleum products used in the text and tables of this chapter.

Electricity generators - Petroleum products delivered for use by major power producers and other companies for electricity generation including those deliveries to the other industries listed below which are used for autogeneration of electricity (Tables 3.4 to 3.6). This includes petroleum products used to generate electricity at oil refineries and is recorded in the Transformation sector, as opposed to other uses of refinery fuels which are recorded in the Energy Industry Use sector. Because delivered fuel may be put to stock and not used immediately and because generators may consume stocks rather than order new deliveries of petroleum products, these numbers may not necessarily be the same as those reported in the **Electricity** chapter (Chapter 5) which gives **consumption** of petroleum products by electricity generators.

Agriculture - Deliveries of fuel oil and gas/diesel oil for use in agricultural power units, dryers and heaters. Burning oil for farm use.

Iron and steel - Deliveries of petroleum products to steel works and iron foundries.

Other industries - The industries covered correspond to the industrial groups shown in Table 1E excluding Iron and Steel of Chapter 1.

Marine - Fuel oil and gas/diesel oil delivered, other than under international bunker contracts, for fishing vessels, UK oil and gas exploration and production, coastal and inland shipping and for use in ports and harbours.

Railways - Deliveries of fuel oil, gas/diesel oil and burning oil to railways, excluding deliveries to railway power stations.

Air transport - Total inland deliveries of aviation turbine fuel and aviation spirit. The figures cover deliveries of aviation fuels in the United Kingdom to international and other airlines, British and foreign governments (including armed services) and for private flying. In order to compile the UK Greenhouse

Gas Inventory, the National Environment Technology Centre (NETCEN) need to estimate how aviation fuel usage splits between domestic and international consumption. Domestic usage is calculated using domestic aircraft kilometres flown (from the Department for Transport) and default fuel consumption factors while international usage is calculated by subtracting domestic and military usage from overall deliveries. NETCEN are currently reviewing this methodology. For further information, see www.naei.org.uk/report_link.php?report_id=191.

Road transport - Deliveries of motor spirit and DERV fuel for use in road vehicles of all kinds. The Department for Transport has provided estimates for the consumption of road transport fuels by different vehicle classes, and these are shown in Table 3F. These are based on details of average vehicle mileages and assumed miles per gallon and while these estimates have remained unchanged for some years, they are still thought to be broadly sound despite the increasing use for vans to transport goods.

Table 3F: Estimated consumption of road transport fuels by vehicle class

Motor spirit:	
Cars and taxis	95%
Goods vehicles, mainly light vans	4%
Remainder, mainly motor cycles, mopeds etc	1%
DERV:	
Goods vehicles	68%
Buses and coaches	7%
Remainder, mainly diesel-engined cars and taxis	25%

Source: Department for Transport

Domestic - Fuel oil and gas/diesel oil delivered for central heating of private houses and other dwellings and deliveries of kerosene (burning oil) and liquefied petroleum gases for domestic purposes (see Tables 3.4 to 3.6).

Public services - Deliveries to national and local government premises (including educational, medical and welfare establishments and British and foreign armed forces) of fuel oil and gas/diesel oil for central heating and of kerosene (burning oil).

Miscellaneous - Deliveries of fuel oil and gas/diesel oil for central heating in premises other than those classified as domestic or public.

Monthly and quarterly data

3.91 Monthly or quarterly aggregate data for certain series presented in this chapter are available. This information can be obtained free of charge by following the links given at the Energy Statistics section of the DTI web site, at: www.dti.gov.uk/energy/inform/energy_stats/.

Contact: Martin Young
martin.young@dti.gsi.gov.uk
020-7215 5184

Clive Evans
clive.evans@dti.gsi.gov.uk
020-7215 5189

Ian Corrie
ian.corrie@dti.gsi.gov.uk
020-7215 2714

3.1 Commodity balances 2003[1]
Primary oil

	Crude oil	Ethane	Propane	Butane	Condensate	Total NGL	Feedstock	Total primary oil
Supply								
Production (2)	97,835	1,531	2,578	1,999	2,130	8,238	-	106,073
Other sources	-	-	-	-	-	-	-	-
Imports	48,589	-	-	-	-	-	5,588	54,177
Exports	-68,823	-24	-1,785	-917	-978	-3,703	-2,372	-74,898
Marine bunkers	-				-		-	-
Stock change (3)	+486	..	..	..	..	-5	-11	+469
Transfers	-	-1,509	-628	-524	-	-2,661	+1,653	-1,008
Total supply	**78,086**	..	..	..	..	**1,869**	**4,859**	**84,814**
Statistical difference (4)(5)	+778	..	..	..	..	+596	-1,145	+229
Total demand (5)	**77,309**	..	..	..	..	**1,273**	**6,004**	**84,585**
Transformation (5)	**77,309**	..	..	..	..	**1,273**	**6,004**	**84,585**
Electricity generation	-	-	-	-	-	-	-	-
Major power producers	-	-	-	-	-	-	-	-
Autogenerators	-	-	-	-	-	-	-	-
Heat generation	-	-	-	-	-	-	-	-
Petroleum refineries	77,309	..	..	..	..	1,273	6,004	84,585
Coke manufacture	-	-	-	-	-	-	-	-
Blast furnaces	-	-	-	-	-	-	-	-
Patent fuel manufacture	-	-	-	-	-	-	-	-
Other	-	-	-	-	-	-	-	-
Energy industry use	-	-	-	-	-	-	-	-
Electricity generation	-	-	-	-	-	-	-	-
Oil & gas extraction (2)(5)	-	-	-	-	-	-	-	-
Petroleum refineries	-	-	-	-	-	-	-	-
Coal extraction	-	-	-	-	-	-	-	-
Coke manufacture	-	-	-	-	-	-	-	-
Blast furnaces	-	-	-	-	-	-	-	-
Patent fuel manufacture	-	-	-	-	-	-	-	-
Pumped storage	-	-	-	-	-	-	-	-
Other	-	-	-	-	-	-	-	-
Losses	-	-	-	-	-	-	-	-

(1) As there is no use made of primary oils and feedstocks by industries other than the oil and gas extraction and
petroleum refining industries, other industry headings have not been included in this table. As such, this table is a
summary of the activity of what is known as the Upstream oil industry.

(2) With the introduction of a new Petroleum Production Reporting System in January 2001, the component of the gas used at
oil terminals is no longer collected. Thus NGL production in 2003 is net compared to the gross production reported in
2000 and earlier years.

(3) Stock fall (+), stock rise (-).

(4) Total supply minus total demand.

(5) Figures for total demand for the individual NGLs (and thus for the statistical differences as well) are not available.

3.2 Commodity balances 2002[1]

Primary oil

	Crude oil	Ethane	Propane	Butane	Condensate	Total NGL	Feedstock	Total primary oil
Supply								
Production (2)	107,430	1,596	2,728	2,071	2,118	8,514	-	115,944
Other sources	-	-	-	-	-	-	-	-
Imports	52,042r	-	-	-	-	-	4,926r	56,968r
Exports	-81,198r	-10	-1,909r	-888r	-1,022r	-3,830r	-2,116r	-87,144r
Marine bunkers	-	-	-	-	-	-	-	-
Stock change (3)	+33	..	..	..	..	+34	+75	+143
Transfers	-	-1,578r	-670	-1,046	-	-3,294r	+1,739r	-1,555r
Total supply	78,306r	..	..	..	..	1,424r	4,625r	84,356r
Statistical difference (4)(5)	+506r	..	..	..	..	-143r	-791r	-428r
Total demand (5)	77,801	..	..	..	..	1,567r	5,416r	84,784r
Transformation (5)	77,801	..	..	..	..	1,567r	5,416r	84,784r
Electricity generation	-	-	-	-	-	-	-	-
Major power producers	-	-	-	-	-	-	-	-
Autogenerators	-	-	-	-	-	-	-	-
Heat generation	-	-	-	-	-	-	-	-
Petroleum refineries	77,801	..	..	..	..	1,567r	5,416r	84,784
Coke manufacture	-	-	-	-	-	-	-	-
Blast furnaces	-	-	-	-	-	-	-	-
Patent fuel manufacture	-	-	-	-	-	-	-	-
Other	-	-	-	-	-	-	-	-
Energy industry use	-	-	-	-	-	-	-	-
Electricity generation	-	-	-	-	-	-	-	-
Oil & gas extraction (2)(5)	-	-	-	-	-	-	-	-
Petroleum refineries	-	-	-	-	-	-	-	-
Coal extraction	-	-	-	-	-	-	-	-
Coke manufacture	-	-	-	-	-	-	-	-
Blast furnaces	-	-	-	-	-	-	-	-
Patent fuel manufacture	-	-	-	-	-	-	-	-
Pumped storage	-	-	-	-	-	-	-	-
Other	-	-	-	-	-	-	-	-
Losses	-	-	-	-	-	-	-	-

(1) As there is no use made of primary oils and feedstocks by industries other than the oil and gas extraction and petroleum refining industries, other industry headings have not been included in this table. As such, this table is a summary of the activity of what is known as the Upstream oil industry.

(2) With the introduction of a new Petroleum Production Reporting System in January 2001, the component of the gas used at oil terminals is no longer collected. Thus NGL production in 2002 is net compared to the gross production reported in 2000 and earlier years.

(3) Stock fall (+), stock rise (-).

(4) Total supply minus total demand.

(5) Figures for total demand for the individual NGLs (and thus for the statistical differences as well) are not available.

3.3 Commodity balances 2001[(1)]

Primary oil

Thousand tonnes

	Crude oil	Ethane	Propane	Butane	Condensate	Total NGL	Feedstock	Total primary oil
Supply								
Production (2)	108,387	1,599	2,718	1,962	2,012	8,292	-	116,678
Other sources	-	-	-	-	-	-	-	-
Imports	48,992	-	-	-	-	-	4,559	53,551
Exports	-80,919r	-11	-1,748	-961	-802	-3,522	-2,489	-86,930r
Marine bunkers	-	-	-	-	-	-	-	-
Stock change (3)	-1,045	..	..	..	..	+17	+414	-614
Transfers	-	-1,587	-967	-1,020	-	-3,575r	+4,328	+753r
Total supply	75,415r	..	..	..	..	1,212r	6,812r	83,438r
Statistical difference (4)(5)	-495r	..	..	..	..	-322r	+913	+96r
Total demand (5)	75,910	..	..	..	..	1,534	5,899	83,343
Transformation (5)	75,910	..	..	..	..	1,534	5,899	83,343
Electricity generation	-	-	-	-	-	-	-	-
Major power producers	-	-	-	-	-	-	-	-
Autogenerators	-	-	-	-	-	-	-	-
Heat generation	-	-	-	-	-	-	-	-
Petroleum refineries	75,910	..	..	..	..	1,534	5,899	83,343
Coke manufacture	-	-	-	-	-	-	-	-
Blast furnaces	-	-	-	-	-	-	-	-
Patent fuel manufacture	-	-	-	-	-	-	-	-
Other	-	-	-	-	-	-	-	-
Energy industry use	-	-	-	-	-	-	-	-
Electricity generation	-	-	-	-	-	-	-	-
Oil & gas extraction (2)(5)	-	-	-	-	-	-	-	-
Petroleum refineries	-	-	-	-	-	-	-	-
Coal extraction	-	-	-	-	-	-	-	-
Coke manufacture	-	-	-	-	-	-	-	-
Blast furnaces	-	-	-	-	-	-	-	-
Patent fuel manufacture	-	-	-	-	-	-	-	-
Pumped storage	-	-	-	-	-	-	-	-
Other	-	-	-	-	-	-	-	-
Losses	-	-	-	-	-	-	-	-

(1) As there is no use made of primary oils and feedstocks by industries other than the oil and gas extraction and petroleum refining industries, other industry headings have not been included in this table. As such, this table is a summary of the activity of what is known as the Upstream oil industry.

(2) With the introduction of a new Petroleum Production Reporting System in January 2001, the component of the gas used at oil terminals is no longer collected. Thus NGL production in 2001 is net compared to the gross production reported in 2000 and earlier years.

(3) Stock fall (+), stock rise (-).

(4) Total supply minus total demand.

(5) Figures for total demand for the individual NGLs (and thus for the statistical differences as well) are not available.

3.4 Commodity balances 2003
Petroleum products

	Ethane	Propane	Butane	Other gases	Naphtha	Aviation spirit	Motor spirit	Industrial spirit	White spirit	Aviation turbine fuel	Burning oil
Supply											
Production	11	1,620	679	2,891	3,516	26	22,627	6	98	5,277	3,521
Other sources	1,509	628	524	-	-	-	-	-	-	-	-
Imports	-	194	172	-	782	12	2,022	27	7	7,346	327
Exports	-	328	16	7	2,461	5	5,603	-	-	587	556
Marine bunkers	-	-	-	-	-	-	-	-	-	-	-
Stock change (1)	-	+5	+22	+1	-74	-1	-88	-	+4	-100	+36
Transfers	-9	-254	-703	-196	+742	-1	+454	-	-	-1,347	+151
Total supply (2)	1,510	1,865	679	2,688	2,506	31	19,412	33	108	10,588	3,479
Statistical difference (3)	-54	-124	-236	-40	+278	-15	-506	-	-6	-176	+22
Total demand	1,564	1,989	915	2,729	2,227	46	19,918	33	114	10,765	3,457
Transformation	-	-	-	191	-	-	-	-	-	-	-
Electricity generation	-	-	-	191	-	-	-	-	-	-	-
Major power producers	-	-	-	-	-	-	-	-	-	-	-
Autogenerators	-	-	-	191	-	-	-	-	-	-	-
Heat generation	-	-	-	-	-	-	-	-	-	-	-
Petroleum refineries	-	-	-	-	-	-	-	-	-	-	-
Coke manufacture	-	-	-	-	-	-	-	-	-	-	-
Blast furnaces	-	-	-	-	-	-	-	-	-	-	-
Patent fuel manufacture	-	-	-	-	-	-	-	-	-	-	-
Other	-	-	-	-	-	-	-	-	-	-	-
Energy industry use	9	17	-	2,215	12	-	-	-	-	-	-
Electricity generation	-	-	-	-	-	-	-	-	-	-	-
Oil & gas extraction	-	-	-	-	-	-	-	-	-	-	-
Petroleum refineries	9	17	-	2,215	12	-	-	-	-	-	-
Coal extraction	-	-	-	-	-	-	-	-	-	-	-
Coke manufacture	-	-	-	-	-	-	-	-	-	-	-
Blast furnaces	-	-	-	-	-	-	-	-	-	-	-
Patent fuel manufacture	-	-	-	-	-	-	-	-	-	-	-
Pumped storage	-	-	-	-	-	-	-	-	-	-	-
Other	-	-	-	-	-	-	-	-	-	-	-
Losses	-	-	-	-	-	-	-	-	-	-	-
Final consumption	1,556	1,972	915	323	2,215	46	19,918	33	114	10,765	3,457
Industry	69	690	154	-	-	-	-	-	-	-	839
Unclassified	69	690	154	-	-	-	-	-	-	-	839
Iron & steel	-	-	-	-	-	-	-	-	-	-	-
Non-ferrous metals	-	-	-	-	-	-	-	-	-	-	-
Mineral products	-	-	-	-	-	-	-	-	-	-	-
Chemicals	-	-	-	-	-	-	-	-	-	-	-
Mechanical engineering, etc	-	-	-	-	-	-	-	-	-	-	-
Electrical engineering, etc	-	-	-	-	-	-	-	-	-	-	-
Vehicles	-	-	-	-	-	-	-	-	-	-	-
Food, beverages, etc	-	-	-	-	-	-	-	-	-	-	-
Textiles, leather, etc	-	-	-	-	-	-	-	-	-	-	-
Paper, printing etc	-	-	-	-	-	-	-	-	-	-	-
Other industries	-	-	-	-	-	-	-	-	-	-	-
Construction	-	-	-	-	-	-	-	-	-	-	-
Transport	-	104	-	-	-	46	19,918	-	-	10,765	12
Air	-	-	-	-	-	46	-	-	-	10,765	-
Rail	-	-	-	-	-	-	-	-	-	-	12
Road	-	104	-	-	-	-	19,918	-	-	-	-
National navigation	-	-	-	-	-	-	-	-	-	-	-
Pipelines	-	-	-	-	-	-	-	-	-	-	-
Other	-	397	48	-	-	-	-	-	-	-	2,606
Domestic	-	294	47	-	-	-	-	-	-	-	2,582
Public administration	-	-	-	-	-	-	-	-	-	-	12
Commercial	-	-	-	-	-	-	-	-	-	-	-
Agriculture	-	103	-	-	-	-	-	-	-6	-	12
Miscellaneous	-	-	-	-	-	-	-	-	-	-	-
Non energy use	1,487	781	714	323	2,215	-	-	33	114	-	-

(1) Stock fall (+), stock rise (-).
(2) Incorporates an extra adjustment for what are thought to be refinery losses. These data are the subject of ongoing investigations.
(3) Total supply minus total demand.

3.4 Commodity balances 2003 (continued)

Petroleum products

Thousand tonnes

Gas oil	Marine diesel oil	Fuel oils	Lubri -cants	Bitu -men	Petroleum wax	Petroleum coke	Orimul -sion	Misc. products	Total Products	
										Supply
27,579	-	11,517	576	1,925	460	1,630	-	569	84,529	Production
-	-	-	-	-	-	-	-	-	2,661	Other sources
3,503	-	1,208	570	249	21	834	-	13	17,286	Imports
5,528	-	6,385	678	329	46	566	-	228	23,323	Exports
861	36	867	-	-	-	-	-	-	1,764	Marine bunkers
-27	-	-3	+46	-9	+3	17	-	-94	-262	Stock change (1)
-779	+155	+136	+454	+43	-375	-22	-	-100	-1,652	Transfers (2)
23,887	119	5,606	968	1,879	64	1,893	-	160	77,475	**Total supply** (2)
-195	-36	+1,231	+101	-441	+7	+130	-	-289	-350	**Statistical difference** (3)
24,083	155	4,375	868	2,320	57	1,762	-	449	77,825	**Total demand**
48	-	745	-	-	-	-	-	-	984	**Transformation**
30	-	376	-	-	-	-	-	-	597	Electricity generation
17	-	83	-	-	-	-	-	-	100	Major power producers
13	-	293	-	-	-	-	-	-	497	Autogenerators
18	-	139	-	-	-	-	-	-	157	Heat generation
-	-	-	-	-	-	-	-	-	-	Petroleum refineries
-	-	1	-	-	-	-	-	-	1	Coke manufacture
-	-	229	-	-	-	-	-	-	229	Blast furnaces
-	-	-	-	-	-	-	-	-	-	Patent fuel manufacture
-	-	-	-	-	-	-	-	-	-	Other
200	-	2,005	-	-	-	933	-	-	5,390	**Energy industry use**
-	-	-	-	-	-	-	-	-	-	Electricity generation
-	-	-	-	-	-	-	-	-	-	Oil & gas extraction
199	-	2,005	-	-	-	933	-	-	5,389	Petroleum refineries
-	-	-	-	-	-	-	-	-	-	Coal extraction
-	-	-	-	-	-	-	-	-	-	Coke manufacture
-	-	-	-	-	-	-	-	-	-	Blast furnaces
-	-	-	-	-	-	-	-	-	-	Patent fuel manufacture
-	-	-	-	-	-	-	-	-	-	Pumped storage
-	-	-	-	-	-	-	-	-	-	Other
-	-	-	-	-	-	-	-	-	-	**Losses**
23,835	155	1,625	868	2,320	57	830	-	449	71,451	**Final Consumption**
3,656	-	1,283	-	-	-	-	-	-	6,691	**Industry**
-	-	-	-	-	-	-	-	-	1,752	Unclassified
1	-	17	-	-	-	-	-	-	19	Iron & steel
21	-	38	-	-	-	-	-	-	59	Non-ferrous metals
206	-	37	-	-	-	-	-	-	243	Mineral products
111	-	249	-	-	-	-	-	-	360	Chemicals
113	-	142	-	-	-	-	-	-	255	Mechanical engineering etc
13	-	39	-	-	-	-	-	-	52	Electrical engineering etc
69	-	45	-	-	-	-	-	-	114	Vehicles
154	-	153	-	-	-	-	-	-	306	Food, beverages etc
78	-	135	-	-	-	-	-	-	212	Textiles, leather, etc
21	-	97	-	-	-	-	-	-	118	Paper, printing etc
2,576	-	328	-	-	-	-	-	-	2,904	Other industries
293	-	3	-	-	-	-	-	-	295	Construction
18,945	155	50	-	-	-	-	-	-	49,995	**Transport**
-	-	-	-	-	-	-	-	-	10,810	Air
302	-	-	-	-	-	-	-	-	314	Rail
17,712	-	-	-	-	-	-	-	-	37,735	Road
930	155	50	-	-	-	-	-	-	1,135	National navigation
-	-	-	-	-	-	-	-	-	-	Pipelines
947	-	292	-	-	-	-	-	-	4,290	**Other**
163	-	6	-	-	-	-	-	-	3,093	Domestic
283	-	185	-	-	-	-	-	-	479	Public administration
258	-	83	-	-	-	-	-	-	341	Commercial
173	-	4	-	-	-	-	-	-	292	Agriculture
70	-	14	-	-	-	-	-	-	84	Miscellaneous
287	-	-	868	2,320	57	830	-	449	10,476	**Non energy use**

3.5 Commodity balances 2002

Petroleum products

	Ethane	Propane	Butane	Other gases	Naphtha	Aviation spirit	Motor spirit	Industrial spirit	White spirit	Aviation turbine fuel	Burning oil
Supply											
Production	50	1,620r	529r	2,928r	3,174r	28	22,944r	6	115	5,365r	3,506r
Other sources	1,578r	670	1,047r	-	-	-	-	-	-	-	-
Imports	-	82r	110r	-	96	9	2,307r	38r	7	6,700r	299r
Exports	-	-448r	-377r	-	-2,077r	-6	-5,532r	-2	-	-588r	-402r
Marine bunkers	-	-	-	-	-	-	-	-	-	-	-
Stock change (1)	-	+80	-11	-3	+20	-4	+273r	-	+2	+269	-8
Transfers	-83r	-259r	-483r	+42r	+743r	+3	+499r	-	-	-1,972r	+150r
Total supply (2)	1,546r	1,744r	815r	2,966r	1,956r	30	20,490r	42	124	9,773r	3,545r
Statistical difference (3)	-45r	-12r	+124r	+63r	+457r	-19r	-319r	+10r	-2r	-746r	+82r
Total demand	1,590r	1,756r	691r	2,903r	1,499r	50r	20,808r	32r	125r	10,519r	3,463r
Transformation	-	-	-	228r	-	-	-	-	-	-	-
Electricity generation	-	-	-	228r	-	-	-	-	-	-	-
Major power producers	-	-	-	-	-	-	-	-	-	-	-
Autogenerators	-	-	-	228r	-	-	-	-	-	-	-
Heat generation	-	-	-	-	-	-	-	-	-	-	-
Petroleum refineries	-	-	-	-	-	-	-	-	-	-	-
Coke manufacture	-	-	-	-	-	-	-	-	-	-	-
Blast furnaces	-	-	-	-	-	-	-	-	-	-	-
Patent fuel manufacture	-	-	-	-	-	-	-	-	-	-	-
Other	-	-	-	-	-	-	-	-	-	-	-
Energy industry use	49	9r	-	2,390r	19r	-	-	-	-	-	-
Electricity generation	-	-	-	-	-	-	-	-	-	-	-
Oil & gas extraction	-	-	-	-	-	-	-	-	-	-	-
Petroleum refineries	49	9r	-	2,390r	19r	-	-	-	-	-	-
Coal extraction	-	-	-	-	-	-	-	-	-	-	-
Coke manufacture	-	-	-	-	-	-	-	-	-	-	-
Blast furnaces	-	-	-	-	-	-	-	-	-	-	-
Patent fuel manufacture	-	-	-	-	-	-	-	-	-	-	-
Pumped storage	-	-	-	-	-	-	-	-	-	-	-
Other	-	-	-	-	-	-	-	-	-	-	-
Losses	-	-	-	-	-	-	-	-	-	-	-
Final consumption	1,541r	1,747r	691r	284	1,480r	50r	20,808r	32r	125r	10,519r	3,463r
Industry	68r	484r	99	-	-	-	-	-	-	-	807r
Unclassified	68r	474r	99	-	-	-	-	-	-	-	807r
Iron & steel	-	10r	-	-	-	-	-	-	-	-	-
Non-ferrous metals	-	-	-	-	-	-	-	-	-	-	-
Mineral products	-	-	-	-	-	-	-	-	-	-	-
Chemicals	-	-	-	-	-	-	-	-	-	-	-
Mechanical engineering, etc	-	-	-	-	-	-	-	-	-	-	-
Electrical engineering, etc	-	-	-	-	-	-	-	-	-	-	-
Vehicles	-	-	-	-	-	-	-	-	-	-	-
Food, beverages, etc	-	-	-	-	-	-	-	-	-	-	-
Textiles, leather, etc	-	-	-	-	-	-	-	-	-	-	-
Paper, printing etc	-	-	-	-	-	-	-	-	-	-	-
Other industries	-	-	-	-	-	-	-	-	-	-	-
Construction	-	-	-	-	-	-	-	-	-	-	-
Transport	-	86	-	-	-	50r	20,808r	-	-	10,519r	12
Air	-	-	-	-	-	50r	-	-	-	10,519r	-
Rail	-	-	-	-	-	-	-	-	-	-	12
Road	-	86	-	-	-	-	20,808r	-	-	-	-
National navigation	-	-	-	-	-	-	-	-	-	-	-
Pipelines	-	-	-	-	-	-	-	-	-	-	-
Other	-	369	48	-	-	-	-	-	-	-	2,644r
Domestic	-	271	48	-	-	-	-	-	-	-	2,620r
Public administration	-	-	-	-	-	-	-	-	-	-	12
Commercial	-	-	-	-	-	-	-	-	-	-	-
Agriculture	-	98	-	-	-	-	-	-	-	-	12
Miscellaneous	-	-	-	-	-	-	-	-	-	-	-
Non energy use	1,473r	808r	544r	284	1,480r	-	-	32r	125r	-	-

(1) Stock fall (+), stock rise (-).
(2) Incorporates an extra adjustment for what are thought to be refinery losses. These data are the subject of ongoing investigations.
(3) Total supply minus total demand.

3.5 Commodity balances 2002 (continued)
Petroleum products

Thousand tonnes

Gas oil	Marine diesel oil	Fuel oils	Lubri -cants	Bitu -men	Petroleum wax	Petroleum coke	Orimul -sion	Misc. products	Total Products	
										Supply
28,393r	-	10,551r	509r	1,918r	430r	1,543r	-	389r	83,996r	Production
-	-	-	-	-	-	-	-	-	3,295r	Other sources
3,219r	-	927r	422r	232r	18r	790	-	13r	15,269r	Imports
-6,352r	-	-5,780r	-521r	-261r	-59r	-541r	-	-497r	-23,444r	Exports
1,108r	36r	769r	-	-	-	-	-	-	1,913r	Marine bunkers
+194r	-	-32	-16r	+24	-4r	16	-	427	1,226r	Stock change (1)
-722r	-	+235r	+442r	+50r	-324	-1	-	-59r	-1,740r	Transfers (2)
23,624r	**-36r**	**5,132r**	**836r**	**1,963r**	**61r**	**1,806r**	**-**	**273r**	**76,689r**	**Total supply (2)**
+588r	-75r	+996r	+7r	-422r	+10r	+23r	-	-334r	+385r	**Statistical difference (3)**
23,036r	**39**	**4,136r**	**829r**	**2,385r**	**51r**	**1,784r**	**-**	**607r**	**76,304r**	**Total demand**
52	**-**	**828r**	**-**	**-**	**-**	**-**	**-**	**-**	**1,108r**	**Transformation**
29r	-	414r	-	-	-	-	-	-	671r	Electricity generation
10	-	108r	-	-	-	-	-	-	119r	Major power producers
18r	-	306r	-	-	-	-	-	-	552r	Autogenerators
23r	-	227r	-	-	-	-	-	-	250r	Heat generation
-	-	-	-	-	-	-	-	-	-	Petroleum refineries
-	-	1r	-	-	-	-	-	-	1r	Coke manufacture
-	-	186r	-	-	-	-	-	-	186r	Blast furnaces
-	-	-	-	-	-	-	-	-	-	Patent fuel manufacture
-	-	-	-	-	-	-	-	-	-	Other
50r	**-**	**2,045r**	**-**	**-**	**-**	**1,010r**	**-**	**11r**	**5,582r**	**Energy industry use**
-	-	-	-	-	-	-	-	-	-	Electricity generation
-	-	-	-	-	-	-	-	-	-	Oil & gas extraction
49r	-	2,045r	-	-	-	1,010r	-	11r	5,582r	Petroleum refineries
-	-	-	-	-	-	-	-	-	-	Coal extraction
-	-	-	-	-	-	-	-	-	-	Coke manufacture
-	-	-	-	-	-	-	-	-	-	Blast furnaces
-	-	-	-	-	-	-	-	-	-	Patent fuel manufacture
-	-	-	-	-	-	-	-	-	-	Pumped storage
-	-	-	-	-	-	-	-	-	-	Other
-	-	-	-	-	-	-	-	-	-	**Losses**
22,935r	**39**	**1,263r**	**829r**	**2,385r**	**51r**	**774r**	**-**	**596r**	**69,614r**	**Final Consumption**
3,305r	**-**	**1,051r**	**-**	**-**	**-**	**-**	**-**	**-**	**5,814r**	**Industry**
-	-	-	-	-	-	-	-	-	1,448r	Unclassified
2r	-	66r	-	-	-	-	-	-	77r	Iron & steel
41	-	39	-	-	-	-	-	-	80	Non-ferrous metals
213	-	31	-	-	-	-	-	-	244	Mineral products
129	-	185r	-	-	-	-	-	-	314r	Chemicals
155	-	108r	-	-	-	-	-	-	263	Mechanical engineering etc
21	-	30	-	-	-	-	-	-	51	Electrical engineering etc
151	-	37	-	-	-	-	-	-	188	Vehicles
180	-	128r	-	-	-	-	-	-	308r	Food, beverages etc
79	-	102	-	-	-	-	-	-	181	Textiles, leather, etc
35	-	74	-	-	-	-	-	-	109r	Paper, printing etc
1,864	-	248r	-	-	-	-	-	-	2,112r	Other industries
435	-	2	-	-	-	-	-	-	437	Construction
17,826r	**39**	**39r**	**-**	**-**	**-**	**-**	**-**	**-**	**49,382r**	**Transport**
-	-	-	-	-	-	-	-	-	10,568r	Air
334	-	-	-	-	-	-	-	-	346	Rail
16,926r	-	-	-	-	-	-	-	-	37,821r	Road
566	39	42r	-	-	-	-	-	-	647r	National navigation
-	-	-	-	-	-	-	-	-	-	Pipelines
1,599r	**-**	**170**	**-**	**-**	**-**	**-**	**-**	**-**	**4,831r**	**Other**
202	-	4	-	-	-	-	-	-	3,145r	Domestic
602	-	96r	-	-	-	-	-	-	710r	Public administration
315	-	56r	-	-	-	-	-	-	371r	Commercial
395	-	3	-	-	-	-	-	-	509r	Agriculture
85r	-	11	-	-	-	-	-	-	96r	Miscellaneous
205	**-**	**-**	**829r**	**2,385r**	**51r**	**774r**	**-**	**596r**	**9,587r**	**Non energy use**

3.6 Commodity balances 2001
Petroleum products

Thousand tonnes

	Ethane	Propane	Butane	Other gases	Naphtha	Aviation spirit	Motor spirit	Industrial spirit	White spirit	Aviation turbine fuel	Burning oil
Supply											
Production	83	1,250	520	2,511r	3,463	101	21,455	9	113	5,910	3,088
Other sources	1,587r	967	1,020	-	-	-	-	-	-	-	-
Imports	-	236r	172r	-	337r	10	3,702r	21	5r	6,217r	203r
Exports	-	-315	-77	-	-1,078	-6	-4,447	-2	-	-456	-167
Marine bunkers	-	-	-	-	-	-	-	-	-	-	-
Stock change (1)	-	-26	-17	+2	+4	+6	-377	+2	-2	-291	+122
Transfers	-101	-258	-314	-	-633	+5	+1,062	+1	-1	+9	+261
Total supply (2)	1,569r	1,854r	1,304r	2,512r	2,093r	114r	21,396r	30	115r	11,388r	3,507r
Statistical difference (3)	-124r	+277r	+778r	-194r	+466r	+55r	+456r	-23	+18r	+774r	-729r
Total demand	1,693	1,578r	526r	2,706r	1,627r	59	20,940r	54	97r	10,614r	4,236r
Transformation	-	36	-	179	-	-	-	-	-	-	-
Electricity generation	-	36	-	179	-	-	-	-	-	-	-
Major power producers	-	-	-	-	-	-	-	-	-	-	-
Autogenerators	-	36	-	179	-	-	-	-	-	-	-
Heat generation	-	-	-	-	-	-	-	-	-	-	-
Petroleum refineries	-	-	-	-	-	-	-	-	-	-	-
Coke manufacture	-	-	-	-	-	-	-	-	-	-	-
Blast furnaces	-	-	-	-	-	-	-	-	-	-	-
Patent fuel manufacture	-	-	-	-	-	-	-	-	-	-	-
Other	-	-	-	-	-	-	-	-	-	-	-
Energy industry use	83	7	-	2,239r	35r	-	-	-	-	-	-
Electricity generation	-	-	-	-	-	-	-	-	-	-	-
Oil & gas extraction	-	-	-	-	-	-	-	-	-	-	-
Petroleum refineries	83	7	-	2,239r	35r	-	-	-	-	-	-
Coal extraction	-	-	-	-	-	-	-	-	-	-	-
Coke manufacture	-	-	-	-	-	-	-	-	-	-	-
Blast furnaces	-	-	-	-	-	-	-	-	-	-	-
Patent fuel manufacture	-	-	-	-	-	-	-	-	-	-	-
Pumped storage	-	-	-	-	-	-	-	-	-	-	-
Other	-	-	-	-	-	-	-	-	-	-	-
Losses	-	-	-	-	-	-	-	-	-	-	-
Final consumption	1,610	1,535r	526r	287r	1,592r	59	20,940r	54	97r	10,614r	4,236r
Industry	82	189r	68r	-	-	-	-	-	-	-	1,561
Unclassified	82	189r	68r	-	-	-	-	-	-	-	1,561
Iron & steel	-	-	-	-	-	-	-	-	-	-	-
Non-ferrous metals	-	-	-	-	-	-	-	-	-	-	-
Mineral products	-	-	-	-	-	-	-	-	-	-	-
Chemicals	-	-	-	-	-	-	-	-	-	-	-
Mechanical engineering, etc	-	-	-	-	-	-	-	-	-	-	-
Electrical engineering, etc	-	-	-	-	-	-	-	-	-	-	-
Vehicles	-	-	-	-	-	-	-	-	-	-	-
Food, beverages, etc	-	-	-	-	-	-	-	-	-	-	-
Textiles, leather, etc	-	-	-	-	-	-	-	-	-	-	-
Paper, printing etc	-	-	-	-	-	-	-	-	-	-	-
Other industries	-	-	-	-	-	-	-	-	-	-	-
Construction	-	-	-	-	-	-	-	-	-	-	-
Transport	-	53	-	-	-	59	20,940r	-	-	10,614r	12
Air	-	-	-	-	-	59	-	-	-	10,614r	-
Rail	-	-	-	-	-	-	-	-	-	-	12
Road	-	53	-	-	-	-	20,940r	-	-	-	-
National navigation	-	-	-	-	-	-	-	-	-	-	-
Pipelines	-	-	-	-	-	-	-	-	-	-	-
Other	-	709r	116r	-	-	-	-	-	-	-	2,663r
Domestic	-	270r	68r	-	-	-	-	-	-	-	2,639r
Public administration	-	-	-	-	-	-	-	-	-	-	12
Commercial	-	324r	47r	-	-	-	-	-	-	-	-
Agriculture	-	115r	1	-	-	-	-	-	-	-	12
Miscellaneous	-	-	-	-	-	-	-	-	-	-	-
Non energy use	1,529	584	342	287r	1,592r	-	-	54	97r	-	-

(1) Stock fall (+), stock rise (-).
(2) Incorporates an extra adjustment for what are thought to be refinery losses. These data are the subject of ongoing investigations.
(3) Total supply minus total demand.

90

3.6 Commodity balances 2001 (continued)
Petroleum products

Thousand tonnes

Gas oil	Marine diesel oil	Fuel oils	Lubri -cants	Bitu -men	Petroleum wax	Petroleum coke	Orimul -sion	Misc. products	Total Products	
										Supply
26,796	-	11,863r	656	1,707	416	1,445r	-	724	82,109r	Production
-	-	-	-	-	-	-	-	-	3,575r	Other sources
4,073r	-	1,212r	319r	251r	19r	688r	-	3r	17,466r	Imports
-5,288	-	-5,440	-806	-269	-56	-460	-	-221	-19,088	Exports
-1,377	-56	-841	-	-	-	-	-	-	-2,274	Marine bunkers
+49	-	+86	-3	-51	-8	-27	-	-66	-598	Stock change (1)
-1,251	+4	-3,174r	+51	+303	-309	-	-	+19	-4,328	Transfers (2)
23,002r	-52r	3,706r	216r	1,941r	61r	1,646r	-	459r	76,863r	**Total supply** (2)
+61r	-178	-788r	-630r	+6r	+28r	+13r	-	-48	+217r	**Statistical difference** (3)
22,941r	126	4,494r	846r	1,935r	33r	1,633r	-	508r	76,646r	**Total demand**
63	-	1,364r	-	-	-	-	-	-	1,642r	**Transformation**
32	-	724r	-	-	-	-	-	-	971r	Electricity generation
10	-	356r	-	-	-	-	-	-	366	Major power producers
22r	-	368r	-	-	-	-	-	-	605	Autogenerators
31r	-	640	-	-	-	-	-	-	671	Heat generation
-	-	-	-	-	-	-	-	-	-	Petroleum refineries
-	-	-	-	-	-	-	-	-	-	Coke manufacture
-	-	-	-	-	-	-	-	-	-	Blast furnaces
-	-	-	-	-	-	-	-	-	-	Patent fuel manufacture
-	-	-	-	-	-	-	-	-	-	Other
49r	-	1,684r	0	0	-	931r	-	32	5,060r	**Energy industry use**
-	-	-	-	-	-	-	-	-	-	Electricity generation
-	-	-	-	-	-	-	-	-	-	Oil & gas extraction
48r	-	1,684r	0	0	-	931r	-	32	5,059r	Petroleum refineries
-	-	-	-	-	-	-	-	-	-	Coal extraction
-	-	-	-	-	-	-	-	-	-	Coke manufacture
-	-	-	-	-	-	-	-	-	-	Blast furnaces
-	-	-	-	-	-	-	-	-	-	Patent fuel manufacture
-	-	-	-	-	-	-	-	-	-	Pumped storage
-	-	-	-	-	-	-	-	-	-	Other
-	-	-	-	-	-	-	-	-	-	**Losses**
22,830r	126	1,446r	846r	1,934r	33r	702r	-	475r	69,945r	**Final Consumption**
3,511r	-	1,188r	-	-	-	-	-	-	6,598r	**Industry**
-	-	-	-	-	-	-	-	-	1,899r	Unclassified
209r	-	75r	-	-	-	-	-	-	284r	Iron & steel
41	-	35r	-	-	-	-	-	-	76r	Non-ferrous metals
238	-	31r	-	-	-	-	-	-	270r	Mineral products
139	-	226r	-	-	-	-	-	-	365r	Chemicals
169	-	85r	-	-	-	-	-	-	254r	Mechanical engineering etc
24	-	35r	-	-	-	-	-	-	59r	Electrical engineering etc
140	-	32r	-	-	-	-	-	-	172r	Vehicles
200	-	147r	-	-	-	-	-	-	347r	Food, beverages etc
90	-	119r	-	-	-	-	-	-	209r	Textiles, leather, etc
37	-	69r	-	-	-	-	-	-	105r	Paper, printing etc
1,756	-	330r	-	-	-	-	-	-	2,086r	Other industries
469	-	2	-	-	-	-	-	-	472	Construction
17,083r	126	34r	-	-	-	-	-	-	48,921r	**Transport**
-	-	-	-	-	-	-	-	-	10,673r	Air
407	-	-	-	-	-	-	-	-	419r	Rail
16,059r	-	-	-	-	-	-	-	-	37,052r	Road
617	126	34r	-	-	-	-	-	-	777r	National navigation
-	-	-	-	-	-	-	-	-	-	Pipelines
1,826	-	224r	-	-	-	-	-	-	5,538r	**Other**
193	-	6	-	-	-	-	-	-	3,177r	Domestic
674	-	132r	-	-	-	-	-	-	818r	Public administration
406	-	57r	-	-	-	-	-	-	834r	Commercial
448	-	12r	-	-	-	-	-	-	587r	Agriculture
105	-	17r	-	-	-	-	-	-	123r	Miscellaneous
411r	-	-	846r	1,934r	33r	702r	-	475r	8,887r	**Non energy use**

3.7 Supply and disposal of petroleum[1]

Thousand tonnes

	1999	2000	2001	2002	2003
Primary oils (Crude oil, NGLs and feedstocks)					
Indigenous production (2)	137,099	126,245	116,678r	115,944	106,073
Imports	44,869	54,387	53,551	56,968r	54,177
Exports (3)	-91,797	-92,918	-86,930r	-87,144r	-74,898
Transfers - Transfers to products (4)	-3,323	-3,383	-3,575r	-3,294r	-2,661
Product rebrands (5)	+2,105	+3,493	+4,328	+1,739r	+1,653
Stock change (6) - Offshore	-83	+550	-378	+68	+12
Oil terminals	-115	+548	-236r	+75	+457
Use during production (7)	-323	-295	-	-	-
Calculated refinery throughput (8)	88,432	88,627	83,438r	84,356r	84,814
Overall statistical difference (9)(10)	+146	+613	+96r	-428r	+229
Actual refinery throughput	**88,286**	**88,014**	**83,343r**	**84,784r**	**84,585**
Petroleum products					
Losses in refining process (11)	+1,554	-168r	+1,261r	+788r	-130
Refinery gross production (11)(12)	86,733	86,341	82,109r	83,996r	84,529
Transfers - Transfers to products (4)	+3,323	+3,383	+3,575r	+3,295r	+2,661
Product rebrands (5)	-2,105	-3,493	-4,328	-1,740r	-1,652
Imports	13,896	14,212	17,466r	15,269r	17,286
Exports (13)	-21,730	-20,677	-19,088r	-23,444r	-23,323
Marine bunkers	-2,329	-2,079	-2,274	-1,913r	-1,764
Stock changes (6) - Refineries	+399	-425	+613	-1,214r	+291
Power generators	+176	+94	-15r	-12	-29
Calculated total supply	78,363	77,397	76,863r	76,689r	77,475
Statistical difference (9)	+388	+201r	+217r	+386r	-350
Total demand (4)	**77,975**	**77,197r**	**76,646r**	**76,304r**	**77,825**
Of which:					
Energy use	67,242	67,142r	67,759r	66,717r	67,349r
Of which, for electricity generation (14)	1,167	978r	971r	671r	597
total refinery fuels (14)	5,969	5,603r	5,059r	5,582r	5,389
Non-energy use	10,733	10,055r	8,887r	9,587r	10,476

(1) Aggregate monthly data on oil production, trade, refinery throughput and inland deliveries are available - see paragraph 3.91 and Annex C.

(2) Crude oil plus condensates and petroleum gases derived at onshore treatment plants.

(3) Includes NGLs, process oils and re-exports.

(4) Disposals of NGLs by direct sale (excluding exports) or for blending.

(5) Product rebrands (inter-product blends or transfers) represent petroleum products received at refineries/ plants as process for refinery or cracking unit operations.

(6) Impact of stock changes on supplies. A stock fall is shown as (+) as it increases supplies, and vice-versa for a stock rise (-).

(7) Own use in onshore terminals and gas separation plants. These figures ceased to be available from January 2001 with the advent of the new PPRS system.

(8) Equivalent to the total supplies reported against the upstream transformation sector in Tables 3.1 to 3.3.

(9) Supply greater than (+) or less than (-) recorded throughput or disposals.

(10) This total includes differences between the figures for indigenous production as recorded by individual fields and indigenous indigenous receipts, which is accounted for by own use in onshore terminals and gas separation plants, losses, platform and other field stock changes and the time lag between production on offshore loaders and tankers arrival at refineries. The size of this component of the overall statistical difference was previously given separately, and is given in the table below for information. See Chapter 3, paragraphs 3.35 to 3.39 for more information on the differences.

	1999	2000	2001	2002	2003
Indigenous receipts	137,220	126,245	116,678	115,944	106,073
Statistical difference - upstream production sector	-527	-166	-	-	-

(11) Data for 1999 to 2003 inc. incorporates adjustments for what are thought to be losses within the refining system. There is ongoing consultation between the DTI and oil companies with a view to resolve this situation. When this investigation is completed the results will be published in the DTI publication Energy Trends.

(12) Includes refinery fuels.

(13) Excludes NGLs.

(14) Figures cover petroleum used to generate electricity by all major power producers and by all other generators, including petroleum used to generate electricity at refineries. These quantities are also included in the totals reported as used as refinery fuel, so there is thus some overlap in these figures.

3.8 Additional information on inland deliveries of selected products[1][2][3]

Thousand tonnes

	1999	2000	2001	2002	2003
Motor spirit					
Retail deliveries (4)					
Hypermarkets (5)					
Leaded premium / Lead Replacement Petrol (6)	641	339	213	138r	92
Super premium unleaded	13	9	24	33	39
Premium unleaded	4,775	5,260	5,498	5,764r	5,803
Total hypermarkets	5,429	5,608	5,735	5,934r	5,935
Refiners/other traders					
Leaded premium / Lead Replacement Petrol (6)	1,988	1,123	624	263r	91
Super premium unleaded	461	395r	396	673r	822
Premium unleaded	13,532	13,748r	13,602r	13,404r	12,488
Total Refiners/other traders	15,981	15,265r	14,622r	14,340r	13,400
Total retail deliveries					
Leaded premium / Lead Replacement Petrol (6)	2,629	1,462r	838r	401r	183
Super premium unleaded	474	403r	420	706r	861
Premium unleaded	18,307	19,008r	19,100r	19,167r	18,291
Total retail deliveries	21,410	20,873r	20,358r	20,274r	19,335
Commercial consumers (7)					
Leaded premium / Lead Replacement Petrol (6)	61	44	34	19	19
Super premium unleaded	6	6	9	17	22
Premium unleaded	311	480	538	499	542
Total commercial consumers	378	530	581	535	583
Total motor spirit	**21,789**	**21,403r**	**20,939r**	**20,809r**	**19,918**
Unleaded as % of Total motor spirit	87.6	93.0	95.8	98.0r	99.0
Gas oil/diesel oil					
DERV fuel:					
Retail deliveries (4):					
Hypermarkets (5)	1,306	1,411	1,633	1,854r	2,135
Refiners/other traders	5,831	5,770r	6,214r	6,300r	6,922
Total retail deliveries	7,137	7,181r	7,846r	8,153r	9,057
Commercial consumers (7)	8,371	8,451r	8,213r	8,774r	8,655
Total DERV fuel	15,508	15,632	16,059r	16,927r	17,712
Gas oil	6,667	7,487	6,834r	6,060r	6,172
Marine diesel oil	15	41	126	39	155
Total gas oil/diesel oil	**22,190**	**23,160**	**23,019r**	**23,026r**	**24,039**
Fuel oils (8)					
Light	74	45	55r	84r	169
Medium	419	390	664r	779r	927
Heavy	1,922	1,399	2,087r	1,226r	1,273
Orimulsion (9)	-	-	-	-	-
Total fuel oils	**2,415**	**1,833**	**2,806r**	**2,088r**	**2,370**

(1) Aggregate monthly data for inland deliveries of oil products are available - see paragraph 3.91 and Annex C.

(2) The end use section analyses are based partly on recorded figures and on estimates made by the Institute of. Petroleum and the Department of Trade and Industry and are intended to be for general guidance only. See also the notes in the main text of this chapter.

(3) For a full breakdown of the end-uses of all oil products, see Commodity Balances in Tables 3.4 to 3.6.

(4) Retail deliveries - deliveries to garages, etc. mainly for resale to final consumers.

(5) Data for sales by super and hypermarket companies are collected via a separate reporting system, but are consistent with the main data collected from UKPIA member companies - see paragraph 3.71.

(6) Sales of Leaded Petrol ceased on 31 December 1999 - see paragraphs 3.46 to 3.48.

(7) Commercial consumers - direct deliveries for use in consumer's business.

(8) Inland deliveries excluding that used as a fuel in refineries, but including that used for electricity generation by major electricity producers and other industries.

3.9 Inland deliveries by country[1]

Thousand tonnes

	England and Wales [2]			Scotland			Northern Ireland		
	2001	2002	2003	2001	2002	2003	2001	2002	2003
Energy use									
Gases for gasworks and other uses									
Butane and propane	995r	880r	1,185	86	91	80	30	29	23
Other gases	1r	-	1	81	68r	68	-	-	-
Aviation spirit	53	48r	42	3	2	3	3	0	1
Motor spirit:									
Dealers	18,999r	18,982r	18,058	1,061	983r	973	298	309	304
Commercial consumers	540	473	518	22	38	40	19	23	25
Total motor spirit	19,539r	19,455r	18,576	1,083	1,022r	1,013	317	332	329
Kerosenes									
Aviation turbine fuel	10,068r	9,971r	10,102	473	476	592	73	72	71
Burning oil	3,308r	2,436r	2,353	232	309	298	696	718	806
Gas oil/diesel oil									
DERV fuel	14,849r	15,715r	16,410	1,039	1,008	1,060	171	203	242
Other [3]	5,056r	4,656r	4,825	980	719	693	450	468	474
Fuel oils	2,446r	1,756r	2,011	207	197	205	153	135	153
Total products used as energy [4]	54,981r	54,179r	54,863	4,184	3,891r	4,012	1,893	1,957	2,100
Non-energy use									
Feedstock for petroleum chemical plants	2,508r	2,154r	3,253	2,211	2,640	2,552	-	2	-
Industrial spirit	54r	32r	33	-	-	-	-	-	-
White spirit	97r	125r	114	-	-	-	-	-	-
Lubricating oils	823r	798r	835	20	27	29	3	3	4
Bitumen	1,629r	2,063r	1,995	197	210	217	109	111	108
Petroleum wax	59r	51r	57	-	-	-	-	-	-
Total products used as non-energy [5]	6,345r	**6,592r**	7,565	2,430	2,879	2,800	112	116	111
Total all products	61,326r	60,771r	62,428	6,614	6,771r	6,812	2,005	2,073	2,211

(1) Excludes products used as a fuel within refineries that are included in Tables 3.4 to 3.6.
(2) Includes the Channel Islands and the Isle of Man.
(3) Includes deliveries of marine diesel oil.
(4) Includes deliveries of LPG road transport fuel.
(5) Includes deliveries of miscellaneous products and petroleum coke.

94

3.10 Stocks of crude oil and petroleum products at end of year[1]

Thousand tonnes

	1999	2000	2001	2002	2003
Crude and process oils					
Refineries (2)	4,560	3,917	4,183	4,508r	4,670
Terminals (3)	2,461	2,556	2,526	2,126	1,509
Offshore (4)	1,000	450	828	760	741
Total crude and process oils (5)	8,080	6,992	7,637	7,504r	7,140
Petroleum products					
Ethane	6	6	6	6r	6
Propane	144	162	188	108r	103
Butane	89	88	105	117r	95
Other petroleum gases	3	-	-	2	2
Naphtha	349	428	424	404r	478
Aviation spirit	5	4	4	2r	3
Motor spirit	1,425	1,078	1,375	1,280r	1,487
Industrial spirit	7	14	12	11	11
White spirit	15	21	23	22	18
Aviation turbine fuel	461	487	779	510r	610
Burning oil	339	414	292	300r	265
Gas oil (6)(7)	2,984	1,908	2,232	2,363r	2,765
Marine diesel oil	1	-	-	-	-
Fuel oils (7)	1,401	1,122	1,180	1,196r	1,237
Lubricating oils	169	199	202	214	166
Bitumen	189	165	215	192r	212
Petroleum wax	36	1	9	15	12
Petroleum coke	327	291	318	302	285
Miscellaneous products	320	1,031	1,097	670r	778
Total all products	8,269	7,419	8,461	7,712r	8,533
Of which : net bilateral stocks (8)	1,307	77	514	1,008	1,500

(1) Aggregate monthly data on the level of stocks of crude oil and oil products are available - see paragraph 3.91 and Annex C.

(2) Stocks of crude oil, NGLs and process oils at UK refineries.

(3) Stocks of crude oil and NGLs at UKCS pipeline terminals.

(4) Stocks of crude oil in tanks and partially loaded tankers at offshore fields.

(5) Includes process oils held abroad for UK use approved by bilateral agreements.

(6) Includes middle distillate feedstock.

(7) The increase in gas oil stocks and the decrease in fuel oil stocks can be attributed to the change in patterns of stocks held abroad, under bilateral agreements, by UK companies as part of their national stocking obligation.

(8) The difference between stocks held abroad for UK use under approved bilateral agreements and the equivalent stocks held in the UK for foreign use.

Chapter 4
Natural gas

Introduction

4.1   This chapter presents figures on the production, transmission and consumption of natural gas and colliery methane. Three tables are presented and a map showing the gas transmission system in Great Britain is included (page 107. The commodity balances for natural gas and colliery methane form the first table (Table 4.1). This is followed by a 5 year table showing the supply, transmission and consumption of these gases as a time series (Table 4.2). A more detailed examination of the various stages of natural gas from gross production through to consumption is given in Table 4.3. Long term trends commentary and table on production and consumption of gas back to 1970 is to be found on the DTI Energy Statistics web site at:
www.dti.gov.uk/energy/inform/dukes/dukes2004/04longterm.pdf.

4.2   Petroleum gases are covered in Chapter 3. Gases manufactured in the coke making and iron and steel making processes (coke oven gas and blast furnace gas) appear in Chapter 2. Biogases (landfill gas and sewage gas) are part of Chapter 7. Details of net selling values of gas for the domestic sector are to be found in Chapter 1.

The gas supply industry Great Britain

4.3   When British Gas was privatised in 1986, it was given a statutory monopoly over supplies of natural gas (methane) to premises taking less than 732,000 kWh (25,000 therms) a year. Under the Oil and Gas (Enterprise) Act 1982, contract customers taking more than this were able to buy their gas from other suppliers but no other suppliers entered the market until 1990.

4.4   In 1991, the Office of Fair Trading (OFT) followed up an examination of the contract market by the Monopolies and Mergers Commission (MMC) that had taken place in 1988. It reviewed progress towards a competitive market and found that the steps taken in 1988 had been ineffective in encouraging self-sustaining competition. British Gas undertook in March 1992 to allow competitors to take by 1995 at least 60 per cent of the contract market above 732,000 kWh (25,000 therms) a year (subsequently redefined as 45 per cent of the market above 73,200 kWh (2,500 therms)); to release to competitors the gas necessary to achieve this; and to establish a separate transport and storage unit with regulated charges. At the same time, the Government took powers in the 1992 Competition and Service (Utilities) Act to reduce or remove the tariff monopoly, and in July 1992 it lowered the tariff threshold to 73,200 kWh.

4.5   Difficulties in implementing the March 1992 undertakings led to further references to the MMC. As a result of the new recommendations made by the MMC in 1993, the President of the Board of Trade decided in December 1993 to require full internal separation of British Gas's supply and transportation activities, but not divestment, and to accelerate removal of the tariff monopoly to April 1996, with a phased opening of the domestic market by the regulator over the following two years.

4.6   In November 1995 the Gas Bill received Royal Assent, clearing the way for the extension of competition into the domestic gas supply market on a phased basis between 1996 and 1998. This was carried out in stages between April 1996 and May 1998. By December 2003, just over 8 million gas consumers (39 per cent) were no longer supplied by British Gas. Table 4A gives market penetration in more detail, by local distribution zone (LDZ). For all types of domestic customer it is in the markets in Northern England that new suppliers have had most success. At the end of Q4 2003, British Gas had lost around 37 per cent of the credit and 44 per cent of the direct debit market compared to 26 per cent of the pre-payment market, although it should be noted that British Gas's pre-payment prices are below the average of new suppliers. At the end of 2003, 22 suppliers were licensed to supply gas to domestic customers.

Table 4A: Domestic gas market penetration (in terms of percentage of customers supplied) by local distribution zone and payment type, fourth quarter of 2003

Region	British Gas Trading			Non-British Gas		
	Credit	Direct Debit	Prepayment	Credit	Direct Debit	Prepayment
Northern	51	49	62	49	51	38
Wales	56	54	52	44	46	48
North East	56	56	70	44	44	30
East Midlands	60	53	73	40	47	27
North West	62	54	81	38	46	19
South East	63	60	82	37	40	18
North Thames	63	54	79	37	46	21
Scotland	64	48	68	36	52	32
Eastern	65	64	80	35	36	20
Southern	67	56	72	33	44	28
South West	68	58	79	32	42	21
West Midlands	69	61	77	31	39	23
Great Britain	63	56	74	37	44	26

4.7   Following the 1995 Act, the business of British Gas was fully separated into two corporate entities. The supply and shipping businesses were devolved to a subsidiary, British Gas Trading Limited, while the transportation business (Transco) remained within British Gas plc. In February 1997, Centrica plc was demerged from British Gas plc (which was itself renamed as BG plc) completing the division of the business into two independent entities. Centrica became the holding company for British Gas Trading, British Gas Services, the Retail Energy Centres and the company producing gas from the North and South Morecambe fields. BG plc comprised the gas transportation and storage business of Transco, along with British Gas's other exploration and production, international downstream, research and technology and property activities. In October 2000 BG plc demerged into two separately listed companies, of which Lattice Group plc was the holding company for Transco, while BG Group plc included the international and gas storage businesses. On 21 October 2002 Transco and the National Grid Company merged to form National Grid Transco.

4.8   From 1 October 2001, under the Utilities Act, gas pipeline companies have been able to apply for their own national Gas Transporter Licences so that they can compete with Transco. In some areas low pressure spur networks had already been developed by new transporters competing with Transco to bring gas supplies to new customers (mainly domestic). In addition, some very large loads (above 60 GWh) are serviced by pipelines operated independently, some by North Sea producers.

4.9   By the end of 1994, competitors had exceeded the target 45 per cent of the market above 73,200 kWh (2,500 therms), but virtually all of this was in the firm gas market. From 1995 British Gas's competitors made inroads into the interruptible market but in 2003 Centrica's share of the industrial and commercial market remained at 11 per cent. At the end of 2003, there were about 50 suppliers active in the UK gas market, but some companies own or part own more than one supplier. The structure of the gas industry in Great Britain as it stood at the end of 2003 is shown in Chart 4.1.

Chart 4.1: Structure of the gas industry in Great Britain in 2003

Regional analysis

4.10   Table 4B gives the number of consumers with a gas demand below 73,200 kWh per year in 2003.   It covers both domestic and small business customers receiving gas from the national transmission system. It is this section of the market that was progressively opened up to competition between April 1996 and May 1998.   The regions shown are Transco's 13 local distribution zones (LDZs). Table 4B also gives the corresponding information for all consumers of gas.

Table 4B: Consumption by gas customers by gas zone in 2003

Local distribution zones	Consumption by customers below 73,200 kWh (2,500 therms) annual demand		Consumption by all customers	
	Number of consumers (thousands)	Gas sales 2003 (GWh)	Number of consumers (thousands)	Gas sales 2003 (GWh)
North Western	2,599	52,749	2,650	90,467
South Eastern	2,367	46,314	2,416	76,552
North Thames	2,203	43,543	2,261	72,100
East Midlands	2,118	42,905	2,156	81,778
West Midlands	1,887	38,272	1,925	64,390
Scotland	1,661	34,200	1,696	63,149
Eastern	1,652	34,011	1,686	53,427
Southern	1,485	30,291	1,515	48,246
South West	1,312	23,854	1,335	38,628
North Eastern	1,282	25,632	1,312	49,554
Northern	1,126	23,899	1,145	44,165
Wales South	775	15,676	787	31,948
Wales North	217	4,602	221	9,339
Great Britain	20,683	415,948	21,105	723,743

Source: National Grid Transco

4.11   In December 2003, DTI published in Energy Trends and on the DTI web site (www.dti.gov.uk/energy/inform/energy_trends/2003/dec_03.pdf) gas consumption data at both regional and local level. The local level data are at "NUTS4" level (see article in December 2003 Energy Trends for definition) and the regional data at "NUTS1" level. Data for 2001 and 2002 were presented and domestic sector sales were shown separately from commercial and industrial sales. Numbers of consumers were also given. It is planned to update the analysis to cover 2003 and publish a further article in Energy Trends by December 2004.

Northern Ireland

4.12   Before 1997, Northern Ireland did not have a public natural gas supply. The construction of a natural gas pipeline from Portpatrick in Scotland to Northern Ireland was completed in 1996 and provided the means of establishing such a system. The primary market is Ballylumford power station, which was purchased by British Gas in 1992 and converted from oil to gas firing (with a heavy fuel oil back up). The onshore line has been extended to serve wider industrial, commercial and domestic markets and this extension is continuing. In 2003, 79 per cent of all gas supplies in Northern Ireland were used to generate electricity.

Competition

4.13   Paragraphs 4.3 to 4.12 above referred to the developments in recent years in opening up the non-domestic market to competition. About three-quarters of this market (by volume) in the United Kingdom was opened to competition at the end of 1982, and the remainder in August 1992 (with the reduction in the tariff threshold). As mentioned above, however, no other suppliers entered the market until 1990. After 1990 there was a rapid increase in the number of independent companies supplying gas, although from 1999 there were signs of some consolidation and in recent years sales of gas have become more concentrated in the hands of the largest companies in the domestic, industrial and commercial sectors. This has come about through larger companies absorbing smaller suppliers and through mergers between already significant suppliers. The three largest suppliers now jointly account for 82 per cent of sales to domestic customers whereas in 2001 the proportion was 76 per cent. For the industrial sector the share of the largest three suppliers rose from 47 per cent in 2001 to 52 per cent in 2003 and through mergers the largest 8 firms have increased their joint share to 94 per cent from 88 per cent in 2001. For commercial sector sales, in 2003 the three largest suppliers accounted for 62 per cent of sales, up from 37 per cent in 2001. Whereas in 2001 the 10 largest suppliers accounted for 63 per cent of sales by 2003 this proportion had moved up to 79 per cent.

Commodity balances for gas (Table 4.1)

4.14   For all three years shown on this table, production of natural gas has been greater than supply because exports have been larger than imports. However, net exports of natural gas, although growing rapidly, were not large in absolute terms, amounting to only 7½ per cent of total production in 2003. Imports and exports of natural gas are described in greater detail below in paragraph 4.19.

4.15   Although demand for natural gas is traditionally less than supply because of the various measurement differences described in paragraphs 4.43 to 4.46, in 2003 they broadly balanced each other.

4.16   In 2003, 29½ per cent of natural gas demand was for electricity generation (transformation sector), a similar proportion to 2002. A further 8 per cent was consumed for heating purposes within the energy industries. A half per cent was accounted for by distribution losses within the gas network. (For an explanation of the items included under losses, see paragraphs 4.43 to 4.46.) Of the remaining 62 per cent, 2 per cent was transformed into heat for sale to a third party, 15½ per cent was accounted for by the industrial sector with the chemicals industry (excluding natural gas for petrochemical feedstocks), food and iron and steel industry being the largest consumers. The chemicals sector accounted for over a quarter of the industrial consumption of natural gas.

4.17   Sales of gas to households (domestic sector) produced 34½ per cent of gas demand, while public administration (including schools and hospitals) consumed 4 per cent of total demand, almost as much gas as the chemicals sector. The commercial, agriculture and miscellaneous sectors together took up 5 per cent. Non energy use of gas accounted for the remaining 1 per cent. As Table 4C, below, shows, non-energy use of gas is small relative to total use (see the technical notes section, paragraph 4.36, for more details on non-energy use of gas).

Table 4C: Non-energy use: share of natural gas demand

	Continental shelf and onshore natural gas
1999	1.2%
2000	1.2%
2001	1.0%
2002	1.0%
2003	1.0%

4.18   Care should be exercised in interpreting the figures for individual industries in these commodity balance tables. As companies switch contracts between gas suppliers, it has not been possible to ensure consistent classification between and within industry sectors and across years. The breakdown of final consumption includes a substantial amount of estimated data. For about 13½ per cent of consumption the allocation to consuming sector is estimated.

4.19   Imports of natural gas from the Norwegian sector of the North Sea began to decline in the late 1980s as output from the Frigg field tailed off. The interconnector linking the UK's transmission network with Belgium via a Bacton to Zeebrugge pipeline began to operate in October 1998. Since 1998 there was an increase in imports brought about by inflows through the Bacton to Zeebrugge interconnector (although the UK has been a net exporter through this interconnector since it began operation). In 2003, imports added about 7 per cent to UK production. Exports to mainland Europe from the United Kingdom's share of the Markham field began in 1992 with Windermere's output being added in 1997. Exports to the Republic of Ireland began in 1995. In 2003, exports accounted for 15 per cent of UK production. Exports of natural gas exceeded imports for the first time in 1997 and grew rapidly to 2000, fell by 5½ per cent in 2001, but rose for the second consecutive year to a new peak in 2003.

4.20   Chart 4.2 shows the increase in indigenous production and consumption of natural gas over the past five years and relative size of net exports.

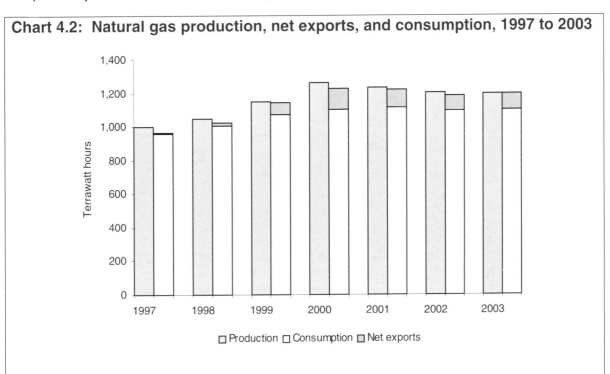

Chart 4.2: Natural gas production, net exports, and consumption, 1997 to 2003

Consumption plus net exports will differ from production plus net imports because of stock changes, losses and the statistical difference item.

Supply and consumption of natural gas and colliery methane (Table 4.2)

4.21   This table summarises the production and consumption of gas from these sources in the United Kingdom over the last 5 years.

4.22   As Chart 4.3 shows, the growth in consumption for electricity generation has dominated the growth in natural gas consumption over the last 10 years. Most of this gas was used in Combined Cycle Gas Turbine (CCGT) stations, although the use of gas in dual fired conventional steam stations was a growth area in 1997 and 1998. However, gas use for electricity generation grew by only 3 per cent in 2000 and in 2001 fell by 4½ per cent as higher gas prices made it more difficult for gas fired stations to compete with large coal fired stations. This was reversed by a 5½ per cent growth in 2002 when gas prices eased but fell again in 2003 by 1½ per cent. Higher gas prices again meant that at times some generators found it more profitable to sell gas than use it for generation, particularly given plentiful supplies of inexpensive coal.   In 2003 the transformation sector as a whole accounted for 31 per cent of gas demand – broadly unchanged over the last 5 years.

4.23   Industrial use of gas grew between 1998 and 2000 by 8 per cent, but fell by 2 per cent in 2001 and by 8 per cent in 2002. In 2003 this was reversed by 4 per cent growth partly due to the downturn in economic activity starting to ease off from the second half of the year. Gas consumption grew sharply in the paper and printing and the chemicals industries but fell in the textiles, mechanical engineering and the iron and steel industries. Use by the public administration sector and the commercial sector were 2 and 1 per cent higher, respectively, in 2003 than in 2002 but consumption in the energy industries other than electricity (and heat) generation fell by 2½ per cent partly due to the closure of one large iron and steel making plant.

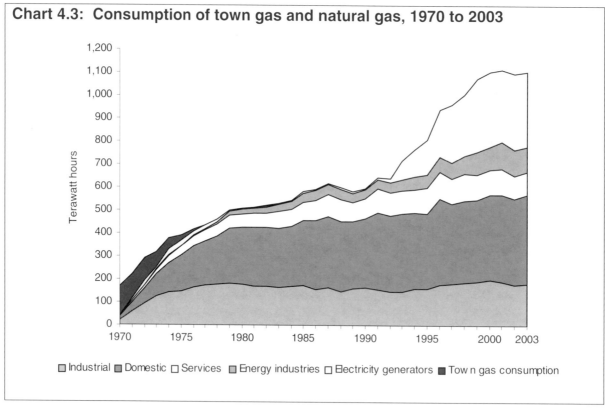

Chart 4.3: Consumption of town gas and natural gas, 1970 to 2003

□ Industrial ■ Domestic □ Services ■ Energy industries □ Electricity generators ■ Tow n gas consumption

4.24   Gas use in the domestic sector is particularly dependent on winter temperatures and in 2003 the average temperature over the winter months was lower than in 2002. This helped domestic sector demand to increase by 2½ a per cent than in 2002 and exceed the previous peak level achieved in the colder year of 2001. Although demand from the domestic sector increased by 7½ per cent between 1999 and 2003, its share of total demand rose less sharply from 33 per cent to 34½ per cent.

4.25   Maximum daily demand for natural gas through the National Transmission System in winter 2003/04 was 4,875 GWh on 29th January 2004. On that day natural gas demand in Northern Ireland was 43 GWh. This total maximum daily demand was just under 2 per cent lower than January 2003's record level.

4.26   It is estimated that sales of gas supplied on an interruptible basis accounted for around 26 per cent of total gas sales in 2003; an increase of around 4 percentage points on 2002.

UK continental shelf and onshore natural gas (Table 4.3)

4.27   Table 4.3 shows the flows for natural gas from production through transmission to consumption. The footnotes to the table give more information about each table row. This table departs from the standard balance methodology and definitions in order to maintain the link with past data and with monthly data given at DTI's energy statistics web site (see paragraph 4.42). The relationship between total UK gas consumption shown in this table and total demand for gas given in the balance tables (4.1 and 4.2) is illustrated for 2003 as follows:

		GWh
Total UK consumption (Table 4.3)		1,018,432
plus Producers' own use		76,839
plus Operators' own use		7,828
equals		
"Consumption of natural gas" (see paragraph 4.32)		1,103,099
plus Other losses and metering differences (upstream)		-
plus Downstream losses - leakage assessment	4,452)	7,088
- own use gas	439)	
- theft	2,197)	
plus Metering differences (transmission)		-1,280
equals		
Total demand (Tables 4.1 and 4.2)		1,108,907

4.28   Gross production rose steadily and peaked in 2000 at 1.3TWh but fell for the third consecutive year in 2003 to stand at broadly the same level (1.2TWh) as in 1999. Gas available at UK terminals has increased by a lesser amount over this period mainly because of the increase in exports and decrease in imports described in paragraph 4.19. Producers' and operators' own use of gas have tended to grow in proportion to the volumes of gas produced and transmitted. Output from the transmission system increased by 1.5 per cent between 1999 and 2003, while total UK consumption of natural gas increased by 1.6 per cent. Consumption increased by more than the output from the transmission system because distribution losses and metering differences have been reduced as a proportion of consumption over these four years.

4.29   For a discussion of the various losses and statistical differences terms in this table, see paragraphs 4.43 to 4.46 in the technical notes and definitions section below. The statistical difference between output from the National Transmission System and total UK consumption has been disaggregated using information obtained from Transco on leakage from local distribution zone pipes, theft and use regarded as own use by pipeline operators. The convention used is set out in paragraph 4.46.

4.30   Losses and metering differences attributable to the information provided on the upstream gas industry are zero from 2001 onwards because these data are no longer reported in the revised Petroleum Production Reporting System. This simplified system for reporting the production of crude oil, NGLs and natural gas in the UK was implemented from 1st January 2001; it reduced the burden on the respondents and improved the quality of data reported on gas production.

Technical notes and definitions

4.31   These notes and definitions are in addition to the technical notes and definitions covering all fuels and energy as a whole in Chapter 1, paragraphs 1.25 to 1.58. For notes on the commodity balances and definitions of the terms used in the row headings see Annex A, paragraphs A.7 to A.42.

Definitions used for production and consumption

4.32   **Natural gas** production in Tables 4.1 and 4.2 relates to the output of indigenous methane at land terminals and gas separation plants (includes producers' and processors' own use). For further explanation, see Annex F, paragraph F.19 on DTI's Energy Statistics web site under 'Production of oil and gas' - www.dti.gov.uk/energy/inform/dukes/dukes2004/annexf.pdf. Output of the Norwegian share of the Frigg and Murchison fields is included under imports. A small quantity of onshore produced methane (other than colliery methane) is also included.

4.33   Table 4.3 shows production, transmission and consumption figures for UK continental shelf and onshore natural gas. Production includes waste and own use for drilling, production and pumping operations, but excludes gas flared. Gas available in the United Kingdom excludes waste, own use for drilling etc, stock change, and includes imports net of exports. Gas transmitted (input into inland transmission systems) is after stock change, own use, and losses at inland terminals. The amount consumed in the United Kingdom differs from the total gas transmitted by the gas supply industry, because of losses in transmission, differences in temperature and pressure between the points at which the gas is measured, delays in reading meters and consumption in the works, offices, shops, etc of the undertakings. The figures include an adjustment to the quantities billed to consumers to allow for the estimated consumption remaining unread at the end of the year.

4.34   **Colliery methane** production is colliery methane piped to the surface and consumed at collieries or transmitted by pipeline to consumers. As the output of deep-mined coal declines so does the production of colliery methane, unless a use can be found for gas that was previously vented. The supply of methane from coal measures that are no longer being worked or from drilling into coal measures is licensed under the same legislation as used for offshore gas production.

4.35   **Transfers** of natural gas include natural gas use within the iron and steel industry for mixing with blast furnace gas to form a synthetic coke oven gas. For further details see paragraph 2.48 in Chapter 2.

4.36   **Non-energy gas**: Non-energy use is gas used as feedstock for petrochemical plants in the chemical industry as raw material for the production of ammonia (an essential intermediate chemical in the production of nitrogen fertilisers) and methanol. The contribution of liquefied petroleum gases (propane and butane) and other petroleum gases is shown in Tables 3.4 to 3.6 of Chapter 3. Firm data for natural gas are not available, but estimates for 1999 to 2003 are shown in Table 4.2 and estimates for 2001 to 2003 in Table 4.1 Estimates for the years up to 2002 have been obtained from the National Atmospheric Emissions Inventory (NAEI); 2003 data are DTI extrapolations.

Sectors used for sales/consumption

4.37   For definitions of the various sectors used for sales and consumption analyses see Chapter 1 paragraphs 1.54 to 1.58 and Annex A, paragraphs A.31 to A.42. However, **miscellaneous** has a wider coverage than in the commodity balances of other fuels. This is because some gas supply companies are unable to provide a full breakdown of the services sector and the gas they supply to consumers is allocated to miscellaneous when there is no reliable basis for allocating it elsewhere.

Data collection

4.38   Production figures are generally obtained from returns made under the Department of Trade and Industry's Petroleum Production Reporting System (PPRS) and from other sources. DTI obtain data on the transmission of natural gas from National Grid Transco (who operate the National Transmission System) and from other pipeline operators. Data on consumption are based on returns from gas suppliers and UKCS producers who supply gas directly to customers.

4.39   The production data are for the United Kingdom (including natural gas from the UKCS - offshore and onshore). The restoration of a public gas supply to parts of Northern Ireland in 1997 (see paragraph 4.12 means that all tables in this chapter (except Tables 4A and 4B) cover the UK.

4.40   DTI carry out an annual survey of gas suppliers to obtain details of gas sales to the various categories of consumer. Estimates are included for the suppliers with the smallest market share since the DTI inquiry covers only the largest suppliers (ie those with more than about a ½ per cent share of the UK market up to 1997 and those known to supply more than 1,750 GWh per year for 1998 onwards).

Period covered
4.41   Figures generally relate to years ended 31 December. However, data for natural gas for electricity generation relate to periods of 52 weeks as set out in Chapter 5, paragraphs 5.56 and 5.58.

Monthly and quarterly data
4.42   Monthly data on natural gas production and supply are available from the DTI's Energy Statistics web site www.dti.gov.uk/energy/inform/energy_stats/ in monthly Table 4.2. A quarterly commodity balance for natural gas (which includes consumption data) is published in DTI's quarterly statistical bulletin *Energy Trends* and is also available from quarterly Table 4.1 at DTI's Energy Statistics web site. See Annex C for more information about *Energy Trends* and the DTI Energy Statistics web site.

Statistical and metering differences
4.43   In Table 4.3 there are several headings that refer to statistical or metering differences. These arise because measurement of gas flows, in volume and energy terms, takes place at several points along the supply chain. The main sub-headings in the table represent the instances in the supply chain where accurate reports are made of the gas flows at that particular key point in the supply process. It is possible to derive alternative estimates of the flow of gas at any particular point by taking the estimate for the previous point in the supply chain and then applying the known losses and gains in the subsequent part of the supply chain. The differences seen when the actual reported flow of gas at any point and the derived estimate are compared are separately identified in the table wherever possible, under the headings statistical or metering differences.

4.44   The differences arise from several factors:-

• Limitations in the accuracy of meters used at various points of the supply chain. While standards are in place on the accuracy of meters, there is a degree of error allowed which, when large flows of gas are being recorded, can become significant.

• Differences in the methods used to calculate the flow of gas in energy terms. For example, at the production end, rougher estimates of the calorific value of the gas produced are used which may be revised only periodically, rather than the more accurate and more frequent analyses carried out further down the supply chain. At the supply end, although the calorific value of gas shows day-to-day variations, for the purposes of recording the gas supplied to customers a single calorific value is used. Until 1997 this was the lowest of the range of calorific values for the actual gas being supplied within each LDZ, resulting in a "loss" of gas in energy terms. In 1997 there was a change to a "capped flow-weighted average" algorithm for calculating calorific values resulting in a reduction in the losses shown in the penultimate row of Table 4.3. This change in algorithm, along with improved meter validation and auditing procedures, also reduced the level of the "metering differences" row within the downstream part of Table 4.3.

• Differences in temperature and pressure between the various points at which gas is measured. Until February 1997 British Gas used "uncorrected therms" on their billing system for tariff customers when converting from a volume measure of the gas used to an energy measure. This made their supply figure too small by a factor of 2.2 per cent, equivalent to about 1 per cent of the wholesale market.

• Differences in the timing of reading meters. While National Transmission System meters are read daily, customers' meters are read less frequently (perhaps only annually for some domestic customers) and profiling is used to estimate consumption. Profiling will tend to underestimate consumption in a strongly rising market.

• Other losses from the system, for example, theft through meter tampering by consumers.

4.45   The headings in Table 4.3 show where, in the various stages of the supply process, it has been possible to identify these metering differences as having an effect. Usually they are aggregated with other net losses as the two factors cannot be separated. Whilst the factors listed above can give rise to either losses or gains, losses are more common. However, the negative downstream gas metering difference within the transmission system in 2003 is an anomaly that was still being investigated by National Grid Transco at the time of compilation of Table 4.3

4.46   The box below shows how in 2003 the wastage, losses and metering differences figures in Table 4.3 are related to the losses row in the balance Tables 4.1 and 4.2. It should be noted that losses from 2001 onwards are lower than in previous years because figures for losses and metering differences in the upstream gas industry are no longer available (see above):

Table 4.3	GWh
Upstream gas industry:	
Other losses and metering differences	-
Downstream gas industry:	
Transmission system metering differences	-1,280
Leakage assessment	4,452
Own use gas	439
Theft	2,197
Tables 4.1 and 4.2	
Losses	5,808

Similarly the statistical difference row in Tables 4.1 and 4.2 is made up of the following components in 2003:

Table 4.3	GWh
Statistical difference between gas available from upstream and gas input to downstream	-1,385
plus Downstream gas industry:	
Distribution losses and metering differences	1,259
Tables 4.1 and 4.2	
Statistical difference	-126

Contact: *Mike Janes (Statistician)*   *John Castle*
              Energy Markets Information and Analysis   *Energy Information Systems*
              mike.janes@dti.gsi.gov.uk   *john.castle@dti.gsi.gov.uk*
              020-7215 5186   *020-7215 2718*

              James Achur
              Energy Markets Information and Analysis
              james.achur@dti.gsi.gov.uk
              020-7215 2717

The National gas transmission system, 2003

Source: National Grid Transco

4.1 Commodity balances

Natural gas

GWh

	2001			2002			2003		
	Natural gas	Colliery methane	Total Natural gas	Natural gas	Colliery methane	Total Natural gas	Natural gas	Colliery methane	Total Natural gas
Supply									
Production	1,230,533	730r	1,231,263r	1,204,713r	692r	1,205,405r	1,196,117	1,050	1,197,167
Other sources	-	-	-	-	-	-	-	-	-
Imports	30,464r	-	30,464r	60,493r	-	60,493r	86,298	-	86,298
Exports	-138,330r	-	-138,330r	-150,731	-	-150,731	-177,039	-	-177,039
Marine bunkers	-	-	-	-	-	-	-	-	-
Stock change (1)	-661		-661	-7,356		-7,356	+3,492		3,492
Transfers (3)	-65		-65	-99		-99	-87		-87
Total supply	1,121,941r	730r	1,122,671r	1,107,020r	692r	1,107,712r	1,108,781	1,050	1,109,831
Statistical difference (2)	+2,618r	-	+2,618r	+1,893r	-	+1,893r	-126	-	-126
Total demand	1,119,323r	730r	1,120,053r	1,105,127r	692r	1,105,819r	1,108,907	1,050	1,109,957
Transformation	335,689r	418r	336,107r	351,623r	406r	352,029r	344,123	788	344,911
Electricity generation	312,103r	418r	312,521r	329,629r	406r	330,035r	324,075	788	324,863
Major power producers	276,764	-	276,764	291,264	-	291,264	284,662	-	284,662
Autogenerators	35,339r	418r	35,757r	38,365r	406r	38,771r	39,413	788	40,201
Heat generation	23,586r		23,586r	21,994r		21,994r	20,048		20,048
Petroleum refineries	-	-	-	-	-	-	-	-	-
Coke manufacture	-	-	-	-	-	-	-	-	-
Blast furnaces	-	-	-	-	-	-	-	-	-
Patent fuel manufacture	-	-	-	-	-	-	-	-	-
Other	-	-	-	-	-	-	-	-	-
Energy industry use	91,244r	207	91,451r	91,064r	196	91,260r	88,421	187	88,608
Electricity generation	-	-	-	-	-	-	-	-	-
Oil and gas extraction	78,457r	-	78,457r	79,364r	-	79,364r	76,839	-	76,839
Petroleum refineries	4,189r	-	4,189r	3,350r	-	3,350r	2,157	-	2,157
Coal extraction	4	207	211	-	196	196	-	187	187
Coke manufacture	9	-	9	-	-	-	-	-	-
Blast furnaces	375	-	375	222	-	222	485	-	485
Patent fuel manufacture	-	-	-	-	-	-	-	-	-
Pumped storage	-	-	-	-	-	-	-	-	-
Other	8,210	-	8,210	8,128	-	8,128	8,940	-	8,940
Losses (4)	8,863r	-	8,863r	9,666	-	9,666	5,808	-	5,808
Final consumption	683,527r	105	683,632r	652,774r	90	652,864r	670,555	75	670,630
Industry	179,738r	105	179,843r	165,330r	90	165,420r	172,084	75	172,159
Unclassified	-	105	105	-	90	90	-	75	75
Iron and steel	20,901r	-	20,901r	19,522r	-	19,522r	19,121	-	19,121
Non-ferrous metals	5,225r	-	5,225r	4,987r	-	4,987r	5,087	-	5,087
Mineral products	13,794r	-	13,794r	12,648r	-	12,648r	13,324	-	13,324
Chemicals	47,448r	-	47,448r	42,252r	-	42,252r	45,154	-	45,154
Mechanical Engineering, etc	8,429r	-	8,429r	8,356r	-	8,356r	8,666	-	8,666
Electrical engineering, etc	4,418r	-	4,418r	4,154r	-	4,154r	4,321	-	4,321
Vehicles	11,162r	-	11,162r	10,735r	-	10,735r	11,150	-	11,150
Food, beverages, etc	27,494r	-	27,494r	27,047r	-	27,047r	27,716	-	27,716
Textiles, leather, etc	7,468r	-	7,468r	7,357r	-	7,357r	7,566	-	7,566
Paper, printing, etc	15,644r	-	15,644r	14,501r	-	14,501r	15,589	-	15,589
Other industries	14,808r	-	14,808r	10,916r	-	10,916r	11,475	-	11,475
Construction	2,947r	-	2,947r	2,855r	-	2,855r	2,915	-	2,915
Transport	-	-	-	-	-	-	-	-	-
Air	-	-	-	-	-	-	-	-	-
Rail	-	-	-	-	-	-	-	-	-
Road (5)	-	-	-	-	-	-	-	-	-
National navigation	-	-	-	-	-	-	-	-	-
Pipelines	-	-	-	-	-	-	-	-	-
Other	492,537r	-	492,537r	476,783r	-	476,783r	487,810	-	487,810
Domestic	379,426r	-	379,426r	376,372r	-	376,372r	385,985	-	385,985
Public administration	46,232r	-	46,232r	42,694r	-	42,694r	43,646	-	43,646
Commercial	37,098r	-	37,098r	36,100r	-	36,100r	36,376	-	36,376
Agriculture	2,329r	-	2,329r	2,346r	-	2,346r	1,494	-	1,494
Miscellaneous	27,452r	-	27,452r	19,271r	-	19,271r	20,309	-	20,309
Non energy use	11,252r	-	11,252r	10,661r	-	10,661r	10,661	-	10,661

(1) Stock fall (+), stock rise (-).
(2) Total supply minus total demand.
(3) Natural gas used in the manufacture of synthetic coke oven gas.
(4) See paragraph 4.45.
(5) See footnote 5 to Table 4.2.

4.2 Supply and consumption of natural gas and colliery methane[1]

GWh

	1999	2000	2001	2002	2003
Supply					
Production	1,152,635	1,260,656	1,231,263r	1,205,405r	1,197,167
Imports	12,862	26,032	30,464r	60,493r	86,298
Exports	-84,433	-146,342	-138,330r	-150,731	-177,039
Stock change (2)	7,787	-11,068	-661	-7,356	3,492
Transfers	-506	-442	-65	-99	-87
Total supply	1,088,345	1,128,836	1,122,671r	1,107,712r	1,109,831
Statistical difference (3)	+704	+3,384	+2,618r	+1,893r	-126
Total demand	1,087,641	1,125,451	1,120,053r	1,105,819r	1,109,957
Transformation	341,678	349,454	336,107r	352,029r	344,911
Electricity generation	315,493	324,563	312,521r	330,035r	324,863
Major power producers	281,988	283,784	276,764	291,264	284,662
Autogenerators	33,505	40,779	35,757r	38,771r	40,201
Heat generation	26,185	24,891	23,586r	21,994r	20,048
Other	-	-	-	-	-
Energy industry use	76,973	77,941	91,451r	91,260r	88,608
Electricity generation	-	-	-	-	-
Oil and gas extraction	64,634	65,555	78,457r	79,364r	76,839
Petroleum refineries	4,155	3,641	4,189r	3,350r	2,157
Coal extraction	252	224	211	196	187
Coke manufacture	13	17	9	-	-
Blast furnaces	643	712	375	222	485
Other	7,276	7,792	8,210	8,128	8,940
Losses (4)	14,678	20,480	8,863r	9,666	5,808
Final consumption	654,312	677,576	683,632r	652,864r	670,630
Industry	176,815	183,440	179,843r	165,420r	172,159
Unclassified	150	120	105	90	75
Iron and steel	21,622	22,551	20,901r	19,522r	19,121
Non-ferrous metals	5,549	5,468	5,225r	4,987r	5,087
Mineral products	14,533	13,894	13,794r	12,648r	13,324
Chemicals	46,792	46,557	47,448r	42,252r	45,154
Mechanical engineering, etc	10,173	9,774	8,429r	8,356r	8,666
Electrical engineering, etc	3,941	4,695	4,418r	4,154r	4,321
Vehicles	10,616	10,824	11,162r	10,735r	11,150
Food, beverages, etc	27,901	27,585	27,494r	27,047r	27,716
Textiles, leather, etc	6,966	7,755	7,468r	7,357r	7,566
Paper, printing, etc	12,532	16,085	15,644r	14,501r	15,589
Other industries	13,905	15,153	14,808r	10,916r	11,475
Construction	2,135	2,979	2,947r	2,855r	2,915
Transport	-	-	-	-	-
Road (5)	-	-	-	-	-
Other	464,553	480,365	492,537r	476,783r	487,810
Domestic	358,066	369,909	379,426r	376,372r	385,985
Public administration	43,253	44,552	46,232r	42,694r	43,646
Commercial	36,622	36,216	37,098r	36,100r	36,376
Agriculture	1,155	1,522	2,329r	2,346r	1,494
Miscellaneous	25,457	28,166	27,452r	19,271r	20,309
Non energy use	12,944	13,771	11,252r	10,661r	10,661

(1) Colliery methane figures included within these totals are as follows:

	1999	2000	2001	2002	2003
Total production	481	488	730r	692r	1,050
Electricity generation	93	150	418r	406r	788
Coal extraction	238	218	207	196	187
Other industries	150	120	105	90	75
Total consumption	481	488	730r	692r	1,050

(2) Stock fall (+), stock rise (-).
(3) Total supply minus total demand.
(4) For an explanation of what is included under losses, see paragraphs 4.46.

(5) A small amount of natural gas is consumed by road transport, but gas use in this sector is predominantly of petroleum gas, hence road use of gas is reported in the petroleum products balances in Chapter 3.

4.3 UK continental shelf and onshore natural gas production and supply[1]

					GWh
	1999	2000	2001	2002	2003
Upstream gas industry:					
Gross production (2)	1,152,154	1,260,168	1,230,533	1,204,713r	1,196,117
Minus Producers' own use (3) (18)	64,634	65,556	78,457r	79,364r	76,839
Exports	84,433	146,342	138,330r	150,731	177,039
Stock change (pipelines) (4) (18)	-842	+161	-	-	-
Waste (5) (18)	-	-	-	-	-
Other losses and metering differences (6)(7)(18)	5,634	10,281	-	-	-
Plus Imports of gas	12,862	26,032	30,464r	60,491	86,298
Gas available at terminals (8)	1,011,157	1,063,858	1,044,210r	1,035,109r	1,028,537
Minus Statistical difference (7)	-127	+251	-690r	-128r	-1,385
Downstream gas industry:					
Gas input into the national transmission system (9)	1,011,284	1,063,607	1,044,900r	1,035,237	1,029,922
Minus Operators' own use (10)	5,626	6,701	6,549	7,017	7,828
Stock change (storage sites) (11)	-6,945	10,907	661	7,356	-3,492
Metering differences (7)	633	2,088	1,798	1,821	-1,280
Gas output from the national transmission system (12)	1,011,970	1,043,911	1,035,892r	1,019,043	1,026,866
Minus Leakage assessment (13)	5,722	5,464	5,360	5,284	4,452
Own use gas (14)	448	442	433	427	439
Theft (15)	2,241	2,206	2,164	2,134	2,197
Transfers (16)	506	441	65	99	87
Statistical difference and metering differences (7)	831	3,128	3,353r	2,031	1,259
Total UK consumption (17)	**1,002,222**	**1,032,230**	**1,024,517**	**1,009,068**	**1,018,432**

(1) For details of where to find monthly updates of natural gas production and supply see paragraph 4.42.

(2) Includes waste and producers' own use, but excludes gas flared.

(3) Gas used for drilling, production and pumping operations.

(4) Gas held within the UKCS pipeline system. As sections are opened and closed between fields, gas moves in and out of the system, hence it is regarded as a change in stocks.

(5) Gas vented from oil and gas platforms as part of the production process. With effect from 1999 gas vented is deducted from the Gross Production figure.

(6) Losses due to pipeline leakage.

(7) Measurement of gas flows, in volume and energy terms, occurs at several points along the supply chain. As such, differences are seen between the actual recorded flow through any one point and estimates calculated for the flow of gas at that point. More detail on the reasons for these differences is given in the technical notes and definitions section of this chapter, paragraphs 4.43 to 4.46.

(8) The volume of gas available at terminals for consumption in the UK as recorded by the terminal operators. The percentage of gas available for consumption in the UK from indigenous sources in 2003 was 91.6 per cent, compared with 94.2 per cent in 2002.

(9) Gas received as reported by the pipeline operators. The pipeline operators include Transco, who run the national pipeline network, and other pipelines that take North Sea gas supplies direct to consumers.

(10) Gas consumed by pipeline operators in pumping operations and on their own sites, office, etc.

(11) Stocks of gas held in specific storage sites, either as liquefied natural gas, pumped into salt cavities or stored by pumping the gas back into an offshore field. Stock rise (+), stock fall (-).

(12) Including public gas supply, direct supplies by North Sea producers, third party supplies and stock changes.

(13) This is a Tranco assessment of leakage through the local distribution system based on the National Leakage Reduction Monitoring Model. The 2003 figure is a DTI estimate.

(14) Equivalent to about 0.06 per cent of LDZ throughput this is an assessment of the energy used to counter the effects of gas cooling on pressure reduction.

(15) Calculated by Transco as 0.3 per cent of LDZ throughput, this is theft before the gas reaches customer meters.

(16) Transfers are the use within the iron and steel industry for use in the manufacture of synthetic coke oven gas.

(17) See paragraph 4.27 for an explanation of the relationship between these "Total UK consumption" figures and "Total demand" shown within the balance tables.

(18) A simplified PPRS reporting system was introduced in January 2001 requiring less data from respondents - see paragraph 4.30.

Chapter 5
Electricity

Introduction

5.1   This Chapter presents statistics on electricity from generation through to sales. In addition, statistics on generating capacity, on fuel used for generation and on load factors and efficiencies are included along with a map showing the transmission system in Great Britain and the location of the main power stations (page 121).

5.2   Commodity balances for electricity, for each of the last three years, form the introductory table (Table 5.1). The supply and consumption elements of the electricity balance are presented as 5-year time series in Table 5.2. Table 5.3 separates out the public distribution system for electricity from electricity generated and consumed by autogenerators and uses a commodity balance format. Fuels used to generate electricity in the United Kingdom in each of the last five years are covered in Table 5.4. Table 5.5 shows the relationship between the commodity balance definitions and traditional Digest definitions for electricity. This enables the most recent data to be linked to the long term trends data, which can be found on the DTI energy statistics web site. Table 5.6 shows the relationship between fuels used, generation and supply in each of the latest five years. Tables on plant capacity (Tables 5.7 and 5.8) and on plant loads and efficiency (Table 5.10) have been included and the table that lists individual power stations in operation is now Table 5.11. Additional information for England and Wales, Scotland, and Northern Ireland on plant capacity (new Table 5.9) and on maximum demand (additional rows in table 5.10) are included for the first time this year. The long term trends commentary and tables on fuel use, generation, supply and consumption back to 1970 are on DTI's energy statistics web site www.dti.gov.uk/energy/inform/dukes/dukes2004/05longterm.pdf.

Structure of the industry

5.3   Since the period immediately after privatisation of the industry in 1989, when there were 7 generating companies in England and Wales and 12 Regional Electricity companies distributing and supplying electricity to customers in their designated area, there have been many structural and business changes. At the end of 2003 there were 33 major power producers operating in England and Wales[1]. Competition developed as follows:

(a)   From 1 April 1990, customers with peak loads of more than 1 MW (about 45 per cent of the non-domestic market) were able to choose their supplier.

(b)   From 1 April 1994, customers with peak loads of more than 100 kW were able to choose their supplier.

(c)   Between September 1998 and May 1999, the remaining part of the electricity market (ie below 100 kW peak load) was opened up to competition. Paragraph 5.8 and Table 5A give more details of the opening up of the domestic gas and electricity markets to competition.

5.4   At the same time, there have been moves to integrate vertically the electricity business with former generating companies acquiring electricity supply companies and supply companies purchasing generating stations or acquiring interests in companies building new power stations. Distribution businesses have been sold or acquired and merged. The National Grid Company, now part of National Grid Transco, operates the high voltage transmission system linking generators to distributors and some large customers. The Grid system of England and Wales is linked to that of Scotland via two interconnectors and to the grid of continental Europe via in interconnector to France under the English Channel. (See Table 5.11).

---

[1] Some of these producers are joint ventures and so the number of generating companies involved is less than 33.

5.5   In Scotland, the two main companies, Scottish Power and Scottish and Southern Energy, cover the full range of electricity provision. They operate generation, transmission, distribution and supply businesses. The entire output of the two nuclear power stations in Scotland, which are owned by British Energy plc, is sold to these two suppliers under long-term contracts. In addition, there are about 25 small independent hydro stations and some independent generators operating fossil-fuelled stations, which sell their output to Scottish Power and Scottish and Southern Energy.

5.6   The electricity supply industry in Northern Ireland is also in private hands. Northern Ireland Electricity plc (NIE) (part of the Viridian Group) is responsible for power procurement, transmission, distribution and supply in the Province. Generation is in the hands of three private sector companies who own the four major power stations. There is a link (re-established in 1996) between the Northern Ireland grid and that of the Irish Republic, along which electricity is both imported and exported. In December 2001, the link between Northern Ireland's grid and that of Scotland was inaugurated.

5.7   In March 2001, the means of trading electricity changed with the introduction in England and Wales of the New Electricity Trading Arrangements (NETA). These arrangements are based on bi-lateral trading between generators, suppliers, traders and customers and are designed to be more efficient and provide greater choice for market participants, whilst maintaining the operation of a secure and reliable electricity system. The system includes forwards and futures markets, a balancing mechanism to enable the National Grid Company, as systems operator, to balance the system, and a settlement process. The system is shown in simplified form in Chart 5.1.

Chart 5.1: Structure of the electricity industry in England and Wales in 2003

5.8   By December 2003, just over 10 million electricity consumers (41 per cent) were no longer with their home supplier. Table 5A gives market penetration in the fourth quarter of 2003. For quarterly credit customers it is in the markets in the North West, West Midlands, North Wales and Merseyside, and the North that new suppliers had the most success. By the end of 2003, the former regional electricity companies had lost around 37 per cent of the credit, 47 per cent of the direct debit, and 38 per cent of the prepayment market.

Table 5A: Domestic electricity market penetration (in terms of percentage of customers supplied) by Public Electricity Supply area and payment type, fourth quarter of 2003

Region	Home Supplier			Non-Home Supplier		
	Credit	Direct Debit	Prepayment	Credit	Direct Debit	Prepayment
North West	51	48	51	49	52	49
West Midlands	54	53	60	46	47	40
Merseyside and North Wales	55	54	52	45	46	48
Northern	58	50	57	42	50	43
Yorkshire	58	48	53	42	52	47
East Midlands	60	52	59	40	48	41
Eastern	64	51	58	36	49	42
South Wales	65	63	86	35	37	14
South East	68	56	53	32	44	47
London	68	48	64	32	44	36
South Scotland	68	61	68	32	52	32
South	71	61	75	29	39	25
South West	72	49	64	28	51	36
North Scotland	84	75	87	16	25	13
Great Britain	63	53	62	37	47	38

Commodity balances for electricity (Table 5.1)

5.9   The first page of this balance table shows that 99½ per cent of UK electricity supply in 2003 was home produced and ½ per cent was from imports net of exports. Just ¾ per cent of home produced electricity was exported. Of the 395,886 GWh produced (excluding pumped storage production), 91 per cent was from major power producers and 9 per cent from autoproducers, 23½ per cent was from primary sources and 76½ per cent from secondary sources.

5.10   Electricity generated by each type of fuel is shown on the second page of the commodity balance table. The link between electricity generated and electricity supplied is made in Table 5.6 and electricity supplied by each type of fuel is illustrated in Chart 5.3. Paragraph 5.26 examines further the ways of presenting each fuel's contribution to electricity production.

5.11   Demand for electricity is predominantly from final consumers, who accounted for 84½ per cent in 2003. The remaining 15½ per cent is split 8 per cent to energy industries' use and 7½ per cent to losses. The electricity industry itself uses 56 per cent of the energy industries' total use of electricity, with a further 11 per cent used for pumping at pumped storage stations. Petroleum refineries are the next most significant consumer. The losses item has three components. First, transmission losses from the high voltage transmission system represented about 19 per cent of total losses in 2003. Second, distribution losses, which occur between the gateways to the public supply system's network and the customers' meters, accounted for about 76 per cent of losses. Third, a small amount was lost through theft or meter fraud (5 per cent) (see also paragraphs 5.64).

5.12   Industrial consumption was 34 per cent of final consumption in 2003, slightly less than the consumption by households (34½ per cent), with transport and the services sector accounting for the remaining 31½ per cent. Within the industrial sector the three largest consuming industries are chemicals, paper and food, which together account for 40 per cent of industrial consumption. The iron and steel sector is also a large user of electricity and would rank fourth largest, but part of its consumption is included against blast furnaces and coke ovens under energy industry uses. This is because electricity is used by coke ovens and blast furnaces in the transformation of solid fuels into coke, coke oven gas and blast furnace gas. Taken together, the engineering industries accounted for a further 18 per cent of final consumption of electricity. A note on the estimates included within these figures is to be found at paragraph 5.65. Chart 5.2 shows diagrammatically the demand for electricity in 2003.

5.13 The transport sector covers electricity consumed by companies involved in transport, storage and communications. Within the overall total of 8,500 GWh, it is known that national railways consume about 2,700 GWh each year for traction purposes, and this figure has been shown separately in the balances.

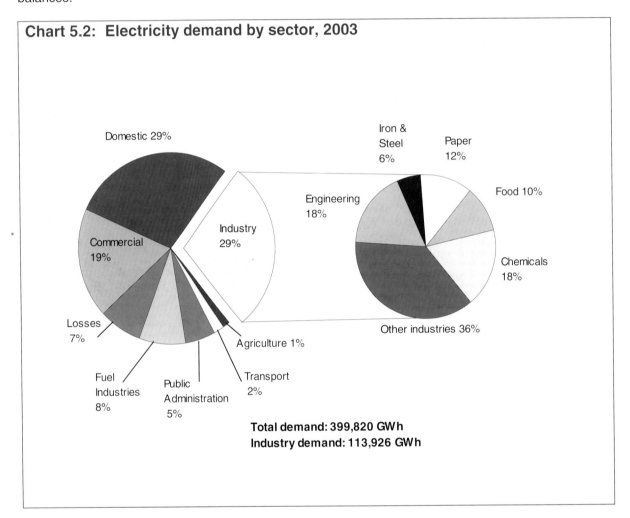

Chart 5.2: Electricity demand by sector, 2003

Domestic 29%
Commercial 19%
Losses 7%
Fuel Industries 8%
Public Administration 5%
Agriculture 1%
Transport 2%
Industry 29%

Iron & Steel 6%
Paper 12%
Engineering 18%
Food 10%
Chemicals 18%
Other industries 36%

Total demand: 399,820 GWh
Industry demand: 113,926 GWh

Supply and consumption of electricity (Table 5.2)

5.14 There was a 1 per cent increase in the supply of electricity in 2003. Production (including pumped storage production) increased by 3 per cent. There was a 44 per cent fall in imports of electricity, because low UK prices made it less attractive to French exporters, while higher prices in continental Europe fostered a growth in exports, which were nearly four times their level in 2002.

5.15 Energy industry use of electricity as a proportion of electricity demand in 2003 (8 per cent) was the same as in 2002, while losses as a proportion of total demand, at 7½ per cent, showed a slight fall. Industrial consumption of electricity was 2 per cent up on 2002's level, while consumption in the services sector rose by 1½ per cent. Consumption by transport, storage and communications fell by 6 per cent but domestic sector consumption rose by 1 per cent. Temperatures influence the actual level of consumption in any one year in the winter months, as customers adjust heating levels in their homes. On average, temperatures in the first and fourth quarters of 2002 were particularly mild while the fourth quarter of 2003 was colder than in any of the 4 preceding years. In addition the warm summer of 2003 led to an increased use of electricity for air conditioning and cooling.

Regional electricity data

5.16 The restructuring of the electricity industry in 1990 and the privatisation of the electricity companies meant that it was no longer possible for this Digest to present regional data on the supply of electricity, as it would disclose information about individual businesses that were in competition with each other. Now that competition has been fully introduced, the Department of Trade and Industry has discussed with electricity suppliers and distributors the way in which electricity data can be collected at a regional (and sub-regional) level, in order to meet the requirements of users. The collection of data relating to regional and local consumption of electricity is expected to begin in autumn 2004. Further information is available on the DTI Energy statistics web site www.dti.gov.uk/energy/inform/energy_stats/. Data on electricity distributed is available at a regional level as is given in Table 5B. However, the regions used are Distribution Network Operator (DNO) areas, which are not aligned with Government Office Regions. An article in the December 2003 edition of *Energy Trends* (see Annex C for more information about *Energy Trends*) explained the differences between the two geographies and estimated 2000, 2001 and 2002 electricity distributed data on a Government Office Regions basis. The DNO areas vary in terms of square kilometres covered, number of customers and electricity distributed within the area. As the map on page 121 shows some companies are now responsible for distribution in more than one area.

5.17 The difference between total electricity distributed, shown in Table 5B, and total consumption is accounted for by electricity sold directly to large users by generators via the high voltage grid without passing through the distribution network of the regional companies, electricity consumed by the company generating the electricity (autogeneration plus electricity industry own use), and transmission losses.

Table 5B: Electricity distributed by public electricity suppliers, 2003[1][2]

	Area (sq km)	Number of customers (thousand)	Customer density (No. per sq. km)	Electricity distributed (GWh)
Eastern	20,300	3,394	167	36,511
South	16,900	2,827	167	33,507
East Midlands	16,000	2,459	154	29,162
Midlands	13,300	2,383	179	27,201
London	665	2,305	3,467	27,040
North West	12,500	2,300	184	25,263
Yorkshire	10,700	2,169	203	24,234
South Scotland	22,950	2,075	90	22,140
South East	8,200	2,136	261	21,687
North East	14,400	1,548	108	16,690
Merseyside & North Wales	12,200	1,443	118	16,614
South West	14,400	1,454	101	15,390
South Wales	11,800	1,053	89	12,354
North Scotland	54,390	830	15	8,708
Northern Ireland	13,506	692	51	7,843
Total	242,211	29,068	120	324,344

(1) The figures for the area and number of customers were provided by OFGEM and Northern Ireland Electricity and relate to 2000; OFGEM have been unable to provide more up to date data at this time. Number of customers figures are number of meter points. Electricity distributed is taken from returns made to DTI for 2003.

(2) The figures for electricity distributed exclude electricity sold directly to customers over high voltage lines.

Commodity balances for the public distribution system and for other generators (Table 5.3)

5.18   Table 5.3 expands on the commodity balance format to show consumption divided between electricity distributed over the public distribution system and electricity provided by other generators (largely autogeneration). Autogeneration is the generation of electricity wholly or partly for a company's own use as an activity which supplements the primary activity. However, most generators of electricity from renewable sources (apart from large scale hydro and some biofuels) are included as other generators because of their comparatively small size, even though their main activity is electricity generation. For a full list of companies included as major power producers see paragraph 5.48.

5.19   Table 5.3 also expands the domestic sector to show consumption by payment type and the commercial sector is expanded to show detailed data beyond that presented in Tables 5.1 and 5.2.

5.20   The proportion of electricity supplied by generators other than major power producers rose slightly in 2003 to 9 per cent, but it is still below the 9½ per cent it reached in 2000 following steady yearly growth. The proportion of this electricity transferred to the public distribution system increased from 23½ per cent in 2000 and 28 per cent in 2001, fell back to 22½ per cent in 2002, but increased to 31½ per cent in 2003. High gas prices and low electricity prices made it more difficult for electricity produced by other generators to compete in the electricity market in 2002, but the position eased in 2003 along with greater generation from renewables and wastes (see Chapter 7).

5.21   In 2003, 5 per cent of final consumption of electricity was by other generators and did not pass over the public distribution system. This was a similar proportion to that in each of the previous two years. A substantial proportion of electricity is self-generated in the energy industries with the proportion close to or above 20 per cent in all three years shown in the table. At petroleum refineries the proportion is even higher and in 2003 nearly three quarters of electricity was self-generated.

5.22   In 2003, about 13 per cent of the industrial demand for electricity was met by autogeneration. There was also a lesser proportion (about 2½ per cent) from autogeneration within the commercial and transport sectors. Transport autogeneration was sharply down in 2003 with the closure of one London Underground generating station. Table 1.9 in Chapter 1 shows the fuels used by autogenerators to generate this electricity within each major sector and also the quantities of electricity generated and consumed.

5.23   Within the domestic sector, about a third of the electricity consumed was purchased under some form of off-peak pricing structure (the same as in the previous two years). About 16 per cent of consumption was through prepayment systems, a proportion that has varied little over the three years shown.

Fuel used in generation (Table 5.4)

5.24   In this table fuel used by electricity generators is measured in both original units and for comparative purposes, in the common unit of million tonnes of oil equivalent. In Table 5.6 figures are quoted in a third unit, namely GWh, in order to show the link between fuel use and electricity generated.

5.25   The energy supplied basis defines the primary input (in million tonnes of oil equivalent) needed to produce 1 TWh of hydro, wind, or imported electricity as:

$$\text{Electricity generated (TWh)} \times 0.085985$$

The primary input needed to produce 1 TWh of nuclear electricity is similarly

$$\frac{\text{Electricity generated (TWh)} \times 0.085985}{\text{Thermal efficiency of nuclear stations}}$$

In the United Kingdom the thermal efficiency of nuclear stations has risen in stages from 32 per cent in 1982 to 38 per cent in 2003 (see Table 5.10 and paragraph 5.55 for the definition)[2]. The factor of

---

[2] Note that the International Energy Agency uses 0.33 in its calculations, which is the European average thermal efficiency of nuclear stations in 1989, measured in net terms rather than the UK's gross terms.

0.085985 is the energy content of one TWh divided by the energy content of one million tonnes of oil equivalent (see page 197 and inside back cover flap).

5.26   Figures on fuel use for electricity generation can be compared in two ways. Table 5.4 illustrates one way by using the volumes of **fuel input** to power stations (after conversion of inputs to an oil equivalent basis), but this takes no account of how efficiently that fuel is converted into electricity. The fuel input basis is the most appropriate to use for analysis of the quantities of particular fuels used in electricity generation (eg to determine the amount of coal at risk from displacement by gas or other fuels). A second way uses the amount of electricity generated and supplied by each fuel. This **output** basis is appropriate for comparing how much, and what percentage, of electricity generation comes from a particular fuel. It is the most appropriate method to use to examine the dominance of any fuel, and for diversity issues. Percentage shares based on fuel outputs reduce the contribution of coal and nuclear, and increase the contribution of gas (by about 5 percentage points in 2003) compared with the fuel input basis, because of the higher conversion efficiency of gas. This output basis is used in Chart 5.3, taking electricity supplied (gross) figures from Table 5.6. Trends in fuel used on this electricity supplied basis are described in the section on Table 5.6, in paragraphs 5.29 to 5.32, below.

5.27   A historical series of fuel used in generation on a consistent, energy supplied, fuel input basis is available at Table 5.1.1 on DTI's energy statistics web site.

Relating measurements of supply, consumption and availability (Table 5.5)

5.28   The balance methodology uses terms that cannot be readily employed for earlier years' data because statistics were not available in sufficient detail. Table 5.5 shows the relationship between these terms for the latest five years. For the full definitions of the terms used in the commodity balances see the Annex A, paragraphs A.7 to A.42.

Electricity generated, and supplied (Table 5.6)

5.29   The main data on generation and supply in Table 5.6 are presented by type of fuel. However, before 1996 data were presented by type of station and in order to maintain a link with this earlier data the final part of the table shows generation from conventional steam stations and from combined cycle gas turbine stations over the most recent five years.

5.30   Total electricity generated in the United Kingdom in 2003 exceeded generation in 2002 by 4 per cent. This rate of growth was above the average rate of growth over the previous four years of 1¾ per cent per year. Major power producers (as defined in paragraph 5.48) accounted for 91 per cent of electricity generation in 2003. Generation by other generators was 7½ per cent up on a year earlier mainly because most of the generation from renewables is included in the "other generators" category.

5.31   Generation from coal-fired stations was 11 per cent higher in 2003 than in 2002 and higher than in the six preceding years. Generation from gas in 2003 was 2½ per cent lower than 2002's record level. In 2002, slightly lower gas prices, except during the winter peak demand period, enabled gas fired generation to recapture some of the generation market that it had lost to coal in 2001, but gas prices remained high during 2003. Generation from nuclear sources rose by 1 per cent following a high level of outages for repairs and maintenance in 2002.

5.32   Table 5.6 also shows electricity supplied data. These data take into account the fact that some stations use relatively more electricity than others in the generation process itself. In total, electricity supplied (gross) was 2½ per cent greater than the volume generated in 2003, but for gas-fired stations it was 2½ per cent less, while for coal fired stations it was 11 per cent more. Chart 5.3 shows how shares of the generation market in terms of electricity output have changed over the last five years. Gas' share of electricity supplied (net) plus imports has moved up from 33 per cent in 1998 to 38 per cent in 2003, but this was below the 40 per cent share in 2002. Coal's share at 35 per cent was 1 percentage point higher than in 1998 and 3 percentage points higher than in 2002. Nuclear's 22 per cent share was not as low as its share in 2000 (21 per cent) but considerably lower than the peak 26 per cent share of 1998. Oil's share has halved to 1 per cent over the five years shown and imports' share has fallen from 4 per cent in 1998 to 1 per cent in 2003.

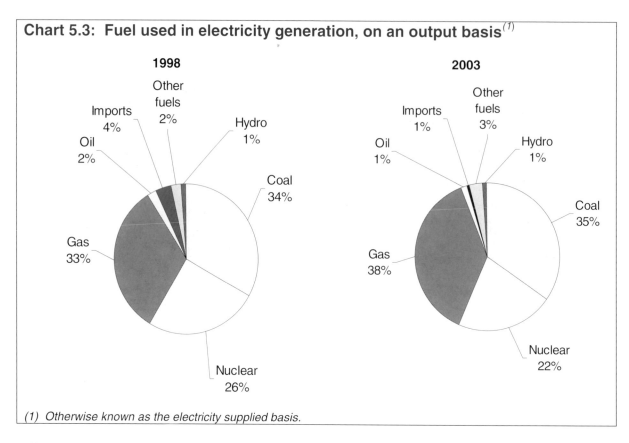

Chart 5.3: Fuel used in electricity generation, on an output basis[1]

1998

- Imports 4%
- Other fuels 2%
- Oil 2%
- Hydro 1%
- Coal 34%
- Gas 33%
- Nuclear 26%

2003

- Imports 1%
- Other fuels 3%
- Oil 1%
- Hydro 1%
- Coal 35%
- Gas 38%
- Nuclear 22%

(1) Otherwise known as the electricity supplied basis.

Plant capacity (Tables 5.7, 5.8 and 5.9)

5.33 Table 5.7 shows capacity, ie the maximum power available at any one time, for major power producers and other generators by type of plant.

5.34 In 2003, there was an increase of just over 1,100 MW (1½ per cent) in the capacity of major power producers. This was due to some coal, oil and CCGT plant being taken out of mothballs in response to signals that the plant margin in England and Wales was becoming tight. New capacity coming on stream in 2003 amounted to 656 MW. In December 2003, major power producers accounted for 91½ per cent of the total generating capacity, the same proportion as at the end of 2002. The capacity of other generators increased by 6½ per cent. Renewables capacity of other generators increased by 266 MW (see Chapter 7) and the capacity of good quality CHP rose by 30 MWe (see Chapter 6).

5.35 A breakdown of the capacity of the major power producers' plants at the end of March each year from 1993 to 1996 and at the end of December for 1996 to 2003 is shown in Chart 5.4.

5.36 A new table (Table 5.8) has been added to this chapter this year separating the capacities of major power producers geographically to show England and Wales, Scotland and Northern Ireland. So as not to disclose data for individual stations that have been provided in confidence, the breakdowns by type of station cannot be given in as much detail as in Table 5.7. In 2003, 84 per cent of the generating capacity in the UK owned by major power producers was in England and Wales, 13 per cent was in Scotland and 3 per cent in Northern Ireland. Out of the net increase in UK capacity of 1,131 MW in 2003, 966 MW was in England and Wales, 66 MW was in Scotland and 100 MW was in Northern Ireland.

5.37 In Table 5.9, data for the generating capacity of industrial, commercial and transport undertakings are shown, according to the industrial classification of the generator. Nearly a fifth of the capacity is in the chemicals sector. Petroleum refineries have 14 per cent of capacity, paper, printing and publishing has a 12 per cent share, and engineering and other metal trades has a 10 per cent share.

Chart 5.4: Capacity of major power producers

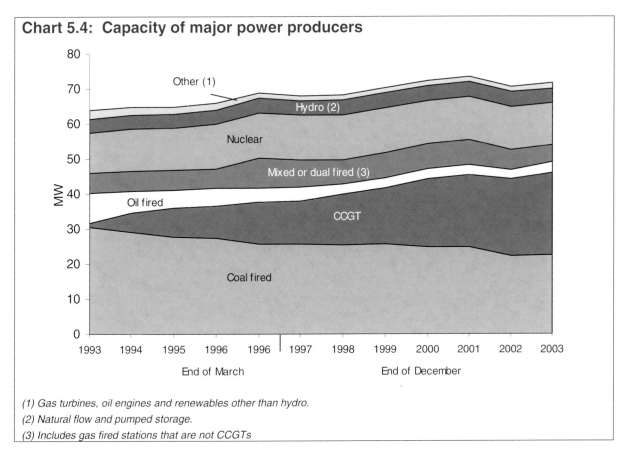

(1) Gas turbines, oil engines and renewables other than hydro.
(2) Natural flow and pumped storage.
(3) Includes gas fired stations that are not CCGTs

Plant loads, demand and efficiency (Table 5.10)

5.38   Table 5.10 shows the maximum load met each year, load factors (by type of plant and for the system in total) and indicators of thermal efficiency. Maximum demand figures cover the winter period ending the following March. For the first time, maximum demand figures for England and Wales, Scotland, and Northern Ireland are shown separately as well as total UK maximum demand.

5.39   Maximum demand in the UK during the winter of 2003/2004 occurred in December 2003. This was 2.0 per cent lower than the previous maximum in December 2002. Maximum demand in 2003/2004 was 84.3 per cent of the UK capacity of major power producers (Table 5.7) as measured at the end of December 2003, compared with 87.4 per cent in 2002/03, and 79.8 per cent in 2001/02. The decrease in this percentage in 2003/4 is partly because major power producers took about 1,100 MW of capacity out of mothballs, see 5.34 above. In England and Wales maximum demand at the end of December 2003 was 87.8 per cent of the England and Wales capacity of major power producers (Table 5.8) compared with 91.7 per cent at the end of 2002. For Scotland the proportion was 62.0 per cent (60 per cent in 2002) and for Northern Ireland 85.0 per cent (88 per cent in 2002). These percentages do not include the capacities available via the interconnectors with neighbouring grid systems.

5.40   Plant load factors measure how intensively each type of plant has been used. The trend up to the end of the 1990s had been for conventional thermal plant to be used less intensively and CCGT stations more intensively. In 2000 increased maintenance and repair at nuclear stations and at CCGT stations, coupled with high gas prices at the end of the year, led to a departure from this trend. Nuclear stations recovered in 2001, suffered further outages in 2002 but recovered again in 2003. Continuing high gas prices since the end of 2000 have brought about the lower CCGT load factors which were particularly marked in 2003. The use of coal-fired stations in competition with gas (see paragraph 5.31) is reflected in the increased load factor for conventional thermal stations, particularly in 2003.

5.41   2003 and 2001 were a particularly dry years, especially in the areas where hydro electricity is produced.   As a result the load factors for natural flow hydro show substantial falls in those years. Pumped storage use was less affected by the dry weather in 2003 than in 2001.   The low availability of hydro was another contributory factor to the high load factor for conventional thermal in 2003.

5.42   Thermal efficiency measures the efficiency with which the heat energy in fuel is converted into electrical energy.   The efficiency of coal-fired stations had been on a downward trend as coal became the marginal fuel for generation, but coal's increased role since 2000 has halted the decline in the thermal efficiency of coal-fired generation.   In 2001 efficiency fell back to 1999 levels, but in 2002 it recovered with the mothballing of some less efficient stations.   In 2003 efficiency again fell back. CCGT efficiency in each of the last eight years has been very consistent with a slight upward trend reflecting the influence of more modern stations coming on stream.   The efficiency of nuclear stations has been on a rising trends in recent years as older, less efficient stations have closed.   The efficiencies presented in this table are calculated using **gross** calorific values to obtain the energy content of the fuel inputs.   If **net** calorific values are used, efficiencies are higher, for example CCGT efficiencies rise by about 5 percentage points.

Power stations in the United Kingdom (Table 5.11)

5.43   Table 5.11 lists the operational power stations in the United Kingdom as at the end of May 2004 along with their installed capacity and the year they began to generate electricity.   Where a company operates several stations the stations are grouped together.   In general the table aims to list all stations of 1 MW installed capacity or over, but for some CHP stations the information is not publicly available and so the data are given in aggregate under "Other power stations" at the end of the table. Generating stations using renewable sources are also listed in aggregate form in this "Other power stations" section apart from hydro stations operated by the major power producers which appear in the main table.   Details of the interconnectors between England and Scotland, England and France, Scotland and Northern Ireland and Northern Ireland and the Irish Republic are also given in this table. The total installed capacity of all the power stations listed in Table 5.11 (including" other generators") is 80,742 MW.

The Electricity Supply System in Great Britain in 2003

This map has been reproduced by permission of Reed Business Publishing and National Grid Transco; it is available in colour on the DTI energy website

Technical notes and definitions

5.44 These notes and definitions are in addition to the technical notes and definitions covering all fuels and energy as a whole in Chapter 1, paragraphs 1.24 to 1.58. For notes on the commodity balances and definitions of the terms used in the row headings see the Annex A, paragraphs A.7 to A.42.

Electricity generation from renewable sources
5.45 Figures on electricity generation from renewable energy sources are included in the tables in this section. Further detailed information on renewable energy sources is included in Chapter 7.

Combined heat and power
5.46 Electricity generated from combined heat and power (CHP) schemes, CHP generating capacities and fuel used for electricity generation are included in the tables in this chapter. However, more detailed analyses of CHP schemes are set out in Chapter 6.

Generating companies
5.47 Following the restructuring of the electricity supply industry in 1990, the term "Major generating companies" was introduced into the electricity tables to describe the activities of the former nationalised industries and distinguish them from those of autogenerators and new independent companies set up to generate electricity. The activities of the autogenerators and the independent companies were classified under the heading "Other generating companies". In the 1994 Digest, a new terminology was adopted to encompass the new independent producers, who were then beginning to make a significant contribution to electricity supply. Under this terminology, all companies whose prime purpose is the generation of electricity are included under the heading "Major power producers" (or MPPs). The term "Other generators" ("Autogenerators" in the balance tables) is restricted to companies who produce electricity as part of their manufacturing or other commercial activities, but whose main business is not electricity generation. "Other generators" also covers generation by energy services companies at power stations on an industrial or commercial site where the main purpose is the supply of electricity to that site, even if the energy service company is a subsidiary of a major power producer. Most generators of electricity from renewable sources (apart from large scale hydro and some biofuels) are also included as "Other generators" because of their comparatively small size, even though their main activity is electricity generation.

5.48 **Major power producers at the end of 2003 were:**
AES Electric Ltd., American Electric Power, Anglian Power Generators Ltd, Baglan Generation Ltd., BNFL Magnox., British Energy plc., Centrica plc., Coolkeeragh Power Ltd., Corby Power Ltd., Coryton Energy Company Ltd., Damhead Creek Ltd., Deeside Power Ltd., Derwent Cogeneration Ltd., Drax Power Ltd., EDF Energy plc., Edison Mission Energy Ltd., Enfield Energy Centre Ltd., Fellside Heat and Power Ltd., Fibrogen Ltd., Fibropower Ltd., Fibrothetford Ltd., Fife Power Ltd., Great Yarmouth Power Ltd, Humber Power Ltd., International Power plc., Killingholme Power Ltd., National Grid Company (Keilder), NIGEN, PowerGen plc., Premier Power Ltd., Regional Power Generators Ltd., Rocksavage Power Company Ltd., RWE Innogy plc., Saltend Co-generation Company Ltd., Scottish Power plc., Scottish and Southern Energy plc., Seabank Power Ltd., SELCHP Ltd., Sita Tyre Recycling Ltd., South Coast Power Ltd., Teesside Power Ltd., Thames Power Services Ltd., Western Power Generation Ltd.

Types of station
5.49 The various types of station identified in the tables of this chapter are as follows:

Conventional steam stations are stations that generate electricity by burning fossil fuels to convert water into steam, which then powers steam turbines.

Nuclear stations are also steam stations but the heat needed to produce the steam comes from nuclear fission.

Gas turbines use pressurised combustion gases from fuel burned in one or more combustion chambers to turn a series of bladed fan wheels and rotate the shaft on which they are mounted. This then drives the generator. The fuel burnt is usually natural gas or gas oil.

Combined cycle gas turbine (CCGT) stations combine in the same plant gas turbines and steam turbines connected to one or more electrical generators. This enables electricity to be produced at higher efficiencies than is otherwise possible when either gas or steam turbines are used in isolation. The gas turbine (usually fuelled by natural gas or oil) produces mechanical power (to drive the generator) and waste heat. The hot exhaust gases (waste heat) are fed to a boiler, where steam is raised at pressure to drive a conventional steam turbine that is also connected to an electrical generator.

Natural flow hydro-electric stations use natural water flows to turn turbines.

Pumped storage hydro-electric stations use electricity to pump water into a high level reservoir. This water is then released to generate electricity at peak times. Where the reservoir is open, the stations also generate some natural flow electricity; this is included with natural flow generation. As electricity is used in the pumping process, pumped storage stations are net consumers of electricity.

Other stations include wind turbines and stations burning fuels such as landfill gas, sewage sludge, biomass and waste.

Public distribution system
5.50   This comprises the grids in England and Wales, Scotland and Northern Ireland.

Sectors used for sales/consumption
5.51   The various sectors used for sales and consumption analyses are standardised across all chapters of the 2004 Digest. For definitions of the sectors see Chapter 1 paragraphs 1.54 to 1.58 and Annex A paragraphs A.31 to A.42.

Declared net capability and declared net capacity
5.52   Declared net capability is the maximum power available for export from a power station on a continuous basis minus any power imported by the station from the network to run its own plant. It represents the nominal maximum capability of a generating set to supply electricity to consumers. The registered capacity of a generating set differs from declared net capability in that, for registered capacity, not all power consumed by the plant is subtracted from the normal full load capacity, only the MW consumed by the generating set through its transformer when generating at its normal full load capacity.

5.53   Declared net capacity is used to measure the maximum power available from generating stations that use renewable resources. For wind and tidal power a factor is applied to declared net capability to take account of the intermittent nature of the energy source (eg 0.43 for wind).

Load factors
5.54   The following definitions are used in Table 5.10:

Maximum load - Twice the largest number of units supplied in any consecutive thirty minutes commencing or terminating at the hour.

Simultaneous maximum load met - The maximum load on the grid at any one time. It is measured by the sum of the maximum load met in England and Wales and the loads met at the same time by companies in other parts of the United Kingdom. In 2003/04 the maximum load in England and Wales occurred on 8 December 2003 at 17.30. However, in Northern Ireland the maximum load occurred on 15 December 2003 at 17.30 (1,629 MW), and in Scotland, while Scottish Power's peak load occurred at the same time as in England and Wales (4,266 MW) Scottish and Southern Energy's peak was on 28 January 2004 at 20.30 (1,694 MW). Northern Ireland's highest ever load met was on 7 January 2003 (1,635 MW), Scottish Power's highest ever load met was on 16 January 2001 (4,382 MW), and Scottish and Southern's highest ever load met was on 7 January 2003 (1,712 MW).

Plant load factor - The average hourly quantity of electricity supplied during the year, expressed as a percentage of the average output capability at the beginning and the end of year.

System load factor - The average hourly quantity of electricity available during the year expressed as a percentage of the maximum demand nearest the end of the year or early the following year.

Thermal efficiency

5.55   Thermal efficiency is the efficiency with which heat energy contained in fuel is converted into electrical energy. It is calculated for fossil fuel burning stations by expressing electricity generated as a percentage of the total energy content of the fuel consumed (based on average gross calorific values). For nuclear stations it is calculated using the quantity of heat released as a result of fission of the nuclear fuel inside the reactor. The efficiency of CHP systems is discussed separately in Chapter 6, paragraph 6.24 and Table 6D. Efficiencies based on gross calorific value of the fuel (sometimes referred to as higher heating values or HHV) are lower than the efficiencies based on net calorific value (or lower heating value LHV). The difference between HHV and LHV is due to the energy associated with the latent heat of the evaporation of water products from the steam cycle which cannot be recovered and put to economic use.

Period covered

5.56   Figures for the major power producers relate to periods of 52 weeks as follows (although some data provided by electricity supply companies relate to calendar months):

Year	53 weeks ended
1998	3 January 1999
	52 weeks ended
1999	2 January 2000
2000	31 December 2000
2001	30 December 2001
2002	29 December 2002
2003	28 December 2003

5.57   Figures for industrial, commercial and transport undertakings relate to years ended 31 December, except for the iron and steel industry where figures relate to the following 52 week periods:

Year	53 weeks ended
1998	2 January 1999
	52 weeks ended
1999	1 January 2000
2000	30 December 2000
2001	29 December 2001
2002	28 December 2002
2003	27 December 2003

5.58   Statistical years that contain 53 weeks are adjusted to 52-week equivalents by taking 5/6ths of the 6-week December period values.

Monthly and quarterly data

5.59   Monthly and quarterly data on fuel use, electricity generation and supply and electricity availability and consumption are available on DTI's Energy Statistics web site www.dti.gov.uk/energy/inform/energy_stats/. Monthly data on fuel used in electricity generation by major power producers are given in Monthly Table 5.3 and monthly data on supplies by type of plant and type of fuel are given in Monthly Table 5.4, while monthly data on availability and consumption of electricity by the main sectors of the economy are given in Monthly Table 5.5. A quarterly commodity balance for electricity is published in DTI's quarterly statistical bulletin *Energy Trends* (Quarterly Table 5.2) along with a quarterly table of fuel use for generation by all generators and electricity supplied by major power producers (Quarterly Table 5.1). Both these quarterly tables are also available from DTI's Energy Statistics web site. See Annex C for more information about *Energy Trends*.

Data collection

5.60 For Major Power Producers, as defined in paragraph 5.47, the data for the tables in this Digest are obtained from the results of an annual DTI inquiry, sent to each company, covering generating capacity, fuel use, generation, sales and distribution of electricity.

5.61 Another annual inquiry is sent to licensed suppliers of electricity to establish electricity sales by these companies. Similarly, an annual inquiry is sent to electricity distributors to establish electricity distributed by these companies.

5.62 Companies that generate electricity mainly for their own use (known as autogenerators or autoproducers - see paragraph 5.47, above) are covered by an annual inquiry commissioned by DTI but carried out by the Office for National Statistics (ONS) from their Newport offices. Where autogenerators operate a combined heat and power (CHP) plant, this survey is now supplemented by information from the CHP Quality Assessment scheme (for autogenerators who have registered under the scheme - see Chapter 6 on CHP). The ONS inquiry only covers generators with capacities greater than 100 kWe and DTI estimates fuel use and electricity generation for smaller companies or includes estimates made by FES for CHP electricity, described in Chapter 6. There are two areas of autogeneration that are covered by direct data collection by DTI, mainly because the return contains additional energy information needed by the Department. These are the Iron and Steel industry, and generation on behalf of London Underground.

Losses and statistical differences

5.63 Statistical differences are included in Tables 5.1, 5.2 and 5.3. These arise because data collected on production and supply do not match exactly with data collected on sales or consumption. One of the reasons for this is that some of the data are based on different calendars as described in paragraphs 5.56 and 5.57, above. Sales data based on calendar years will always include more electricity consumption than the slightly shorter statistical year of exactly 52 weeks.

5.64 Of the losses shown in the commodity balance for electricity of almost 30,000 GWh in 2003, it is estimated that about 5,700 GWh (1½ per cent of electricity available) were lost from the high voltage transmission system of the National Grid and 22,700 GWh (6 per cent) between the grid supply points (the gateways to the public supply system's distribution network) and customers' meters. The balance (about ½ per cent of electricity available) is accounted for by theft and meter fraud, accounting differences and calendar differences (as described in paragraph 5.63, above).

5.65 Care should be exercised in interpreting the figures for individual industries in the commodity balance tables. As new suppliers have entered the market and companies have moved between suppliers, it has not been possible to ensure consistent classification between and within industry sectors and across years. The breakdown of final consumption includes some estimated data. For about 4 per cent of consumption of electricity supplied by the public distribution system, the sector figures are partially estimated.

Contact: *Mike Janes (Statistician)*   *Joe Ewins*
          Energy Markets Information and Analysis   *Energy Information Systems*
          mike.janes@dti.gsi.gov.uk   *joe.ewins@dti.gsi.gov.uk*
          020-7215 5186   *020-7215 5190*

5.1 Commodity balances

Electricity

GWh

	2001	2002	2003
Total electricity			
Supply			
Production	382,355r	384,854r	395,886
Other sources (1)	2,422r	2,652	2,734
Imports	10,663	9,182	5,119
Exports	-264	-768	-2,959
Marine bunkers	-	-	-
Stock change (2)	-	-	-
Transfers			
Total supply	**395,177r**	**395,921r**	**400,780**
Statistical difference (3)	+1,167r	+1,049r	+960
Total demand	**394,010r**	**394,872r**	**399,820**
Transformation	-		
Electricity generation	-	-	-
Major power producers	-	-	-
Autogenerators	-	-	-
Heat generation	-	-	-
Petroleum refineries	-	-	-
Coke manufacture	-	-	-
Blast furnaces	-	-	-
Patent fuel manufacture	-	-	-
Other	-	-	-
Energy industry use	**30,387r**	**31,736r**	**32,515**
Electricity generation	17,394r	17,172r	18,238
Oil and gas extraction	675	540	551
Petroleum refineries	5,231	6,577r	5,724
Coal extraction	-	-	-
Coke manufacture	1,223	1,218	1,244
Blast furnaces	885	815	841
Patent fuel manufacture	-	-	-
Pumped storage	3,210	3,463	3,546
Other	1,769	1,950r	2,371
Losses	**30,902**	**29,980**	**29,862**
Final consumption	**332,721r**	**333,156r**	**337,444**
Industry	**111,337r**	**112,368r**	**113,926**
Unclassified	-	-	-
Iron and steel	8,429r	6,354r	6,545
Non-ferrous metals	7,172	6,296r	6,571
Mineral products	6,991r	6,997	7,540
Chemicals	20,598r	22,613r	21,750
Mechanical engineering, etc	8,228r	8,635r	8,741
Electrical engineering, etc	5,464r	5,788r	5,955
Vehicles	5,591r	5,505r	5,588
Food, beverages, etc	11,182r	11,979r	11,820
Textiles, leather, etc	3,206	3,419r	3,418
Paper, printing, etc	11,192r	11,831r	12,519
Other industries	21,727	21,337r	21,846
Construction	1,559	1,613	1,632
Transport	**8,828r**	**8,478r**	**8,528**
Air	-	-	-
Rail (4)	2,700	2,700	2,700
Road	-	-	-
National navigation	-	-	-
Pipelines	-	-	-
Other	**212,557r**	**212,311r**	**214,990**
Domestic	115,337r	114,534r	115,761
Public administration	21,105r	20,668r	20,966
Commercial	72,014	72,963r	74,238
Agriculture	4,100r	4,145r	4,025
Miscellaneous	-	-	-
Non energy use	**-**	**-**	**-**

5.1 Commodity balances (continued)
Electricity

GWh

	2001	2002	2003
Electricity production			
Total production (5)	**382,355r**	**384,854r**	**395,886**
Primary electricity			
Major power producers	**93,307r**	**91,776r**	**91,254**
Nuclear	90,093r	87,848r	88,686
Large scale hydro (5)	3,215	3,927r	2,568
Small scale hydro	-	-	-
Wind	-	-	-
Autogenerators	**1,805**	**2,119r**	**1,948**
Nuclear	-	-	-
Large scale hydro	630	657	545
Small scale hydro	210	204	115
Wind	965	1,259	1,288
Secondary electricity			
Major power producers	**257,328r**	**259,566r**	**268,612**
Coal	127,128r	120,958	134,023
Oil	2,472	2,011	2,197
Gas	126,999	135,741	131,238
Renewables	729r	856r	1,154
Other	-	-	-
Autogenerators	**29,915r**	**31,393r**	**34,071**
Coal	4,333r	3,339r	4,219
Oil	2,781	2,798r	2,672
Gas	14,906r	16,576r	17,409
Renewables	4,318	4,769r	5,554
Other	3,577r	3,912r	4,218
Primary and secondary production (6)			
Nuclear	90,093r	87,848r	88,686
Hydro	4,055	4,788r	3,228
Wind	965	1,259	1,288
Coal	131,461r	124,296r	138,242
Oil	5,253	4,809r	4,869
Gas	141,905r	152,317r	148,646
Other renewables	5,047r	5,625r	6,708
Other	3,577r	3,912r	4,218
Total production	**382,355r**	**384,854r**	**395,886**

(1) Pumped storage production.
(2) Stock fall (+), stock rise (-).
(3) Total supply minus total demand.
(4) See paragraph 5.13.
(5) Excludes pumped storage production.
(6) These figures are the same as the electricity generated figures in Table 5.6 except that they exclude pumped storage production. Table 5.6 shows that electricity used on works is deducted to obtain electricity supplied. It is electricity supplied that is used to produce Chart 5.3 showing each fuel's share of electricity output (see paragraph 5.26).

5.2 Electricity supply and consumption

GWh

	1999	2000	2001	2002	2003
Supply					
Production	365,250	374,375	382,355r	384,854r	395,886
Other sources (1)	2,902	2,694	2,422r	2,652	2,734
Imports	14,507	14,308	10,663	9,182	5,119
Exports	-263	-134	-264	-768	-2,959
Total supply	**382,396**	**391,243**	**395,177r**	**395,921r**	**400,780**
Statistical difference (2)	+1,564	+1,494	+1,167r	+1,049r	+960
Total demand	**380,832**	**389,749**	**394,010r**	**394,872r**	**399,820**
Transformation	-	-	-	-	-
Energy industry use	**29,790**	**30,681**	**30,387r**	**31,736r**	**32,515**
Electricity generation	16,707	16,304	17,394r	17,172r	18,238
Oil and gas extraction	408	527	675	540	551
Petroleum refineries	4,981	6,362	5,231	6,577r	5,724
Coal and coke	1,358	1,283	1,223	1,218	1,244
Blast furnaces	948	877	885	815	841
Pumped storage	3,774	3,499	3,210	3,463	3,546
Other	1,614	1,829	1,769	1,950r	2,371
Losses	**28,298**	**29,649**	**30,902**	**29,980**	**29,862**
Final consumption	**322,744**	**329,419**	**332,721r**	**333,156r**	**337,444**
Industry	**110,978**	**114,112**	**111,337r**	**112,368r**	**113,926**
Unclassified	-	-	-	-	-
Iron and steel	9,779	9,229	8,429r	6,354r	6,545
Non-ferrous metals	5,895	6,002	7,172	6,296r	6,571
Mineral products	7,265	7,864	6,991r	6,997r	7,540
Chemicals	21,677	23,242	20,598r	22,613r	21,750
Mechanical engineering. etc	8,824	9,097	8,228r	8,635r	8,741
Electrical engineering, etc	6,006	5,985	5,464r	5,788r	5,955
Vehicles	5,615	6,093	5,591r	5,505r	5,588
Food, beverages, etc	12,524	11,329	11,182r	11,979r	11,820
Textiles, leather, etc	3,751	3,470	3,206	3,419r	3,418
Paper, printing, etc	10,989	11,141	11,192r	11,831r	12,519
Other industries	17,125	19,074	21,727	21,337r	21,846
Construction	1,528	1,586	1,559	1,613	1,632
Transport	**8,579**	**8,623**	**8,828r**	**8,477r**	**8,528**
Other	**203,187**	**206,684**	**212,557r**	**212,311r**	**214,990**
Domestic	110,308	111,842	115,337r	114,534r	115,761
Public administration	21,951	20,913	21,105r	20,668r	20,966
Commercial	66,748	69,571	72,014	72,963r	74,238
Agriculture	4,180	4,358	4,100r	4,145r	4,025
Miscellaneous	-	-	-	-	-
Non energy use	**-**	**-**	**-**	**-**	**-**

(1) Pumped storage production.
(2) Total supply minus total demand.

5.3 Commodity balances
Public distribution system and other generators

GWh

	2001			2002			2003		
	Public distribution system	Other generators	Total	Public distribution system	Other generators	Total	Public distribution system	Other generators	Total
Supply									
Major power producers	350,635r	-	350,635r	351,342r	-	351,342r	359,866	-	359,866
Other generators	-	31,720r	31,720r	-	33,513r	33,513r	-	36,019	36,019
Other sources *(1)*	2,422r	-	2,422r	2,652	-	2,652	2,734	-	2,734
Imports	10,663	-	10,663	9,182	-	9,182	5,119	-	5,119
Exports	-264	-	-264	-768	-	-768	-2,959	-	-2,959
Transfers	8,897r	-8,897r	-	7,564r	-7,564r	-	11,317	-11,317	-
Total supply	**372,354r**	**22,823r**	**395,177r**	**369,972r**	**25,949r**	**395,921r**	**376,078**	**24,702**	**400,780**
Statistical difference *(2)*	1,167r	-r	1,167r	1,049r	-r	1,049r	960	-	960
Total demand	**371,187r**	**22,823r**	**394,010r**	**368,923r**	**25,949r**	**394,872**	**375,118**	**24,702**	**399,820**
Transformation	-	-	-	-	-	-	-	-	-
Energy industry use	**24,481r**	**5,906r**	**30,387r**	**23,959r**	**7,776r**	**31,736r**	**25,133**	**7,381**	**32,515**
Electricity generation	16,066r	1,328r	17,394r	15,746r	1,426r	17,172r	16,747	1,491	18,238
Oil and gas extraction	675	-	675	540	-	540	551	-	551
Petroleum refineries	1,912	3,319	5,231	1,598	4,979r	6,577r	1,550	4,174	5,724
Coke manufacture	1,047	176	1,223	1,064	154	1,218	1,091	153	1,244
Blast furnaces	-	885	885	-	815	815	-	841	841
Pumped storage	3,210	-	3,210	3,463	-	3,463	3,546	-	3,546
Other fuel industries	1,571	198	1,769	1,548	402r	1,950r	1,649	722	2,371
Losses	**30,843**	**59**	**30,902**	**29,914**	**66**	**29,980**	**29,794**	**68**	**29,862**
Final consumption	**315,862**	**16,859r**	**332,721r**	**315,050**	**18,106r**	**333,156r**	**320,192**	**17,252**	**337,444**
Industry	**97,021**	**14,316r**	**111,337r**	**96,843**	**15,525r**	**112,368r**	**99,007**	**14,919**	**113,926**
Iron and steel	7,768	660	8,429	5,690	664r	6,354r	5,580	965	6,545
Non-ferrous metals	4,157	3,015	7,172	4,180	2,115r	6,296r	4,347	2,224	6,571
Mineral products	6,987	3r	6,991r	6,997	-	6,997	7,354	185	7,540
Chemicals	14,410	6,188r	20,598r	14,984	7,630r	22,613r	15,300	6,450	21,750
Mechanical engineering, etc	8,122	106r	8,228r	8,370	265r	8,635r	8,399	342	8,741
Electrical engineering, etc	5,450	14r	5,464r	5,777	11r	5,788r	5,944	11	5,955
Vehicles	5,452	138r	5,591r	5,360	145r	5,505r	5,456	132	5,588
Food, beverages, etc	10,216	966r	11,182r	10,541	1,438r	11,979r	10,699	1,121	11,820
Textiles, leather, etc	3,097	109	3,206	3,305	114r	3,419r	3,305	114	3,418
Paper, printing, etc	8,572	2,619r	11,192r	9,392	2,439r	11,831r	9,476	3,043	12,519
Other industries	21,246	481	21,727	20,649	688r	21,337r	21,528	318	21,846
Construction	1,544	15	1,559	1,598	15	1,613	1,617	15	1,632
Transport	**7,452**	**1,376r**	**8,828r**	**7,051**	**1,427r**	**8,477r**	**7,734**	**794**	**8,528**
Of which National Rail *(3)*	2,700	-	2,700	2,700	-	2,700	2,700	-	2,700
Other	**211,389**	**1,168r**	**212,557r**	**211,156**	**1,154r**	**212,311r**	**213,451**	**1,539**	**214,990**
Domestic	115,337	-	115,337	114,534	-	114,534	115,761	-	115,761
Standard	63,377	-	63,377	63,225	-	63,225	64,381	-	64,381
Economy 7 and other off-peak	32,949	-	32,949	32,207	-	32,207	32,109	-	32,109
Prepayment (standard)	12,474	-	12,474	12,608	-	12,608	12,643	-	12,643
Prepayment (off-peak)	6,163	-	6,163	6,055	-	6,055	6,191	-	6,191
Sales under any other arrangement	373	-	373	440	-	440	437	-	437
Public administration	19,938	1,168r	21,105r	19,514	1,154r	20,668r	19,427	1,539	20,966
Public lighting *(4)*	2,044	-	2,044	1,923	-	1,923	2,050	-	2,050
Other public sector	17,894	1,168r	19,062r	17,591	1,154r	18,745r	17,377	1,539	18,916
Commercial	72,014	-	72,014	72,963	-	72,963	74,238	-	74,238
Shops	32,652	-	32,652	33,769	-	33,769	34,180	-	34,180
Offices	21,765	-	21,765	21,928	-	21,928	22,105	-	22,105
Hotels	8,206	-	8,206	8,253	-	8,253	8,611	-	8,611
Combined domestic/ commercial premises	1,746	-	1,746	1,767	-	1,767	1,896	-	1,896
Post and telecommunications	5,545	-	5,545	5,597	-	5,597	5,746	-	5,746
Unclassified	2,100	-	2,100	1,650	-	1,650	1,700	-	1,700
Agriculture	4,100	-r	4,100r	4,145	-r	4,145r	4,025	-	4,025

(1) Pumped storage production.
(2) Total supply minus total demand.
(3) See paragraph 5.15.
(4) Sales for public lighting purposes are increasingly covered by wider contracts that cannot distinguish the public lighting element.

5.4 Fuel used in generation[1]

	Unit	1999	2000	2001	2002	2003
					Original units of measurement	
Major power producers (2)						
Coal	M tonnes	39.58	44.76	49.29	46.14	51.55
Oil (3)	"	0.79	0.75	0.79	0.67	0.63
Gas	GWh	281,988	283,784	276,764	291,264	284,662
Other generators (2)						
Transport undertakings:						
Gas	GWh	2,496	2,194	2,238	1,793	93
Undertakings in industrial and commercial sectors:						
Coal (4)	M tonnes	1.59	1.47	1.65r	1.61r	1.55
Oil (5)	"	0.76	0.71	0.55r	0.54r	0.55
Gas (6)	GWh	31,009	38,585	33,519r	36,978r	40,108
					Millions of tonnes of oil equivalent	
Major power producers (2)						
Coal		24.506	27.765	30.575	28.623	31.976
Oil (3)		0.817	0.772	0.818	0.689	0.654
Gas		24.247	24.401	23.797	25.044	24.476
Nuclear		22.216	19.635	20.768r	20.100r	20.041
Hydro (natural flow) (7)		0.381	0.372	0.276	0.338r	0.221
Other renewables (7)		0.223	0.237	0.253	0.274	0.381
Net imports		1.225	1.219	0.894	0.724	0.186
Total major power producers (2)		**73.615**	**74.401**	**77.381r**	**75.792r**	**77.935**
Of which: conventional thermal and other stations (9)		28.626	32.793	32.629r	30.574r	33.694
combined cycle gas turbine stations		21.167	21.775r	22.814r	24.056r	23.793
Other generators (2)						
Transport undertakings:						
Gas		0.215	0.189	0.192	0.154	0.008
Undertakings in industrial and commercial sectors:						
Coal (4)		1.006	0.905	1.031r	1.003r	0.973
Oil (5)		0.724	0.777	0.605r	0.599r	0.606
Gas (6)		2.666	3.318	2.882r	3.180r	3.449
Hydro (natural flow) (7)		0.078	0.065	0.072	0.074	0.057
Other renewables (7)		1.248	1.416	1.704	1.907r	2.178
Other fuels (8)		1.392	1.354	1.036r	1.061r	1.455
Total other generators (2)		**7.329**	**8.024**	**7.522r**	**7.978r**	**8.726**
All generating companies						
Coal (4)		25.512	28.670	31.606r	29.626r	32.949
Oil (3)(5)		1.541	1.549	1.423r	1.288r	1.260
Gas (6)		27.128	27.908	26.871r	28.378r	27.933
Nuclear		22.216	19.635	20.768r	20.100r	20.041
Hydro (natural flow) (7)		0.459	0.437	0.348	0.412r	0.278
Other renewables (7)		1.471	1.653	1.957	2.181r	2.559
Other fuels (8)		1.392	1.354	1.036r	1.061r	1.455
Net imports		1.225	1.219	0.894	0.724	0.186
Total all generating companies		**80.944**	**82.425**	**84.903r**	**83.770r**	**86.661**

(1) For details of where to find monthly updates of fuel used in electricity generation by major power producers and quarterly updates of fuel used in electricity generation by all generating companies see paragraph 5.59.

(2) See paragraphs 5.47 and 5.48 for information on companies covered.

(3) Includes Orimulsion, oil used in gas turbine and diesel plants, and oil used for lighting up coal fired boilers.

(4) Includes coke oven coke

(5) Includes refinery gas.

(6) Includes colliery methane.

(7) Renewable sources, which are included under hydro and other renewables in this table, are shown separately in Table 7.6 of Chapter 7.

(8) Main fuels included are coke oven gas, blast furnace gas, and waste products from chemical processes.

(9) Includes gas turbines, oil engines and plants producing electricity from renewable sources other than hydro.

5.5 Electricity supply, electricity supplied (net), electricity available, electricity consumption and electricity sales

GWh

	1999	2000	2001	2002	2003
Total supply					
(as given in Tables 5.1 and 5.2)	382,396	391,243	395,177r	395,921r	400,780
less imports of electricity	-14,507	-14,308	-10,663	-9,182	-5,119
plus exports of electricity	+263	+134	+264	+768	+2,959
less electricity used in pumped storage	-3,774	-3,499	-3,210	-3,463	-3,546
less electricity used on works	-16,707	-16,304	-17,394	-17,172r	-18,238
equals					
Electricity supplied (net)	347,671	357,267	364,174r	366,871r	376,836
(as given in Tables, 5.6, 5.1.2 and 5.1.3)					
Total supply					
(as given in Tables 5.1 and 5.2)	382,396	391,243	395,177r	395,921r	400,780
less electricity used in pumped storage	-3,774	-3,499	-3,210	-3,463	-3,546
less electricity used on works	-16,707	-16,304	-17,394r	-17,172r	-18,238
equals					
Electricity available	361,915	371,440	374,573r	375,286r	378,996
(as given in Table 5.1.2)					
Final consumption					
(as given in Tables 5.2 and 5.3)	322,744	329,419	332,721	333,156r	337,444
plus Iron and steel consumption counted as energy industry use	+1,272	+1,174	+1,158	+1,074	+1,102
equals					
Final users	324,016	330,593	333,879r	334,230r	338,546
(as given in Table 5.1.2)					
Final consumption					
Public distribution system					
(as given in Table 5.3)	304,255	309,957	315,862	315,050	320,192
plus Oil and gas extraction use	+408	+527	+675	+540	+551
plus Petroleum refineries use	+1,214	+1,665	+1,912	+1,598	+1,550
plus Coke manufacture use	+1,174	+1,097	+1,047	+1,064	+1,091
plus Other fuel industries use	+1,307	+1,420	+1,571	+1,548	+1,649
equals					
UK Electricity sales (1)	308,358	314,666	321,067	319,800	325,033

(1) The renewables obligation percentage is calculated using total renewables generation on an obligation basis from Table 7.4 (x 100) as the numerator, and this figure as the denominator. Separate electricity sales data for public electricity suppliers are given for England and Wales, Scotland and Northern Ireland in Table 5.5 of Energy Trends on the DTI web site at www.dti.gov.uk/energy/inform/energy_stats/electricity/5_5elecconsumption-ettab23.xls

5.6 Electricity fuel use, generation and supply

GWh

	Thermal sources							Non-thermal sources			Total
	Coal	Oil	Gas	Nuclear	Renew-ables (1)	Other (3)	Total	Hydro-natural flow	Hydro-pumped storage	Other (4)	All sources
1999											
Major power producers (2)											
Fuel used	285,004	9,500	281,986	258,374	2,546	-	837,410	4,431	2,902	-	844,744
Generation	102,074	2,943	128,365	95,133	761	-	329,276	4,431	2,902	-	336,608
Used on works	4,725	210	2,759	7,461	187	-	15,342	21	98	-	15,461
Supplied (gross)	97,348	2,733	125,606	87,672	574	-	313,933	4,409	2,804	-	321,147
Used in pumping	-	-	-	-	-	-	-	-	-	-	3,774
Supplied (net)	-	-	-	-	-	-	-	-	-	-	317,373
Other generators (2)											
Fuel used	11,702	8,420	33,562	-	13,659	16,187	83,531	905	-	851	85,287
Generation	4,106	3,606	14,537	-	3,227	4,312	29,787	905	-	851	31,543
Used on works	197	267	471	-	100	198	1,233	11	-	-	1,245
Supplied	3,909	3,339	14,066	-	3,126	4,113	28,554	894	-	851	30,298
All generating companies											
Fuel used	296,706	17,920	315,548	258,374	16,205	16,187	920,941	5,336	2,902	851	930,030
Generation	106,179	6,549	142,902	95,133	3,988	4,312	359,063	5,336	2,902	851	368,151
Used on works	4,922	477	3,230	7,461	287	198	16,576	33	98	-	16,706
Supplied (gross)	101,257	6,072	139,672	87,672	3,700	4,113	342,487	5,303	2,804	851	351,445
Used in pumping	-	-	-	-	-	-	-	-	-	-	3,774
Supplied (net)	-	-	-	-	-	-	-	-	-	-	347,671
2000											
Major power producers (2)											
Fuel used	322,907	8,981	283,781	228,358	2,921	-	846,949	4,331	2,694	-	853,974
Generation	117,025	2,415	129,558	85,063	698	-	334,758	4,331	2,694	-	341,783
Used on works	5,175	292	2,592	6,729	58	-	14,846	15	91	-	14,952
Supplied (gross)	111,850	2,123	126,965	78,334	640	-	319,912	4,316	2,603	-	326,831
Used in pumping	-	-	-	-	-	-	-	-	-	-	3,499
Supplied (net)	-	-	-	-	-	-	-	-	-	-	323,332
Other generators (2)											
Fuel used	10,522	9,042	40,779	-	15,517	15,743	91,603	755	-	947	93,304
Generation	2,925	4,109	18,519	-	3,630	4,401	33,584	755	-	947	35,285
Used on works	39	304	592	-	203	202	1,340	12	-	-	1,352
Supplied	2,887	3,805	17,927	-	3,427	4,198	32,244	743	-	947	33,933
All generating companies											
Fuel used	333,429	18,023	324,560	228,358	18,439	15,743	938,551	5,085	2,694	947	947,278
Generation	119,950	6,524	148,077	85,063	4,328	4,401	368,342	5,085	2,694	947	377,069
Used on works	5,214	596	3,184	6,729	261	202	16,186	27	91	-	16,304
Supplied (gross)	114,736	5,928	144,892	78,334	4,067	4,198	352,156	5,058	2,603	947	360,764
Used in pumping	-	-	-	-	-	-	-	-	-	-	3,499
Supplied (net)	-	-	-	-	-	-	-	-	-	-	357,266
2001											
Major power producers (2)											
Fuel used	355,582r	9,510r	276,761	241,537r	3,102r	-	886,492r	3,215	2,422r	-	892,129r
Generation	127,128r	2,472	126,999	90,093r	729r	-	347,420r	3,215	2,422r	-	353,057r
Used on works	5,830r	281r	2,709r	7,108r	46r	-	15,973r	11	82r	-	16,066r
Supplied (gross)	121,298	2,192	124,289	82,985	683	-	331,447	3,203r	2,340	-	336,991
Used in pumping											3,210
Supplied (net)											333,781
Other generators (2)											
Fuel used	11,987r	7,035r	35,757r	-	18,851r	12,053r	85,684r	840	-	965	87,489r
Generation	4,333r	2,781	14,906r	-	4,318	3,577r	29,915r	840	-	965	31,721r
Used on works	230r	196r	480r	-	246	165r	1,316r	12r	-	-	1,328r
Supplied	4,104r	2,585r	14,426r	-	4,072	3,412r	28,599r	829	-	965	30,393r
All generating companies											
Fuel used	367,569r	16,545r	312,518r	241,537r	21,953r	12,053r	972,176r	4,055	2,422r	965	979,618r
Generation	131,461r	5,253	141,905r	90,093r	5,048r	3,577r	377,336r	4,055	2,422r	965	384,778r
Used on works	6,059r	476r	3,189r	7,108r	292r	165r	17,289r	23r	82r	-	17,394r
Supplied (gross)	125,402r	4,777r	138,716r	82,985	4,755	3,412r	360,047r	4,032r	2,340	965	367,384r
Used in pumping											3,210
Supplied (net)											364,174r

5.6 Electricity fuel use, generation and supply (cont'd)

GWh

	Coal	Oil	Gas	Nuclear	Renew-ables (1)	Other (3)	Total	Hydro-natural flow	Hydro-pumped storage	Other (4)	Total All sources
2002											
Major power producers (2)											
Fuel used	332,889r	8,011	291,264	233,765r	3,186r	-	869,115r	3,927	2,652	-	875,694r
Generation	120,958	2,011	135,741	87,848r	856r	-	347,414r	3,927r	2,652	-	353,994r
Used on works	5,574	378	2,877	6,758r	55r	-	15,643r	14r	90	-	15,746r
Supplied (gross)	115,383	1,633	132,864	81,090	802	-	331,772	3,914	2,562	-	338,248
Used in pumping											3,463
Supplied (net)											334,785
Other generators (2)											
Fuel used	11,663r	6,968r	38,771r	-	20,923r	12,339r	90,664r	860	-	1,259	92,783r
Generation	3,339r	2,798r	16,576r	-	4,769r	3,912r	31,393r	860	-	1,259	33,513r
Used on works	230	207	533r	-	264r	181r	1,414r	11	-	-	1,426r
Supplied	3,108r	2,592r	16,043r	-	4,505r	3,731r	29,979r	849	-	1,259	32,087r
All generating companies											
Fuel used	344,552r	14,979r	330,035r	233,765r	24,108r	12,339r	959,779r	4,788	2,652	1,259	968,477r
Generation	124,296r	4,809r	152,317r	87,848r	5,625r	3,912r	378,808r	4,788r	2,652	1,259	387,506r
Used on works	5,805	585r	3,410r	6,758r	318r	181r	17,057r	25r	90	-	17,172r
Supplied (gross)	118,492r	4,225r	148,907r	81,090	5,306r	3,731r	361,751r	4,763	2,562	1,259	370,334r
Used in pumping											3,463
Supplied (net)											366,871r
2003											
Major power producers (2)											
Fuel used	371,878	7,604	284,662	233,080	4,187	-	901,410	2,568	2,734	-	906,712
Generation	134,023	2,197	131,238	88,686	1,154	-	357,299	2,568	2,734	-	362,600
Used on works	6,325	249	3,201	6,775	95	-	16,645	9	92	-	16,747
Supplied (gross)	127,698	1,948	128,037	81,911	1,059	-	340,654	2,559	2,641	-	345,854
Used in pumping											3,546
Supplied (net)											342,308
Other generators (2)											
Fuel used	11,318	7,048	40,201	-	24,042	16,924	99,533	660	-	1,288	101,481
Generation	4,219	2,672	17,409	-	5,554	4,218	34,071	660	-	1,288	36,019
Used on works	217	197	540	-	335	195	1,484	7	-	-	1,491
Supplied	4,002	2,475	16,869	-	5,218	4,022	32,587	653	-	1,288	34,528
All generating companies											
Fuel used	383,196	14,652	324,862	233,080	28,229	16,924	1,000,943	3,228	2,734	1,288	1,008,193
Generation	138,242	4,869	148,646	88,686	6,708	4,218	391,370	3,228	2,734	1,288	398,620
Used on works	6,541	446	3,741	6,775	431	195	18,129	16	92	-	18,238
Supplied (gross)	131,701	4,423	144,906	81,911	6,277	4,022	373,240	3,212	2,641	1,288	380,382
Used in pumping											3,546
Supplied (net)											376,836

	1999 Conv-entional thermal (5)	1999 CCGT	2000 Conv-entional thermal (5)	2000 CCGT	2001 Conv-entional thermal (5)	2001 CCGT	2002 Conv-entional thermal (5)	2002 CCGT	2003 Conv-entional thermal (5)	2003 CCGT
Major power producers (2)										
Generated	119,523	114,620	131,760	117,935	133,482r	123,846r	127,550r	132,016r	147,536	121,076
Supplied (gross)	113,493	112,768	125,468	116,110	127,118r	121,344r	121,297r	129,384r	140,196	118,546
Other generators										
Generated	22,646	7,141	22,724	10,859	20,937r	8,979	20,820r	10,577r	23,320	10,759
Supplied (gross)	21,769	6,785	21,926	10,318	20,068r	8,531	19,933r	10,049r	22,373	10,222
All generating companies										
Generated	142,169	121,761	154,485	128,794	154,418r	132,825r	148,370r	142,593r	170,857	131,835
Supplied (gross)	135,262	119,553	147,394	126,428	147,186r	129,875r	141,230r	139,433r	162,569	128,768

(1) Thermal renewable sources are those included under biofuels and non-biodegradable wastes in Chapter 7.
(2) See paragraphs 5.47 and 5.48 on companies covered.
(3) Other thermal sources include coke oven gas, blast furnace gas and waste products from chemical processes.
(4) Other non-thermal sources include wind, wave and solar photovoltaics.
(5) Includes gas turbines, oil engines and plants producing electricity from renewable sources other than hydro.

5.7 Plant capacity - United Kingdom

MW

	1999	2000	2001	2002	end December 2003
Major power producers *(1)*					
Total declared net capability	**70,245r**	**72,193r**	**73,382r**	**70,615r**	**71,746**
Of which:					
Conventional steam stations:	35,647r	34,835r	34,835r	30,687r	30,367
Coal fired	25,581	24,810r	24,810r	22,427r	22,524
Oil fired	2,829	2,933	2,933	2,708	2,930
Mixed or dual fired *(2)*	7,237r	7,092r	7,092r	5,552r	4,913
Combined cycle gas turbine stations	16,110	19,349	20,517	21,800r	23,577
Nuclear stations	12,956	12,486	12,486	12,486	12,098
Gas turbines and oil engines	1,301r	1,291r	1,291r	1,432r	1,497
Hydro-electric stations:					
Natural flow	1,327	1,327	1,348	1,304	1,302
Pumped storage	2,788	2,788	2,788	2,788	2,788
Renewables other than hydro	117	117	117	117	117
Other generators *(1)*					
Total capacity of own generating plant	**5,388**	**6,258**	**6,296**	**6,376r**	**6,798**
Of which:					
Conventional steam stations *(3)*	3,315	3,544	3,464	3,345r	3,405
Combined cycle gas turbine stations	1,243	1,709	1,777	1,854r	1,950
Hydro-electric stations (natural flow)	150	158	160	162	166
Renewables other than hydro	680	847	895	1,015	1,277
All generating companies					
Total capacity	**75,633**	**78,451**	**79,678r**	**76,991r**	**78,544**
Of which:					
Conventional steam stations *(3)*	38,962	38,379	38,299r	34,032r	33,772
Combined cycle gas turbine stations	17,353	21,058	22,294	23,654r	25,535
Nuclear stations	12,956	12,486	12,486	12,486	12,098
Gas turbines and oil engines	1,301r	1,291r	1,291r	1,432r	1,489
Hydro-electric stations:					
Natural flow	1,477	1,485	1,508	1,466	1,468
Pumped storage	2,788	2,788	2,788	2,788	2,788
Renewables other than hydro	797	964	1,012	1,132	1,394

(1) See paragraphs 5.47 and 5.48 for information on companies covered.
(2) Includes gas fired stations that are not Combined Cycle Gas Turbines.
(3) For other generators, conventional steam stations include combined heat and power plants (electrical capacity only), but exclude combined cycle gas turbine plants, hydro-electric stations and plants using renewable sources.

5.8 Plant capacity - England and Wales, Scotland, and Northern Ireland

MW

	1999	2000	2001	2002	2003
				end December	
Major power producers in England and Wales *(1)*					
Total declared net capability	**58,485**	**60,585**	**61,850**	**59,333**	**60,299**
Of which:					
Conventional steam stations:	28,713	28,128	28,128	25,634	26,211
Coal fired	21,954	21,240	21,240	18,971	19,068
Oil fired	2,649	2,753	2,753	2,528	2,750
Mixed or dual fired *(2)*	4,110	4,135	4,135	4,135	4,393
Combined cycle gas turbine stations	16,110	19,275	20,443	20,186	20,967
Nuclear stations	10,516	10,046	10,046	10,046	9,658
Gas turbines and oil engines	817	807	897	1,131	1,127
Hydro-electric stations:					
Natural flow	124	124	131	131	131
Pumped storage	2,088	2,088	2,088	2,088	2,088
Renewables other than hydro	117	117	117	117	117
Major power producers in Scotland *(1)*					
Total declared net capability	**9,776**	**9,677**	**9,601**	**9,465**	**9,531**
Of which:					
Conventional steam and combined cycle gas turbine stations	5,169	5,070	5,070	5,069	5,070
Nuclear stations	2,440	2,440	2,440	2,440	2,440
Gas turbines and oil engines	264	264	174	83	150
Hydro-electric stations:					
Natural flow	1,203	1,203	1,217	1,173	1,171
Pumped storage	700	700	700	700	700
Major power producers in Northern Ireland *(1)*					
Total declared net capability	**1,984**	**1,930**	**1,930**	**1,816**	**1,915**

(1) See paragraphs 5.47 and 5.48 for information on companies covered.

(2) Includes gas fired stations that are not Combined Cycle Gas Turbines.

5.9 Capacity of other generators

MW

	1999	2000	2001	2002	2003
				end-December	
Capacity of own generating plant *(1)*					
Undertakings in industrial and commercial sector:					
Petroleum refineries	887	1,003	1,000r	954	950
Iron and steel	355	373	379	310r	310
Chemicals	1,253	1,266	1,296r	1,341r	1,231
Engineering and other metal trades	518	615	617r	621r	670
Food, drink and tobacco	406	409	394r	404r	379
Paper, printing and publishing	483	573	544	598r	804
Other *(2)*	1,204	1,736	1,783r	2,046r	2,350
Total industrial and commercial sector	5,105	5,975	6,013r	6,273r	6,695
Undertakings in transport sector	283	283	283	103	103
Total other generators	**5,388**	**6,258**	**6,296r**	**6,376r**	**6,798**

(1) For combined heat and power plants the electrical capacity only is included. Further CHP capacity is included under major power producers in Table 5.7. A detailed analysis of CHP capacity is given in the tables of Chapter 6.

(2) Includes companies in the commercial sector.

5.10 Plant loads, demand and efficiency

Major power producers [1]

	Unit	1999	2000	2001	2002	2003
Simultaneous maximum load met [2][3]	MW	57,849	58,452	58,589	61,717	60,501
of which England and Wales	MW	50,560	51,020	51,548	54,430	52,965
Scotland	MW	5,847	5,861	5,504	5,688	5,909
Northern Ireland	MW	1,442	1,571	1,537	1,599	1,627
Maximum demand as a percentage of UK capacity	Per cent	82.6r	81.1r	80.0	87.6	84.3
Plant load factor						
Combined cycle gas turbine stations	Per cent	84.0	75.0	66.6	68.4	59.8
Nuclear stations	"	77.5	70.5	76.1	74.3	76.3
Hydro-electric stations:						
Natural flow	"	38.0	37.2	27.4	33.8	22.5
Pumped storage	"	11.5	10.7	9.6	10.5	10.8
Conventional thermal and other stations [4]	"	35.3	39.4r	42.1r	42.3	50.0
All plant	"	**53.1**	**52.7r**	**53.1**	**53.9**	**55.7**
System load factor	"	**66.7**	**67.4**	**68.7**	**64.8r**	**67.0**
Thermal efficiency (gross calorific value basis)						
Combined cycle gas turbine stations	"	46.6	46.6	46.7	47.2r	46.4
Coal fired stations	"	35.8	36.2	35.7	36.4r	36.0
Nuclear stations	"	36.8	37.3	37.3	37.6r	38.1

(1) See paragraphs 5.47 and 5.48 for information on companies covered.
(2) Data cover the 12 months ending March of the following year eg 2003 data are for the year ending March 2004.
(3) The demands shown are those that occurred in Scotland and Northern Ireland at the same time as England and Wales had their maximum demand. See paragraph 5.54 for further details .
(4) Conventional steam plants, gas turbines and oil engines and plants producing electricity from renewable sources other than hydro.

5.11 Power Stations in the United Kingdom
(operational at the end of May 2004)[1]

Company Name	Station Name	Fuel	Installed Capacity (MW)	Year of Commission or year generation began
AES	Kilroot	coal/oil	520	1981
	Indian Queens	gas oil/kerosene	140	1996
AES Fifoots Point Ltd	Fifoots Point (2)	coal	393	2000
American Electric Power	Ferrybridge C	coal	1,955	1966
	Fiddler's Ferry	coal	1,961	1971
	Ferrybridge GT	gas oil	34	1966
	Fiddler's Ferry GT	gas oil	34	1969
Alcan	Lynemouth	coal	420	1995
	Fort William	hydro	62	1929
	Kinlochleven	hydro	30	1907
Baglan Generation Ltd	Baglan Bay	CCGT	575	2002
Barking Power	Barking	CCGT	1,000	1994
British Energy	Dungeness B	nuclear	1,110	1985
	Hartlepool	nuclear	1,210	1989
	Heysham1	nuclear	1,150	1989
	Heysham 2	nuclear	1,250	1989
	Hinkley Point B	nuclear	1,220	1976
	Sizewell B	nuclear	1,188	1995
	Hunterston B	nuclear	1,190	1976
	Torness	nuclear	1,250	1988
	Eggborough	coal	1,960	1967
	Bridgewater District Energy	gas	10	2000
	Solutia District Energy	gas	10	2000
	Sevington District Energy	gas	10	2000
BNFL British Nuclear Group	Chapelcross	nuclear	196	1959
	Dungeness A	nuclear	450	1965
	Oldbury	nuclear	434	1967
	Sizewell A	nuclear	420	1966
	Wylfa	nuclear	980	1971
	Maentwrog	hydro	20	1928
Calpine Corporation	Saltend	CCGT	1,200	2000
Centrica	Barry	CCGT	250	1998
	Kings Lynn	CCGT	340	1996
	Peterborough	CCGT	380	1993
	Roosecote	CCGT	229	1991
Citigen (London) Ltd	Charterhouse St, London	gas/gas oil	31	1995
Coolkeeragh Power	Coolkeeragh	oil	120	1959
Corby Power	Corby	CCGT	401	1993
Coryton Energy Company Ltd	Coryton	CCGT	753	2001
Damhead Creek Limited (3)	Damhead Creek	CCGT	792	2000
Derwent Cogeneration	Derwent	CHP	236	1994
Drax Power Ltd	Drax	coal	3,870	1974
	Drax GT	gas oil	75	1971

5.11 Power Stations in the United Kingdom
(operational at the end of May 2004)[1] (continued)

Company Name	Station Name	Fuel	Installed Capacity (MW)	Year of Commission or year generation began
EDF Energy	Sutton Bridge	CCGT	803	1999
	Cottam	coal	2,008	1969
	West Burton	coal	1,972	1967
	West Burton GT	gas oil	40	1967
Edison Mission Energy	Dinorwig	pumped storage	1,728	1983
	Ffestiniog	pumped storage	360	1961
Enfield Energy Centre Ltd	Brimsdown	CCGT	390	1999
Fellside Heat and Power	Fellside	CHP	168	1993
Fibrogen	Glanford	meat & bone meal	13	1993
Fibropower Ltd	Eye, Suffolk	poultry litter	13	1992
Fibrothetford	Thetford	poultry litter	39	1998
Great Yarmouth Power Ltd	Great Yarmouth	CCGT	420	2001
Humber Power	South Humber Bank 1	CCGT	785	1996
	South Humber Bank 2	CCGT	527	1998
Immingham CHP LLP	Immingham CHP	CHP	734	2004
International Power	Deeside (4)	CCGT	500	1994
	Rugeley	coal	1,006	1972
	Rugeley GT	gas oil	50	1972
Killingholme Power Ltd (5)	Killingholme	CCGT	650	1994
National Grid	Kielder	hydro	5.5	1984
PowerGen	Kingsnorth	coal/oil	1,940	1970
	Ironbridge	coal	970	1970
	Ratcliffe	coal	2,000	1968
	Grain (6)	oil	650	1979
	Grain GT	gas oil	55	1978
	Kingsnorth GT	gas oil	34	1967
	Ratcliffe GT	gas oil	34	1966
	Taylor's Lane GT	gas oil	132	1979
	Connahs Quay	CCGT	1,380	1996
	Cottam Development Centre	CCGT	400	1999
	Rheidol	hydro	50	1961
Premier Power Ltd	Ballylumford	oil/gas	1,216	1968
Regional Power Generators Ltd	Glanford Brigg	CCGT	240	1993
Rocksavage Power Co. Ltd	Rocksavage	CCGT	750	1997
RWE Innogy Plc	Aberthaw B	coal	1,455	1971
	Tilbury B (7)	coal/oil	1,020	1968
	Didcot A	coal/gas	1,925	1972
	Aberthaw GT	gas oil	51	1971
	Cowes	gas oil	70	1982
	Didcot GT	gas oil	100	1972

5.11 Power Stations in the United Kingdom
(operational at the end of May 2004)[1] (continued)

Company Name	Station Name	Fuel	Installed Capacity (MW)	Year of Commission or year generation began
RWE Innogy Plc (continued)	Fawley GT	gas oil	34	1969
	Littlebrook GT	gas oil	105	1982
	Tilbury GT	gas oil	34	1968
	Fawley (7)	oil	484	1969
	Littlebrook D (7)	oil	685	1982
	Didcot B	CCGT	1,370	1998
	Little Barford	CCGT	655	1995
	Cwm Dyli	hydro	10	1989 (8)
	Dolgarrog	hydro	37	1924
Scottish & Southern Energy plc **Schemes:**				
Affric/Beauly	Mullardoch Tunnel	hydro	2.4	1955
	Fasnakyle	hydro	69	1951
	Deanie	hydro	38	1963
	Culligran	hydro	19.1	1962
	Aigas	hydro	20	1962
	Kilmorack	hydro	20	1962
Breadalbane	Lubreoch	hydro	4	1958
	Cashlie	hydro	11	1959
	Lochay	hydro	47	1958
	Finlarig	hydro	16.5	1955
	Lednock	hydro	3	1961
	St. Fillans	hydro	16.8	1957
	Dalchonzie	hydro	4	1958
Conon	Achanalt	hydro	3	1956
	Grudie Bridge	hydro	18.7	1950
	Mossford	hydro	18.7	1957
	Luichart	hydro	34	1954
	Orrin	hydro	18	1959
	Torr Achilty	hydro	15	1954
Foyers	Foyers	hydro/pumped storage	300	1974
Great Glen	Foyers Falls	hydro	5.2	1968
	Mucomir	hydro	2	1962
	Ceannacroc	hydro	20	1956
	Livishie	hydro	15	1962
	Glenmoriston	hydro	37	1957
	Quoich	hydro	18.5	1955
	Ivergarry	hydro	20	1956
Shin	Cassley	hydro	10	1959
	Lairg	hydro	3.5	1959
	Shin	hydro	18.7	1958
Sloy/Awe	Sloy	hydro	152.5	1950
	Sron Mor	hydro	5	1957
	Clachan	hydro	40	1955
	Alt-na-Lairgie	hydro	6	1956
	Nant	hydro	15	1963
	Inverawe	hydro	25	1963
	Kilmelfort	hydro	2	1956
	Loch Gair	hydro	6	1961
	Lussa	hydro	2.4	1952
	Striven	hydro	8	1951

5.11 Power Stations in the United Kingdom
(operational at the end of May 2004)[1] (continued)

Company Name	Station Name	Fuel	Installed Capacity (MW)	Year of Commission or year generation began
Scottish & Southern Energy plc (continued)				
Tummel	Gaur	hydro	7.9	1953
	Cuaich	hydro	2.5	1959
	Loch Ericht	hydro	2.2	1962
	Rannoch	hydro	44.1	1930
	Tummel	hydro	34	1933
	Errochty	hydro	75	1955
	Clunie	hydro	61.2	1950
	Pitlochry	hydro	15	1950
Small Hydros:	Chliostair	hydro	1.1	1960
	Kerry Falls	hydro	1.3	1951
	Loch Dubh	hydro	1.2	1954
	Nostie Bridge	hydro	1.3	1950
	Storr Lochs	hydro	2.4	1952
	Cuileag	hydro	3.2	2002
Thermal:	Peterhead (9)	CCGT oil/gas	1,540	1980
	Medway	CCGT	688	1995
	Fife Power Station	CCGT	120	2000
	Keadby	CCGT	745	1994
	Chickerell	gas	45	1998
	Burghfield	gas	45	1998
	Thatcham	diesel	8.9	1994
	Five Oaks	diesel	8.9	1995
	Chippenham	gas	10	2002
	Wheldale	gas	10	2002
Island Generation	Stornoway	diesel	23.5	1950
	Lerwick	diesel	67.2	1953
	Arnish	diesel	3	2001
	Kirkwall	diesel	16.2	1953
	Loch Carnan, South Uist	diesel	11.8	1971
	Bowmore	diesel	6	1946
	Tiree	diesel	2.5	1945
	Barra	diesel	2.1	1990
Scottish Power **Schemes:**				
Galloway	Carsfad	hydro	12	1936
	Drumjohn	hydro	2	1985
	Earlstoun	hydro	14	1936
	Glenlee	hydro	24	1935
	Kendoon	hydro	24	1936
	Tongland	hydro	33	1935
Lanark	Bonnington	hydro	11	1927
	Stonebyres	hydro	5	1927
Cruachan	Cruachan	pumped storage	399	1966
Thermal:	Cockenzie	coal	1,152	1967
	Longannet	coal	2,304	1970
	Knapton	gas oil	40	1994
	Rye House	CCGT	715	1993
Seabank Power Limited	Seabank 1	CCGT	812	1998
	Seabank 2	CCGT	410	2000

5.11 Power Stations in the United Kingdom
(operational at the end of May 2004)[1] (continued)

Company Name	Station Name	Fuel	Installed Capacity (MW)	Year of Commission or year generation began
Sita Tyre Recycling Ltd	Wolverhampton(10)	waste	20	1994
South Coast Power	Shoreham	CCGT	400	2000
South East London Combined Heat & Power Ltd	Landmann Way, London	waste	32	1994
Spalding Energy Company Ltd	Spalding	CCGT	903	2004
Teesside Power Ltd	Teesside Power Station	CCGT	1,875	1992
Western Power Generation	St Marys	gas oil	6	1958
	Princetown	kerosene	3	1959
	Lynton	gas oil	2	1961
	Roseland	kerosene	5	1963
Total			**73,855**	

(1) This list covers stations of more than 1 MW capacity, but excludes some renewables stations of over 1 MW which are included in the section below.
(2) AES Fifoots is in administration and not currently operating although it did operate under lease in winter 2003/04.
(3) Purchased by Scottish Power in June 2004
(4) Includes 250 MW re-instated in October 2003.
(5) Purchased by Centrica in June 2004
(6) As re-instated in October 2003; 650 MW remain mothballed.
(7) Excludes mothballed capacity.
(8) Recommissioning date.
(9) Total capacity is 2,319 MW but because of transmission constraints only 1,540 MW can be used at any one time.
(10) There has been no generation from this site for several years.

Other power stations[11]

Station type	Fuel	Capacity (MW)
Renewable sources and combustible wastes	wind	742
	landfill gas	619
	sewage gas	101
	hydro	133
	waste	269
	other	119
CHP schemes other than major power producers and renewables	mainly gas	3,978
Other autogenerators	various fuels	926

(11) As at end December 2003.

Interconnectors

	Capacity (MW)
England - Scotland	2,200
England - France	2,000
Scotland - Northern Ireland	500
Northern Ireland - Irish Republic	600

Chapter 6
Combined heat and power

Introduction

6.1   This chapter sets out the contribution made by Combined Heat and Power (CHP) to the United Kingdom's energy requirements.   The data presented in this Chapter have been derived from information submitted to the CHP Quality Assurance programme (CHPQA).   This programme was introduced by Government to provide the methods and procedures to assess and certify the quality of the full range of CHP schemes.   It is a rigorous system for the Government to ensure that the incentives on offer are targeted fairly and benefit schemes in relation to their environmental performance.   The data presented in this chapter have been derived from information submitted to CHPQA or by following the same procedures where no information has been provided directly.

6.2   CHP is the simultaneous generation of usable heat and power (usually electricity) in a single process.   The term CHP is synonymous with cogeneration and total energy, which are terms often used in other Member States of the European Community and the United States. CHP uses a variety of fuels and technologies across a wide range of sites and scheme sizes.   The basic elements of a CHP plant comprise one or more prime movers (a reciprocating engine, gas turbine, or steam turbine) driving electrical generators, where the steam or hot water generated in the process is utilised via suitable heat recovery equipment for use either in industrial processes, or in community heating and space heating.

6.3   A CHP plant provides primary energy savings compared to separate generation of heat and power.   In addition, CHP is typically sized to make use of the available heat, and connected to the lower voltage distribution system (ie embedded).   This provides efficiency gains compared to electricity-only plant, which is larger, and connected at very high voltage to the grid transmission system, by avoiding significant transmission and distribution losses. CHP can also provide important network services such as black start, improvements to power quality, and the ability to operate in island mode if the grid goes down.

6.4   There are four principal types of CHP systems: steam turbine, gas turbine, combined cycle systems and reciprocating engines. Each of these is defined in paragraph 6.34 below.

Government policy towards CHP

6.5   To reduce carbon emissions and help deliver the UK's Climate Change Programme, the Government has a target of achieving at least 10,000 MWe of Good Quality CHP capacity by 2010. At the end of the year 2002, installed Good Quality CHP capacity was 4,849 MWe. This figure is based on all submissions to the CHPQA programme and is higher than the end of year 2002 figure reported in the 2003 DUKES. The increase is due to a small number of schemes that submitted information to CHPQA after the statistics were prepared in 2003. During 2003, there was a decrease in the total number of CHP schemes from 1,541 at the beginning of the year to 1,506 at the end, but a slight increase in capacity to 4,879 MWe.

6.6   In April 2004, the Government published its strategy to reach the 2010 target (www.defra.gov.uk/environment/energy/chp/chp-strategy.pdf). The Strategy incorporates the full range of measures to lay the foundation for long-term growth in CHP.

6.7   The Chancellor announced in the Budget of 2002 that the Government is committed to providing relief from the Climate Change Levy (CCL) for electricity generated by CHP. The Budget contained measures that provide a framework for relief from CCL by extending the exemption from levy to electricity from Good Quality CHP schemes if the electricity is sold to end-users via third party electricity utilities (www.hmce.gov.uk/business/othertaxes/ccl/tec18.pdf). During 2003, a system of Levy Exemption Certificates (LECs) was set up to facilitate this relief. CHP station operators are able to sell or transfer their LECs with the amount of electricity supplied indirectly from the station. The scheme allows commercial freedom to maximise the benefit. It enables supplies of "Good Quality" electricity to be identified as such, as part of an auditable process.

International context

6.8   The EU Directive "On the promotion of cogeneration (CHP) based on useful heat demand in the energy market" came into force in February 2004. Its purpose is to increase energy efficiency and improve security of supply by creating a framework for the promotion and development of high efficiency cogeneration.

6.9   The EU Emissions Trading Scheme (EU-ETS) is due to commence on 1st January 2005 and involves the trading of emissions allowances. The purpose of the EU-ETS is to reduce emissions by a fixed amount at least cost to the regulated sources. Each year participants in the scheme are allocated a set number of allowances and the number of allowances equal to the reported emissions must be given up. If participants reduce emissions below their allocations, they will have allowances to trade or keep for use in future years. If emissions rise above their allocations allowances must be purchased. Although the EU-ETS is expected to encourage lower carbon technologies such as CHP, the exact impact on will depend on:

- the effect of the EU-ETS on electricity prices. If electricity prices were to rise due to EU-ETS, this would be beneficial to the economics for CHP.
- the need to account for carbon emissions from fuel use in CHP. The net effect will depend on the allocation, in developing the National Allocation Plan, the UK Government sought to ensure that CHP was not disadvantaged by the allocation. There are ring-fenced allowances for new entrant CHP (CHP schemes coming on line during the first phase of the EU-ETS).

UK Energy markets, and their effect on CHP

6.10   Two major factors affecting the economics of CHP are the relative cost of fuel (principally natural gas) and the value that can be realised for electricity. Over the last ten years, electricity prices have declined in real terms. For most of that time gas prices have also fallen, but rose significantly in 2000 and 2001, due to structural changes in the gas market. Electricity prices have increased slightly over the last few months.

Use of CHPQA in producing CHP statistics

6.11   The CHPQA programme is now the major source for CHP statistics. The following factors need to be kept in mind when using the statistics produced:

- Scheme operators have previously determined the boundary of a CHP scheme (what is regarded as part of the CHP installation and what is not). Now, through CHPQA, scheme operators have been given guidance on how to determine scheme boundaries. A scheme can include multiple CHP prime movers, along with supplementary boilers and generating plant, subject to appropriate metering installed to support the CHP scheme boundaries proposed, and subject to appropriate metering and threshold criteria (see CHPQA Guidance Note 11 available at www.chpqa.com).

- The output of a scheme is based on gross power output, ignoring parasitic loads (ie ignoring power used in pumps, fans, etc within the scheme itself).

- The main purpose of a number of CHP schemes is the generation of electricity including export to others. Such schemes may not be sized to use all of the available heat. The total capacity and output of these schemes have been scaled back using the methodologies outlined in CHPQA. Only the portion of the capacity and output that qualifies as Good Quality is counted in this chapter and the remaining capacity and output are regarded as power only and reported in Chapter 5. In previous years the fuel use for these partial schemes was scaled back by assigning fuel use to the power-only portion of the output based on the overall electrical efficiency of the scheme. For the 2001-2003 figures presented here, a new convention has been adopted so that the fuel allocated to the power-only portion of the output is calculated from the power efficiency of the prime mover. This is a better representation of the fuel used for the power, but needed additional information from schemes. This information was requested for the 2003 self-assessment forms (submitted to CHPQA in 2004).

- The load factor presented in Table 6A is based on the Good Quality Power Output and Good Quality Power Capacity reported in this Chapter. For schemes that are scaled back, this load factor is likely to be smaller than the actual load factor (hours run) for the prime mover in these schemes.

Chart 6.1: Installed CHP capacity by year

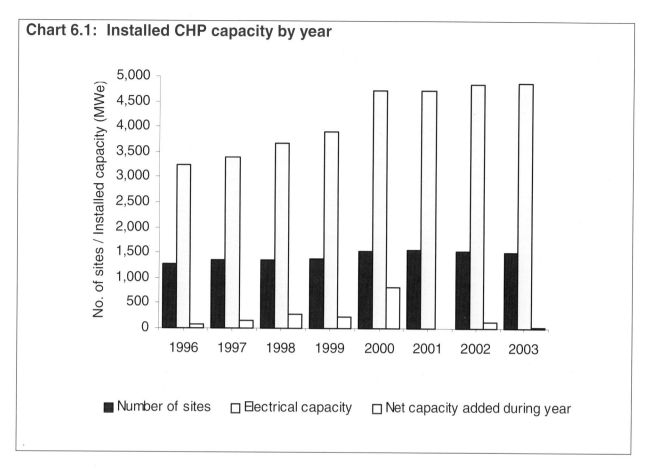

Progress towards the Government's targets

6.12   Chart 6.1 shows the change in installed CHP capacity over the last eight years. Installed capacity at the end of 2003 stood at 4,879 MWe. In the decade to 2000, capacity more than doubled, representing an average growth rate over the period of 8 per cent per annum. However, difficult market conditions slowed this growth rate from 2001. Despite a decreasing number of CHP schemes, the overall capacity has still been increasing slowly, in part because of better use of heat in some partial schemes. Table 6A summarises the latest figures.

Capacity in 2003

6.13   In 2002, 8 new schemes came into operation and 43 ceased to operate. The net loss in the number of schemes reflects the slowing of the market in 2001 and 2002 due to unfavourable energy prices.

6.14   In the current market conditions, a number of operators have chosen to mothball their CHP schemes rather than continue to operate. As these schemes are still able to operate they have been included in the total capacity. At the end of 2003, there were 64 mothballed schemes with a total capacity of 31 MWe.

6.15   Over 65 per cent of capacity is now gas turbine based, with about 80 per cent of this in combined cycle mode. Capacity in all technologies, except combined cycle gas turbines, decreased (see Tables 6A and 6.5). Heat generation has been falling slightly each year since 2000, reflecting decreasing demand for heat in industry. There was a dip in electricity generation in 2001. This reflected the difficulties encountered by smaller generators faced with rising gas prices, and falling electricity prices under NETA. As a result CHP plants were used less and the average load factor fell from 64 per cent in 2000 to 54 per cent in 2001. Since 2001, the generation has recovered slightly and the load factor has increased by 3-4 percentage points. There was a slight decrease in generation between 2002 and 2003, but efficiency has improved. The overall efficiency for 2001 and 2002 is lower than previously reported because of the change in methodology for allocating fuels to partial CHP schemes (discussed in paragraph 6.11).

Table 6A: A summary of the recent development of CHP

	Unit	1999	2000	2001	2002	2003
Number of schemes		1,383	1,522	1,552	1,541	1,506
Net number of schemes added during		*27*	*139*	*30*	*-11*	*-35*
Electrical capacity (CHP$_{QPC}$)	MWe	3,912	4,730	4,732	4,849	4,879
Net capacity added during year		*232*	*818*	*2*	*117*	*30*
Capacity added in percentage terms	Per cent	*6*	*21*	*-*	*2*	*1*
Heat capacity	MWth	14,800	11,888	11,898	11,560	11,168
Heat to power ratio *(1)*		3.78	2.51	2.69	2.45	2.45
Fuel input *(3)*	GWh	113,01	117,450	119,735	123,888	120,937
Electricity generation (CHP$_{QPO}$)	GWh	20,256	26,539	22,444	24,485	24,244
Heat generation (CHP$_{QHO}$)	GWh	60,439	62,121	60,584	59,902	59,284
Overall efficiency *(2)*	Per cent	71.4	75.5	69.3	68.1	69.1
Load factor *(4)*	Per cent	59.1	64.1	54.1	57.6	56.7

(1) Heat to power ratios are calculated from the qualifying heat output (QHO) and the qualifying power output (QPO).
(2) These are calculated using gross calorific values; overall net efficiencies are some 5 percentage points higher.
(3) The fuel figures from 2001 are based on a new methodology for assigning fuel to partial CHP schemes (see paragraph 6.11)
(4) The load factor reported in this table is based on the qualifying power generation and capacity and does not correspond exactly to the number of hours run by the prime movers in a year (see paragraph 6.23)

Installed capacity and output in 2003

6.16   Table 6A gives a summary of the overall CHP market. The electricity generated by CHP schemes was 24,244 GWh. This represents 6 per cent of the total electricity generated in the UK in 2003. Across the commercial and industrial sectors (including the fuel industries other than electricity generation) electrical output from CHP accounted for around 10 per cent of electricity consumption. CHP schemes in total supplied 59,284 GWh of heat.

6.17   In terms of electrical capacity, schemes larger than 10 MWe represent 81 per cent of the total electrical capacity of CHP schemes as shown in Table 6B. However, in terms of number of schemes, the largest share (>80 per cent) is in schemes less than 1 MWe. Schemes of 1 MWe or larger make up 17 per cent of the total number of schemes. Table 6.5 provides data on electrical capacity for each type of CHP installation.

Table 6B: CHP schemes by capacity size ranges in 2003

Electrical capacity size range	Number of schemes	Share of total (per cent)	Total electricity capacity (MWe)	Share of total (per cent)
Less than 100 kWe	628	41.7	38	0.8
100 kWe - 999 kWe	624	41.4	149	3.1
1 MWe - 9.9 MWe	182	12.1	733	15.0
Greater than 10 MWe	72	4.8	3,958	81.1
Total	**1,506**	**100.0**	**4,879**	**100.0**

6.18   In terms of heat capacity, combined cycle gas turbines now make up the largest proportion, 44½ per cent, with steam turbines providing the next largest proportion, 32 per cent. Table 6.7 provides data on heat capacity for each type of CHP installation.

Fuel used by types of CHP installation

6.19   Table 6.2 shows the fuel used to generate electricity and heat in CHP schemes, (see paragraphs 6.35 to 6.37, below for an explanation of the convention for dividing fuel between electricity and heat production). Table 6.3 gives the overall fuel used by types of CHP installation (which are explained in paragraph 6.34). Total fuel use is summarised in Chart 6.2. In 2003, 66 per cent of the total fuel use was natural gas, the same proportion as in 2002. CHP schemes accounted for 8 per cent of UK gas consumption in 2003 (see Table 4.3).

6.20   Non-conventional fuels (liquids, solids or gases which are by-products or waste products from industrial processes, or are renewable fuels) account for a quarter of fuel used in CHP. These are fuels that are not commonly used by the mainstream electricity generating industry, and some would otherwise be flared or disposed of by some means. These fuels (with the exception of some waste gases) will always be burnt in external combustion engines, such as boilers feeding steam turbines. In almost all cases, the technical nature of the combustion process (lower calorific value of the fuel, high moisture content of the fuel, the need to maintain certain combustion conditions to ensure complete disposal etc) will always imply a lower efficiency. However, given that the use of such fuels avoids the use of fossil fuels, and since they need to be disposed of in some way, the use of these fuels in CHP provides environmental benefits.

Chart 6.2: Types of fuel used by CHP schemes in 2003

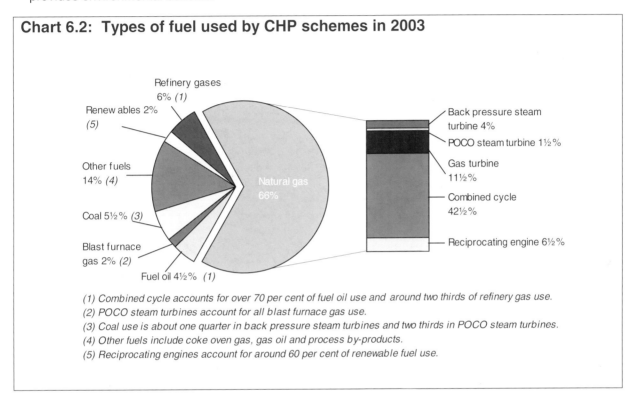

(1) Combined cycle accounts for over 70 per cent of fuel oil use and around two thirds of refinery gas use.
(2) POCO steam turbines account for all blast furnace gas use.
(3) Coal use is about one quarter in back pressure steam turbines and two thirds in POCO steam turbines.
(4) Other fuels include coke oven gas, gas oil and process by-products.
(5) Reciprocating engines account for around 60 per cent of renewable fuel use.

CHP capacity, output and fuel use by sector

6.21   Table 6.8 gives data on all operational schemes by economic sector. A definition of the sectors used in this table can be found in Chapter 1, paragraph 1.57 and Table 1F:

- 389 schemes (94 per cent of electrical capacity) are in the industrial sector and 1,117 schemes (6 per cent of capacity) are in the agricultural, commercial, public administration, residential and transport sectors.

- Four industrial sectors account for three quarters of the CHP electrical capacity - chemicals (29½ per cent of capacity), oil refineries (19½ per cent), paper, publishing and printing (14 per cent) and food, beverages and tobacco (8 per cent). Capacity by sector is shown in Chart 6.3.

Table 6C: Number and capacity of CHP schemes installed in buildings by sector in 2003

	Number of schemes	Electrical capacity (MWe)	Heat capacity (MWth)
Leisure	426	44.7	68.1
Hotels	299	37.4	58.8
Health	208	105.1	220.8
Residential Group Heating	48	44.1	84.8
Universities	32	29.5	85.7
Offices	25	18.4	22.3
Education	23	10.3	26.1
Government Estate	15	12.2	17.8
Retail	10	6.1	5.4
Other *(1)*	5	14.7	22.8
Total	**1,091**	**322.6**	**612.4**

(1) Other includes: agriculture, airports, and domestic buildings

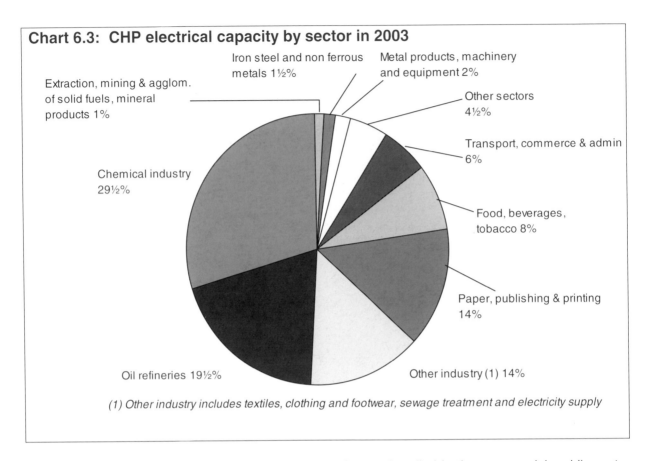

Chart 6.3: CHP electrical capacity by sector in 2003

Iron steel and non ferrous metals 1½%

Metal products, machinery and equipment 2%

Extraction, mining & agglom. of solid fuels, mineral products 1%

Other sectors 4½%

Chemical industry 29½%

Transport, commerce & admin 6%

Food, beverages, tobacco 8%

Paper, publishing & printing 14%

Oil refineries 19½%

Other industry (1) 14%

(1) Other industry includes textiles, clothing and footwear, sewage treatment and electricity supply

6.22   Table 6C gives a summary of the 1,091 schemes installed in the commercial, public sector and residential buildings. These schemes form a major part of the "Transport, commerce and administration" and "Other" sectors in Tables 6.8 and 6.9. The vast majority of these schemes (98 per cent) are based on spark ignition reciprocating engines fuelled with natural gas, though the larger schemes use compression ignition reciprocating engines or gas turbines. The largest proportion of the capacity is in the health sector, mainly hospitals. Leisure and hotels account for more than half the total number of schemes. Table 6.9 gives details of the quantities of fuels used in each sector.

CHP performance by main prime mover

6.23   Table 6D gives a summary of the performance of schemes in 2003 by main prime mover type. Combined cycle gas turbines have the highest average operating hours at 5,705 hours. The average for all schemes of 4,969 hours is slightly lower than in 2002 (5,069 hours).

6.24   The average electrical efficiency is 20 per cent and heat efficiency 49 per cent, giving an overall average of 70 per cent.

Table 6D: A summary of scheme performance in 2003

	Typical operating hours per annum (Full load equivalent)	Average electrical efficiency (% GCV)	Average heat efficiency (% GCV)	Average overall efficiency (% GCV)	Average heat to power ratio
Main prime mover in CHP plant					
Back pressure steam turbine	4,459	11	62	74	5.5
Pass out condensing steam turbine	3,277	12	59	67	4.8
Gas turbine	5,309	22	48	71	2.2
Combined cycle	5,705	23	45	68	2.0
Reciprocating engine	3,860	25	44	68	1.8
All schemes	**4,969**	**20**	**49**	**69**	**2.5**

148

CHP schemes which export and schemes with mechanical power output

6.25   For 2002, a large number of CHP schemes have provided information on the amount of electricity they export (Table 6E). It is estimated that this accounts for almost all the electricity exported from schemes in 2003. Where a scheme that exports is Good Quality for only a portion of its capacity and output, the exports have been scaled back in the same way as power output has been scaled back (see paragraph 6.11, above). Exports accounted for about 35 per cent of power generation from CHP.

6.26   Table 6E also shows revised figures for exports for 2001 and 2002. Exports have generally been increasing since 2001, with an increase of 8 per cent in 2003 relative to 2002. In 2002, there was an increase in exports via direct supply as these exports were exempt from the climate change levy. In 2003, this exemption was extended to exports via licensed suppliers and the percentage of direct exports decreased again.

Table 6E: Electrical exports from CHP

GWh

	2001	2002	2003
To part of same qualifying group (1)	499	820	431
To a firm NOT part of same qualifying group	1,425	3,527	1,923
To an electricity supplier	4,881	3,584	6,241
Customer not specified	2	27	-
Total	**6,807**	**7,958**	**8,584**

(1) A qualifying group is a group of two or more corporate consumers that are connected or related to each other, for example, as a subsidiary, or via a parent or holding company, or in terms of share capital.

6.27   Around 40 large schemes also export heat, some larger schemes to more than one customer. Together they supplied 9,415 GWh of heat, an increase of around 10 per cent compared to 2002.

6.28   There are an estimated 11 schemes with mechanical power output. For those schemes, mechanical power accounts for around 18 per cent of their capacity (Table 6F). These schemes are predominantly on petro-chemicals or steel sites, using by-product fuels in boilers to drive steam turbines. The steam turbine is used to provide mechanical rather than electrical power, driving compressors, blowers or fans, rather than an alternator.

Table 6F: CHP schemes with mechanical power output in 2003

	Unit	
Number of schemes		11
Total Power Capacity of these schemes (CHP_{TPC})	MWe	811
Mechanical power capacity of these schemes	MWe	153

Emissions savings

6.29   The calculation of emissions savings from CHP is important, given the substantial contribution of CHP to the Climate Change Programme, but complex given that CHP displaces a variety of fuels, technologies and sizes of plant. Using the methodology and assumptions outlined in Energy Trends www.dti.gov.uk/energy/inform/energy_stats/. CHP saved 3.0 - 4.1 MtC in 2003 compared to equivalent electricity-only and heat-only generation. This is equivalent to 0.65 – 0.89 MtC per 1,000 MWe[1]. The carbon savings are lower than previously reported, largely because the change in the allocation of fuel to partial schemes discussed in paragraph 6.11.

---

[1] *This range is obtained by assuming that electricity displaced is either at the average carbon intensity for the whole generating system, giving 0.70 MtC per 1,000 MWe, or at the carbon intensity of the fossil fuel basket, giving 0.96 MtC per 1,000 MWe.*

Technical notes and definitions

6.30 These notes and definitions are in addition to the technical notes and definitions covering all fuels and energy as a whole in Chapter 1, paragraphs 1.24 to 1.58.

Data for 2003

6.31 The data are summarised from the results of a long-term project being undertaken by Future Energy Solutions on behalf of the Department of Trade and Industry (DTI), the Department for Environment, Food and Rural Affairs (Defra), and the Statistical Office of the European Communities (Eurostat). Data are included for CHP schemes installed in all sectors of the UK economy.

6.32 The project continues to be overseen by a Steering Group that comprises officials from the DTI, Defra, the Office of Gas and Electricity Markets (OFGEM) and the Combined Heat and Power Association (CHPA), all of whom have an interest in either the collection of information on CHP schemes or the promotion of the wider use of CHP in the UK.

6.33 Data for 2003 were based largely on data supplied to the CHPQA programme, supplemented by a survey carried out by the Office for National Statistics (ONS) between December 2003 and March 2004 of companies (other than major power producers) who generate their own electricity, either in CHP schemes or in electricity-only schemes. Information on the CHP plant included in the major power producers category comes from surveys conducted by DTI as part of the electricity statistics system. For 2003, the Iron and Steel Statistics Bureau agreed with the industry a method for calculating CHP fuel inputs and electricity and heat outputs at integrated steel works. The information on CHP in iron and steel is largely based on statistics collected in previous years. Over half of CHP schemes and around 82 per cent of capacity are based on returns under CHPQA, while around 3 per cent of schemes and 6 per cent of CHP capacity are based on data from ONS. Data for schemes not applying for CHPQA and not included in the ONS survey (eg because they were below the cut off capacity for the survey) were interpolated from historical data.

Definitions of schemes

6.34 There are four principal types of CHP systems:

- **Steam turbine,** where steam at high pressure is generated in a boiler. In **back pressure steam turbine systems**, the steam is wholly or partly used in a turbine before being exhausted from the turbine at the required pressure for the site. In **pass-out condensing steam turbine systems**, a proportion of the steam used by the turbine is extracted at an intermediate pressure from the turbine with the remainder being fully condensed before it is exhausted at the exit. (Condensing steam turbines without passout and which do not utilise steam are not included in these statistics as they are not CHP). The boilers used in such schemes can burn a wide variety of fuels including coal, gas, oil, and waste-derived fuels. With the exception of waste-fired schemes, steam turbine plant has often been in service for several decades. Steam turbine schemes capable of supplying useful steam have electrical efficiencies of between 10 and 20 per cent, depending on size, and thus between 70 per cent and 30 per cent of the fuel input is available as useful heat. Steam turbines used in CHP applications typically range in size from a few MWe to over 100 MWe.

- **Gas turbine systems**, often aero-engine derivatives, where fuel (gas, or gas-oil) is combusted in the gas turbine and the exhaust gases are normally used in a waste heat boiler to produce usable steam, though the exhaust gases may be used directly in some process applications. Gas turbines range from 30kWe upwards, achieving electrical efficiency of 23 to 30 per cent (depending on size) and with the potential to recover up to 50 per cent of the fuel input as useful heat. They have been common in CHP since the mid 1980s. The waste heat boiler can include supplementary or auxiliary firing using a wide range of fuels, and thus the heat to power ratio of the scheme can vary.

- **Combined cycle systems**, where the plant comprises more than one prime mover. These are usually gas turbines where the exhaust gases are utilised in a steam generator, the steam from which is passed wholly or in part into one or more steam turbines. In rare cases reciprocating engines may be linked with steam turbines. Combined cycle is suited to larger installations of 7 MWe and over. They achieve higher electrical efficiency and a lower heat to power ratio than steam turbines or gas turbines. Recently installed combined cycle gas turbine (CCGT) schemes have achieved an electrical efficiency approaching 50 per cent, with 20 per cent heat recovery, and a heat to power ratio of less than 1:1.

- **Reciprocating engine systems** range from less than 100 kWe up to around 5 MWe, and are found in applications where production of hot water (rather than steam) is the main requirement, for example, on smaller industrial sites as well as in buildings. They are based on auto engine or marine engine derivatives converted to run on gas. Both compression ignition and spark ignition firing is used. Reciprocating engines operate at around 28 to 33 per cent electrical efficiency with around 50 per cent to 33 per cent of the fuel input available as useful heat. Reciprocating engines produce two grades of waste heat: high grade heat from the engine exhaust and low grade heat from the engine cooling circuits.

Determining fuel consumption for heat and electricity

6.35   In order to provide a comprehensive picture of electricity generation in the United Kingdom and the fuels used to generate that electricity, the energy input to CHP schemes has to be allocated between heat and electricity production. This allocation is notional and is not determinate.

6.36   The convention used to allocate the fuels to heat and electricity relates the split of fuels to the relative efficiency of heat and electricity supply. The efficiency of utility plants varies widely: electricity generation from as little as 25 per cent to more than 50 per cent and boilers from as little as 50 per cent to more than 90 per cent. Thus it is around twice as hard to generate a unit of electricity as it is to generate a unit of heat. Accordingly a simple convention can be implemented whereby twice as many units of fuel are allocated to each unit of electricity generated, as to each unit of heat supplied. This approach is consistent with the Defra Guidelines for Company Reporting on greenhouse gas emissions and for Negotiated Agreements on energy efficiency agreed between Government and industry as part of the Climate Change Levy (CCL) package. It recognises that in developing a CHP scheme, both the heat customer(s) and the electricity generator share in the savings, reflecting the fact that more than three-quarters of CHP build in the last few years has been supplied under an energy services arrangement.

6.37   The assumption in this convention, that it is twice as hard to generate a unit of electricity as heat, is appropriate for the majority of CHP schemes. However, for some types of scheme (for example in the iron and steel sector) this allocation is less appropriate and can result in very high apparent heat efficiencies. These however are only notional efficiencies.

The effects on the statistics of using CHPQA

6.38   Paragraph 6.11 described how schemes were scaled back so that only CHP_{QPC} and CHP_{QPO} were included in the CHP statistics. This is illustrated in Table 6G. In 2003, 64 schemes have been scaled back. The power output from these schemes was scaled back from a total of 31,029 GWh to 6,680 GWh. The total fuel input to these schemes is 89,440 GWh of which 59,674 GWh is regarded as power only.

Table 6G: CHP capacity, output and fuel use which has been scaled back in 2003

	Units	
Number of schemes requiring scaling back		64
Total Power Capacity of these schemes (CHP_{TPC})	MWe	7,531
Qualifying Power Capacity of these schemes (CHP_{QPC})	MWe	1,601
Total power output of these schemes (CHP_{TPO})	GWh	31,029*
Qualifying Power Output of these schemes (CHP_{QPO})	GWh	6,680
Electricity regarded as "Power only" not from CHP (CHP_{TPO} - CHP_{QPO})	GWh	24,348
Total Fuel Input of these schemes (CHP_{TFI})	GWh	89,440
Fuel input regarded as being for "Power only" use ie not for CHP	GWh	59,674

*This figure includes generation from major power producers

Contacts:
Adrian Crispin, Future Energy Solutions
adrian.crispin@aeat.co.uk
0870 1906085

Mike Janes (Statistician), DTI
mike.janes@dti.gsi.gov.uk
020-7215 5186

6.1 CHP installations by capacity and size range

	1999	2000	2001	2002	2003
Number of schemes (1)	**1,383**	**1,522**	**1,552r**	**1,541r**	**1,506**
Less than 100 kWe	627	667	664r	647r	628
100 kWe to 999 kWe	509	593	631r	638r	624
1 MWe to 9.9 MWe	174	192	185r	184r	182
10.0 MWe and above	73	70	72	72r	72
					MWe
Total capacity	**3,912**	**4,730**	**4,732r**	**4,849r**	**4,879**
Less than 100 kWe	38	41	40	39r	38
100 kWe to 999 kWe	127	145	155	155r	149
1 MWe to 9.9 MWe	740	803	747	750r	733
10.0 MWe and above	3,007	3,741	3,790	3,906r	3,958

(1) A site may contain more than one CHP scheme.

6.2 Fuel used to generate electricity and heat in CHP installations

				GWh	
	1999	2000	2001	2002	2003
Fuel used to generate electricity (1)					
Coal (2)	2,333	1,524	2,412r	2,388r	2,282
Fuel oil	4,433	3,071	2,817r	2,237r	2,200
Natural gas	27,075	37,842	35,422r	40,334r	39,796
Renewable fuels (3)	1,187	943	1,076r	1,083r	1,147
Other fuels (4)	9,238	10,530	9,379r	9,563r	8,685
Total all fuels	**44,266**	**53,908**	**51,106r**	**55,606r**	**54,110**
Fuel used to generate heat					
Coal (2)	6,682	3,845	4,825r	4,923r	4,575
Fuel oil	9,414	3,342	5,244r	3,210r	3,195
Natural gas	31,718	37,618	38,501r	41,619r	39,990
Renewable fuels (3)	1,051	1,024	1,090r	1,183r	1,332
Other fuels (4)	19,889	17,714	18,968r	17,347r	17,735
Total all fuels	**68,753**	**63,542**	**68,629r**	**68,282r**	**66,827**
Overall fuel use					
Coal (2)	9,015	5,369	7,237r	7,311r	6,857
Fuel oil	13,847	6,412	8,061r	5,447r	5,395
Natural gas	58,793	75,459	73,923r	81,953r	79,786
Renewable fuels (3)	2,238	1,967	2,166r	2,267r	2,479
Other fuels (4)	29,127	28,243	28,348r	26,910r	26,420
Total all fuels	**113,019**	**117,450**	**119,735r**	**123,888r**	**120,937**

(1) The allocation of fuel use between heat generation and electricity generation has been changed to match that used in CHPQA. See paragraphs 6.35 to 6.37 for an explanation of the method used.
(2) includes coke and semi-coke.
(3) Renewable fuels include: sewage gas; other biogases; municipal waste and refuse derived fuels.
(4) Other fuels include: process by-products, coke oven gas, blast furnace gas, gas oil and uranium.

6.3 Fuel used by types of CHP installation

GWh

	1999	2000	2001	2002	2003
Coal					
Back pressure steam turbine	3,940	2,333	2,103	1,923r	1,853
Gas turbine	31	30	34	46	42
Combined cycle	271	347	466r	503r	362
Reciprocating engine	-	-	-	-	-
Pass out condensing steam turbine	4,774	2,659	4,810r	4,839r	4,601
Total coal	**9,015r**	**5,369**	**7,414r**	**7,311**	**6,857**
Fuel oil					
Back pressure steam turbine	2,215	555	551r	452r	487
Gas turbine	503	651	403r	288r	519
Combined cycle	4,798	4,361	5,995r	4,077r	3,967
Reciprocating engine	387	226	175r	221r	197
Pass out condensing steam turbine	5,943	619	937r	409r	225
Total fuel oil	**13,847**	**6,412**	**8,061r**	**5,447r**	**5,395**
Natural gas					
Back pressure steam turbine	7,613	6,116	5,267r	5,212r	4,773
Gas turbine	13,160	16,050	13,025r	13,790r	13,941
Combined cycle	25,229	39,256	43,878r	51,147r	51,320
Reciprocating engine	5,659	7,455	7,436r	8,570r	7,948
Pass out condensing steam turbine	7,132	6,583	4,317r	3,233r	1,803
Total natural gas	**58,793**	**75,459**	**73,923r**	**81,953r**	**79,786**
Renewable fuels (1)					
Back pressure steam turbine	119	8	10	14r	13
Gas turbine	-	-	19	21r	21
Combined cycle	20	20	40r	28r	271
Reciprocating engine	1,633	1,417	1,573r	1,564r	1,434
Pass out condensing steam turbine	466	522	524r	640r	740
Total renewable fuels	**2,238**	**1,966**	**2,166r**	**2,267r**	**2,479**
Other fuels (2)					
Back pressure steam turbine	5,537	4,847	5,811	5,310r	5,280
Gas turbine	2,244	3,185	1,481r	1,577r	1,436
Combined cycle	7,514	6,863	7,409r	7,817r	6,506
Reciprocating engine	77	107	89r	58r	61
Pass out condensing steam turbine	13,754	13,241	13,381r	12,149r	13,139
Total other fuels	**29,127**	**28,243**	**28,171r**	**26,910r**	**26,420**
Total - all fuels					
Back pressure steam turbine	19,425	13,859	13,743r	12,911r	12,406
Gas turbine	15,938	19,916	20,553r	15,722r	15,958
Combined cycle	37,832	50,847	52,165r	63,572r	62,426
Reciprocating engine	7,756	9,205	10,036r	10,413r	9,640
Pass out condensing steam turbine	32,069	23,623	23,208r	21,271r	20,508
Total all fuels	**113,019**	**117,450**	**119,735r**	**123,888r**	**120,937**

(1) Renewable fuels include: sewage gas; other biogases; municipal waste and refuse derived fuels.
(2) Other fuels include: process by-products, coke oven gas, blast furnace gas, gas oil and uranium.

6.4 CHP - electricity generated by fuel and type of installation

GWh

	1999	2000	2001	2002	2003
Coal					
Back pressure steam turbine	278r	192r	151	151	140
Gas turbine	5	6	6	7	7
Combined cycle	44	45	56	46r	49
Reciprocating engine	-	-	-	-	-
Pass out condensing steam turbine	661	396	771	732r	718
Total coal	**987**	**639**	**984**	**937r**	**914**
Fuel oil					
Back pressure steam turbine	181	54	51	51r	54
Gas turbine	81	116	84	60r	91
Combined cycle	625	1,245	902	765r	765
Reciprocating engine	118	69	54	67r	61
Pass out condensing steam turbine	862	109	145	46r	34
Total fuel oil	**1,866**	**1,593**	**1,236**	**989r**	**1,005**
Natural gas					
Back pressure steam turbine	557	515	437r	508r	543
Gas turbine	3,185	4,022	2,936r	2,846r	3,217
Combined cycle	6,765	11,362	10,134r	12,330r	12,328
Reciprocating engine	1,667	2,237	1,991r	2,164r	1,968
Pass out condensing steam turbine	961	987	432r	266r	180
Total natural gas	**13,135**	**19,124**	**15,930r**	**18,114r**	**18,236**
Renewable fuels *(1)*					
Back pressure steam turbine	18	1	1	1	1
Gas turbine	-	-	3	4	4
Combined cycle	5	5	6	2r	18
Reciprocating engine	408	370	365	368r	352
Pass out condensing steam turbine	48	46	57	60r	80
Total renewable fuels	**479**	**422**	**432**	**436**	**455**
Other fuels *(2)*					
Back pressure steam turbine	734	624	661	678r	675
Gas turbine	336	536	293	314r	268
Combined cycle	975r	1,800	1,174r	1,509r	1,280
Reciprocating engine	25	35	28	17	16
Pass out condensing steam turbine	1,719r	1,767	1,705r	1,492r	1,395
Total other fuels	**3,788**	**4,761**	**3,862r**	**4,010**	**3,634**
Total - all fuels					
Back pressure steam turbine	1,768r	1,385	1,301	1,389	1,412
Gas turbine	3,606	4,680	3,323	3,231	3,587
Combined cycle	8,413r	14,457	12,272	14,653	14,440
Reciprocating engine	2,219r	2,711	2,437	2,616	2,397
Pass out condensing steam turbine	4,250r	3,306	3,110	2,597	2,408
Total all fuels	**20,256r**	**26,539**	**22,444**	**24,485**	**24,244**

(1) Renewable fuels include: sewage gas; other biogases; municipal waste and refuse derived fuels.
(2) Other fuels include: process by-products, coke oven gas, blast furnace gas, gas oil and uranium.

6.5 CHP - electrical capacity by fuel and type of installation

MWe

	1999	2000	2001	2002	2003
Coal					
Back pressure steam turbine	82	63	55r	48	40
Gas turbine	1	1	1	1	1
Combined cycle	8	8	11r	11r	10
Reciprocating engine	-	-	-	-	-
Pass out condensing steam turbine	176	93	195	208	203
Total coal	**267**	**165**	**261r**	**268r**	**254**
Fuel oil					
Back pressure steam turbine	42	16	17	14	14
Gas turbine	25	31	27	23r	40
Combined cycle	116	201	251	144r	148
Reciprocating engine	27	20	16	20	19
Pass out condensing steam turbine	185	24	33	13r	9
Total fuel oil	**395**	**291**	**344**	**213r**	**231**
Natural gas					
Back pressure steam turbine	173	145	143r	177r	154
Gas turbine	477	594	521r	533r	555
Combined cycle	1,238	1,785	1,834	2,040r	2,114
Reciprocating engine	336	437	473	514r	514
Pass out condensing steam turbine	177	214	97	79r	60
Total natural gas	**2,401**	**3,175**	**3,068r**	**3,342r**	**3,398**
Renewable fuels (1)					
Back pressure steam turbine	13	-	-	-	-
Gas turbine	-	-	-r	-	1
Combined cycle	1	1	1r	-r	3
Reciprocating engine	92	86	85	84r	83
Pass out condensing steam turbine	18	18	16	18	23
Total renewable fuels	**124**	**105**	**103**	**104r**	**110**
Other fuels (2)					
Back pressure steam turbine	134	111	109	109r	109
Gas turbine	107	129	97	99r	79
Combined cycle	170r	288	292	269	256
Reciprocating engine	8	11	9	4r	5
Pass out condensing steam turbine	306r	456	448r	441r	440
Total other fuels	**726**	**993**	**955r**	**923r**	**887**
Total - all fuels					
Back pressure steam turbine	444	336	323r	347r	316
Gas turbine	609	754	646r	655r	676
Combined cycle	1,533	2,282	2,389r	2,464r	2,531
Reciprocating engine	463	552	584	622r	621
Pass out condensing steam turbine	862	804	790r	759r	735
Total all fuels	**3,912**	**4,729**	**4,732r**	**4,849r**	**4,879**

(1) Renewable fuels include: sewage gas; other biogases; municipal waste and refuse derived fuels.
(2) Other fuels include: process by-products and uranium.

6.6 CHP - heat generated by fuel and type of installation

					GWh
	1999	2000	2001	2002	2003
Coal					
Back pressure steam turbine	2,650	1,493	1,342	1,226r	1,180
Gas turbine	19	17	18	27	31
Combined cycle	191	179	219	174r	149
Reciprocating engine	-	-	-	-	-
Pass out condensing steam turbine	2,765	1,546	2,370	2,451r	2,358
Total coal	**5,625r**	**3,235r**	**3,949**	**3,878r**	**3,718**
Fuel oil					
Back pressure steam turbine	1,485	399	394r	329r	352
Gas turbine	193	274r	231	167r	251
Combined cycle	2,593	2,460r	3,419	2,110r	2,119
Reciprocating engine	119	55r	60r	71r	63
Pass out condensing steam turbine	3,529	376	518	180r	117
Total fuel oil	**7,920**	**3,564r**	**4,622r**	**2,858**	**2,901**
Natural gas					
Back pressure steam turbine	5,322	4,125	3,867r	3,637r	3,278
Gas turbine	5,607	7,154r	6,389r	6,130r	6,747
Combined cycle	11,421r	19,097r	18,904	22,442r	22,404
Reciprocating engine	2,317r	3,072r	3,314r	3,644r	3,545
Pass out condensing steam turbine	5,032r	4,380r	3,032	1,854r	1,337
Total natural gas	**29,699r**	**37,828**	**35,507r**	**37,707r**	**37,310**
Renewable fuels (1)					
Back pressure steam turbine	36	4	5	6r	5
Gas turbine	-	-	9	11	11
Combined cycle	16	16	16	7r	61
Reciprocating engine	634	514	577r	580r	562
Pass out condensing steam turbine	165	253	223	267r	324
Total renewable fuels	**852**	**787**	**830r**	**870r**	**964**
Other fuels (2)					
Back pressure steam turbine	2,840	2,562	3,145	2,943r	2,923
Gas turbine	1,000	1,446	838	871r	687
Combined cycle	4,134	4,358	3,877	3,822r	3,459
Reciprocating engine	24	41	35	27r	29
Pass out condensing steam turbine	8,345	8,300	7,781r	6,924r	7,294
Total other fuels	**16,343**	**16,707**	**15,676r**	**14,588r**	**14,392**
Total - all fuels					
Back pressure steam turbine	12,333	8,582	8,753r	8,142r	7,738
Gas turbine	6,819	8,890	7,487r	7,207r	7,727
Combined cycle	18,356	26,111	26,435	28,556r	28,191
Reciprocating engine	3,094	3,682	3,986r	4,321r	4,198
Pass out condensing steam turbine	19,837	14,856	13,924r	11,677r	11,430
Total all fuels	**60,439**	**62,121**	**60,584**	**59,902**	**59,284**

(1) *Renewable fuels include: sewage gas; other biogases; municipal waste and refuse derived fuels.*
(2) *Other fuels include: process by-products and uranium.*

6.7 CHP - heat capacity by fuel and type of installation

MWth

	1999	2000	2001	2002	2003
Coal					
Back pressure steam turbine	742	446	405	305r	246
Gas turbine	3	3	3	4	3
Combined cycle	25	25	34	28r	24
Reciprocating engine	-	-	-	-	-
Pass out condensing steam turbine	1,326	314	573	606	591
Total coal	**2,096**	**787**	**1,014**	**943r**	**865**
Fuel oil					
Back pressure steam turbine	402	124	128	90r	94
Gas turbine	90	103r	95	87r	164
Combined cycle	389	474r	572	357	369
Reciprocating engine	34	21	20	21r	20
Pass out condensing steam turbine	1,572	70	104	51r	26
Total fuel oil	**2,486**	**791**	**920**	**605r**	**674**
Natural gas					
Back pressure steam turbine	1,266	830	761r	685r	585
Gas turbine	1,140	1,286	1,146r	1,121r	1,134
Combined cycle	2,592	3,315	3,417	3,774r	3,778
Reciprocating engine	570	774	918r	931r	868
Pass out condensing steam turbine	1,270	820	573	400r	253
Total natural gas	**6,838**	**7,025**	**6,815r**	**6,911r**	**6,618**
Renewable fuels (1)					
Back pressure steam turbine	46	1	1	5r	5
Gas turbine	-	-	2	2	2
Combined cycle	2	2	2	1r	9
Reciprocating engine	150	138	139r	136r	136
Pass out condensing steam turbine	57	57	46	62r	73
Total renewable fuels	**255**	**199**	**190**	**206r**	**226**
Other fuels (2)					
Back pressure steam turbine	420	358	357	357r	355
Gas turbine	411	466	384	388r	306
Combined cycle	641	777	787	793r	772
Reciprocating engine	7	11	9	6r	6
Pass out condensing steam turbine	1,645	1,475	1,421r	1,350r	1,347
Total other fuels	**3,124**	**3,086**	**2,959r**	**2,895r**	**2,787**
Total - all fuels					
Back pressure steam turbine	2,876	1,758	1,652r	1,442r	1,286
Gas turbine	1,645	1,858	1,630r	1,602r	1,609
Combined cycle	3,649	4,593	4,812	4,953r	4,953
Reciprocating engine	761	944	1,087r	1,094r	1,030
Pass out condensing steam turbine	5,870	2,736	2,717r	2,469r	2,290
Total all fuels	**14,800**	**11,888**	**11,898r**	**11,560r**	**11,168**

(1) Renewable fuels include: sewage gas; other biogases; municipal waste and refuse derived fuels.
(2) Other fuels include: process by-products and uranium.

6.8 CHP capacity, output and total fuel use[1] by sector

	Unit	1999	2000	2001	2002	2003
Iron and steel and non ferrous metals						
Number of sites		6	6	7	5	5
Electrical capacity	MWe	74	74	80	63	63
Heat capacity	MWth	491	491	497	285r	285
Electrical output	GWh	492	486	493	367r	243
Heat output	GWh	2,361	2,377	2,197	1,325r	1,705
Fuel use	GWh	2,728	2,751	3,251r	1,914r	3,053
of which : for electricity	GWh	826	818	984r	693r	628
for heat	GWh	1,902	1,933	2,267r	1,221r	2,425
Chemicals						
Number of sites		59	55	49r	50r	47
Electrical capacity	MWe	1,243	1,524	1,517r	1,475r	1,445
Heat capacity	MWth	6,340	4,022	3,940r	3,763r	3,606
Electrical output	GWh	6,839	9,675	8,344r	8,016r	7,793
Heat output	GWh	24,213	22,959	21,645r	21,087r	20,199
Fuel use	GWh	42,041	45,838	43,839r	44,435r	41,150
of which : for electricity	GWh	14,897	20,390	19,048r	18,985r	17,844
for heat	GWh	27,144	25,448	24,792r	25,450r	23,305
Oil refineries						
Number of sites		13	10	10	9	8
Electrical capacity	MWe	870	986	984	954	950
Heat capacity	MWth	3,648	2,995	3,098	3,066	3,058
Electrical output	GWh	4,017	5,710	4,214	5,222r	4,968
Heat output	GWh	15,699	14,667	14,823	14,676r	14,406
Fuel use	GWh	29,495	25,249	27,472r	28,396r	26,826
of which : for electricity	GWh	9,845	11,676	10,119r	11,993r	10,857
for heat	GWh	19,649	13,574	17,352r	16,403r	15,969
Paper, publishing and printing						
Number of sites		37	36	35	37r	36
Electrical capacity	MWe	472	559	529	596r	690
Heat capacity	MWth	1,422	1,331	1,316	1,390r	1,340
Electrical output	GWh	3,023	3,827	3,413	3,661r	3,822
Heat output	GWh	7,166	9,065	8,852	8,593r	8,542
Fuel use	GWh	14,082	16,718	16,611r	16,710r	16,758
of which : for electricity	GWh	6,239	7,526	7,145r	7,603r	7,906
for heat	GWh	7,842	9,192	9,466r	9,107r	8,852
Food, beverages and tobacco						
Number of sites		46	47	45r	45	42
Electrical capacity	MWe	400	405	393r	404r	379
Heat capacity	MWth	1,349	1,166	1,121	1,108r	979
Electrical output	GWh	2,201	2,113	1,674r	1,953r	1,963
Heat output	GWh	5,143	5,536	5,101r	5,768r	5,665
Fuel use	GWh	10,523	10,089	8,706	9,990r	9,737
of which : for electricity	GWh	4,652	4,316	3,402r	3,984r	3,932
for heat	GWh	5,872	5,772	5,304r	6,005r	5,805
Metal products, machinery and equipment						
Number of sites		9	15	16	14r	15
Electrical capacity	MWe	31	86	82r	78	101
Heat capacity	MWth	60	90	91	66r	82
Electrical output	GWh	153	523	182	202r	339
Heat output	GWh	179	302	388	344r	400
Fuel use	GWh	520	1,446	821	800r	1,076
of which : for electricity	GWh	328	1,132	391r	430r	661
for heat	GWh	192	313	430r	370r	415

For footnotes see page 160

6.8 CHP capacity, output and total fuel use[1] by sector

	Unit	1999	2000	2001	2002	2003
Mineral products, extraction, mining and agglomeration of solid fuels						
Number of sites		6	10	10	10	10
Electrical capacity	MWe	24	56	56	54r	57
Heat capacity	MWth	100	180	180	180	180
Electrical output	GWh	149	313	242	225	225
Heat output	GWh	573	913	848	819	793
Fuel use	GWh	989	1,592	1,474r	1,443r	1,397
of which : for electricity	GWh	339	666	536r	514r	525
for heat	GWh	649	927	938r	929r	872
Sewage treatment						
Number of sites		112	113	113	113	112
Electrical capacity	MWe	107	102	102	101	101
Heat capacity	MWth	172	160	162	159r	158
Electrical output	GWh	463	428	424	429r	414
Heat output	GWh	711	586	654	659r	643
Fuel use	GWh	1,840	1,624	1,782	1,776r	1,653
of which : for electricity	GWh	1,043	931	997	992r	921
for heat	GWh	797	692	786	784r	731
Electricity supply						
Number of sites		6	6	6	7r	7
Electrical capacity	MWe	243	437	470	555r	527
Heat capacity	MWth	321	370	370	462r	462
Electrical output	GWh	774	874	1,157	2,025r	2,021
Heat output	GWh	1,077	1,500	1,837	2,408r	2,332
Fuel use	GWh	2,297	2,624	6,173r	7,969r	8,524
of which : for electricity	GWh	1,316	1,397	3,577r	4,995r	5,389
for heat	GWh	981	1,228	2,596r	2,974r	3,135
Other industrial branches (2)						
Number of sites		15	17	16	15	14
Electrical capacity	MWe	41	58	57	56	51
Heat capacity	MWth	148	206	181	161	109
Electrical output	GWh	229	348	333	333r	308
Heat output	GWh	402	528	699	649r	531
Fuel use	GWh	1,038	1,135	1,419	1,448r	1,132
of which : for electricity	GWh	542	600	680	728r	608
for heat	GWh	495	534	739	720r	524
Total industry						
Number of sites		309	315	307r	305r	296
Electrical capacity	MWe	3,504	4,288	4,269r	4,336r	4,364
Heat capacity	MWth	14,051	11,011	10,954r	10,640r	10,258
Electrical output	GWh	18,338	24,295	20,474r	22,433r	22,096
Heat output	GWh	57,524	58,432	57,042r	56,326r	55,216
Fuel use	GWh	105,552	109,065	111,548r	114,880r	111,305
of which : for electricity	GWh	40,029	49,452	46,877r	50,916r	49,271
for heat	GWh	65,524	59,612	64,671r	63,964r	62,034

6.8 CHP capacity, output and total fuel use[1] by sector (continued)

	Unit	1999	2000	2001	2002	2003
Transport, commerce and administration						
Number of sites		993	1,110	1,148r	1,141	1,117
Electrical capacity	MWe	250	268	293r	294r	292
Heat capacity	MWth	450	586	657r	556r	547
Electrical output	GWh	1,226	1,347	1,337r	1,295r	1,306
Heat output	GWh	1,798	2,219	2,388r	2,337r	2,396
Fuel use	GWh	4,465	4,870	5,289r	5,310r	5,182
of which : for electricity	GWh	2,602	2,645	2,798r	2,784r	2,689
for heat	GWh	1,864	2,225	2,491r	2,527r	2,493
Other (3)						
Number of sites		81	97	97r	95	93
Electrical capacity	MWe	159	174	170r	219r	224
Heat capacity	MWth	299	292	287r	364r	363
Electrical output	GWh	692	897	633r	756r	843
Heat output	GWh	1,118	1,470	1,156r	1,239r	1,673
Fuel use	GWh	3,001	3,515	2,898	3,698r	4,451
of which : for electricity	GWh	1,635	1,811	1,431r	1,906r	2,150
for heat	GWh	1,366	1,705	1,467r	1,792r	2,301
Total CHP usage by all sectors						
Number of sites		1,383	1,522	1,552r	1,541r	1,506
Electrical capacity	MWe	3,912	4,730	4,732r	4,849r	4,879
Heat capacity	MWth	14,801	11,888	11,898r	11,560r	11,168
Electrical output	GWh	20,256	26,539	22,445r	24,485r	24,244
Heat output	GWh	60,439	62,121	60,586r	59,902r	59,285
Fuel use	GWh	113,019	117,450	119,735r	123,888r	120,937
of which : for electricity	GWh	44,266	53,908	51,106r	55,606r	54,110
for heat	GWh	68,753	63,542	68,629r	68,282r	66,828

(1) The allocation of fuel use between electricity and heat is largely notional and the methodology is outlined in paragraphs 6.35 to 6.37.

(2) Other industry includes Textiles, clothing and footwear sector.

(3) Sectors included under Other are agriculture, community heating, leisure, landfill and incineration.

6.9 CHP - use of fuels by sector

GWh

	1999	2000	2001	2002	2003
Iron and steel and non ferrous metals					
Coal	89	97	97	-	-
Fuel oil	153	160	179r	49r	45
Natural gas	413	422	513r	247r	185
Blast furnace gas	1,643	1,643	1,971r	1,256r	2,401
Coke oven gas	406	405	445r	363r	422
Other fuels (2)	24	24	46r	-	-
Total iron and steel and non ferrous metals	**2,728**	**2,751**	**3,251r**	**1,914r**	**3,053**
Chemicals					
Coal	4,821	2,416	4,479	4,473r	4,479
Fuel oil	3,951	868	1,182r	526r	350
Gas oil	78	80	98	74r	34
Natural gas	21,689	31,116	27,584r	28,862r	25,915
Refinery gas	347	393	66r	28r	-
Renewable fuels (1)	-	-	19	21	21
Other fuels (2)	11,156	10,965	10,412r	10,451r	10,350
Total chemical industry	**42,041**	**45,838**	**43,839r**	**44,435r**	**41,150**
Oil refineries					
Fuel oil	8,404	4,596	5,946	4,136	4,309
Gas oil	266	266	134	134	134
Natural gas	6,319	7,050	7,794r	10,248r	10,103
Refinery gas	9,128	7,961	7,526	8,152r	7,345
Other fuels (2)	5,377	5,377	6,072	5,727r	4,934
Total oil refineries	**29,495**	**25,249**	**27,472r**	**28,396r**	**26,826**
Paper, publishing and printing					
Coal	1,777	731	797r	713r	388
Fuel oil	474	366	361	313	268
Gas oil	79	21	43	43r	22
Natural gas	11,749	15,441	15,217r	15,450r	15,933
Renewable fuels (1)	2	2	4	3r	2
Other fuels	-	157	188	188	145
Total paper, publishing and printing	**14,082**	**16,718**	**16,611r**	**16,710r**	**16,758**
Food, beverages and tobacco					
Coal	1,806	1,521	1,292	1,241r	1,179
Fuel oil	465	194	184	188r	214
Gas oil	45	56	66	11r	19
Natural gas	8,205	8,316	7,164r	8,550r	8,316
Renewable fuels (1)	2	2	-r	-r	-
Other fuels (2)	-	-	-	-	8
Total food, beverages and tobacco	**10,523**	**10,088**	**8,706**	**9,990r**	**9,737**
Metal products, machinery and equipment					
Coal	20	32	32	-	-
Fuel oil	106	107	51r	92	91
Gas oil	1	-	-	-	-
Natural gas	395	1,306	737r	708r	985
Total metal products, machinery and equipment	**520**	**1,446**	**821**	**800r**	**1,076**
Mineral products, extraction, mining and agglomeration of solid fuels					
Coal	-	69	176r	245r	209
Fuel oil	-	-	-	-	2
Natural gas	769	1,373	1,148r	1,048r	1,036
Coke oven gas	219	150	150	150	150
Total mineral products, extraction, mining and agglomeration of solid fuels	**989**	**1,592**	**1,474r**	**1,443r**	**1,397**

For footnotes see page 162

6.9 CHP - use of fuels by sector (cont'd)

GWh

	1999	2000	2001	2002	2003
Sewage treatment					
Fuel oil	116	71	71	71	61
Gas oil	-	30	30	30	30
Natural gas	116	114	114	114	130
Renewable fuels *(1)*	1,608	1,408	1,567	1,561r	1,432
Total sewage treatment	**1,840**	**1,624**	**1,782**	**1,776r**	**1,653**
Electricity supply					
Coal	178	178	178	216	288
Fuel oil	-	-	3	3r	3
Natural gas	1,860	1,857	5,213r	7,576r	7,893
Other fuels *(2)*	260	590	780r	174r	339
Total electricity supply	**2,297**	**2,625**	**6,173r**	**7,969r**	**8,524**
Other industrial branches *(3)*					
Fuel oil	2	2	2	-	-
Gas oil	2	3	1	-r	-
Natural gas	1,029	1,125	1,411	1,442r	1,126
Renewable fuels *(1)*	6	6	5r	5r	5
Total other industrial branches	**1,038**	**1,135**	**1,419**	**1,448r**	**1,132**
Transport, commerce and administration					
Coal	30	30	34	46	42
Fuel oil	158	32	67r	64r	50
Gas oil	44	74	65r	18r	20
Natural gas	4,223	4,727	5,116r	5,179r	5,068
Refinery gas	1	1	1	1	-
Renewable fuels *(1)*	5	5	5	2	2
Other fuels *(2)*	5	1	1r	1r	1
Total transport, commerce and administration	**4,465**	**4,870**	**5,289r**	**5,310r**	**5,182**
Other *(4)*					
Coal	294	294	329r	377r	273
Fuel oil	18	18	14	6r	-
Gas oil	44	44	22r	17r	15
Natural gas	2,027	2,613	1,913r	2,531r	3,095
Renewable fuels *(1)*	615	543	566r	675r	1,017
Other fuels *(2)*	3	3	54r	92r	51
Total other	**3,001**	**3,515**	**2,898**	**3,698r**	**4,451**
Total - all sectors					
Coal	9,015	5,369	7,414r	7,311r	6,857
Fuel oil	13,847	6,412	8,061r	5,447r	5,395
Gas oil	559	573	458r	327r	275
Natural gas	58,793	75,459	73,923r	81,953r	79,786
Blast furnace gas	1,643	1,643	1,971r	1,256r	2,401
Coke oven gas	625	555	595r	513r	572
Refinery gas	9,476	8,355	7,594r	8,182r	7,345
Renewable fuels *(1)*	2,238	1,967	2,166r	2,267r	2,479
Other fuels *(2)*	16,825	17,117	17,553r	16,633r	15,827
Total CHP fuel use	**113,019**	**117,450**	**119,735r**	**123,888r**	**120,937**

(1) Renewable fuels include: sewage gas; other biogases; clinical waste; municipal waste.

(2) Other fuels include: process by-products and uranium.

(3) Other industry now includes textiles, clothing and footwear which was shown as a separate sector in previous Digests.

(4) Sectors included under Other are agriculture, community heating, leisure, landfill and incineration.

Chapter 7
Renewable sources of energy

Introduction

7.1   This chapter provides information on the contribution of renewable energy sources to the United Kingdom's energy requirements. It includes sources that under international definitions are not counted as renewable sources or are counted only in part. This is to ensure that this Digest covers all sources of energy available in the United Kingdom. In previous years wastes have been added in with renewables. However, from this year the international definition of total renewables has been adopted and this excludes non-biodegradable wastes. Wastes are still shown in the tables of this chapter but as "below the line" items. This chapter covers both the use of renewables to generate electricity and the burning of renewable fuels to produce heat either in boilers (or cookers) or in combined heat and power plants.

7.2   The data summarise the results of an ongoing study undertaken by the Future Energy Solutions (FES - part of AEA Technology (AEAT) Environment), on behalf of the Department of Trade and Industry, to update a database containing information on all relevant renewable energy sources in the United Kingdom. This database is called RESTATS, the Renewable Energy STATisticS database.

7.3   The study started in 1989, when all relevant renewable energy sources were identified and, where possible, information was collected on the amounts of energy derived from each source. The renewable energy sources identified were the following: active solar heating; photovoltaics; onshore and offshore wind power; wave power; large and small scale hydro; biofuels; geothermal aquifers. The technical notes at the end of this chapter define each of these renewable energy sources. The database now contains 15 years of data from 1989 to 2003.

7.4   The information contained in the database is collected by a number of methods. For larger projects, an annual survey is carried out in which questionnaires are sent to project managers. For technologies in which there are large numbers of small projects, the values given in this chapter are estimates based on information collected from a sub-sample of the projects. Further details about the data collection methodologies used in RESTATS, including the quality and completeness of the information, are given in the technical notes at the end of this chapter.

7.5   Commodity balances for renewable energy sources covering each of the last three years form the first three tables (Tables 7.1 to 7.3). These are followed by the 5-year table showing capacity of and electricity generation from renewable sources (Table 7.4), and a table summarising all the renewable orders (Table 7.5). Table 7.6 shows renewable sources used to generate electricity and heat in each of the last five years. A long-term trends commentary and table (Table 7.1.1) covering the use of renewables to generate electricity and heat is available on DTI's energy statistics web site: www.dti.gov.uk/energy/inform/dukes/dukes2004/07longterm.pdf .

7.6   Unlike in the commodity balance tables in other chapters of the Digest, Tables 7.1 to 7.3 have zero statistical differences. This is because the data for each category of fuel are, in the main, taken from a single source where there is less likelihood of differences due to timing or measurement.

Renewables Obligation and Renewables Directive

7.7   In April 2002 the Renewables Obligation (RO) (and the analogous Renewables (Scotland) Obligation) came into effect[1]. It is an obligation on all electricity suppliers to supply a specific proportion of electricity from eligible renewable sources. Eligible sources include all those covered by this chapter but with specific exclusions. These are: existing hydro plant of over 20 MW; all plant using renewable sources built before 1990 (unless re-furbished and less than 20 MW); and energy from mixed waste combustion unless the waste is first converted to fuel using advanced conversion technology. Only the biodegradable fraction of any waste is eligible (in line with the EU Directive, see paragraph 7.8, below). All stations outside the United Kingdom (the UK includes its territorial waters

---

[1] Parliamentary approval of the Renewables Obligation Orders under The Utilities Act 2000 was given in March 2002.

and the continental shelf) are also excluded. In Table 7.4 a row gives total electricity generation on an RO basis. Strictly speaking the RO covers only Great Britain, but in these UK based statistics Northern Ireland renewable sources have been treated as if they were also part of the RO.

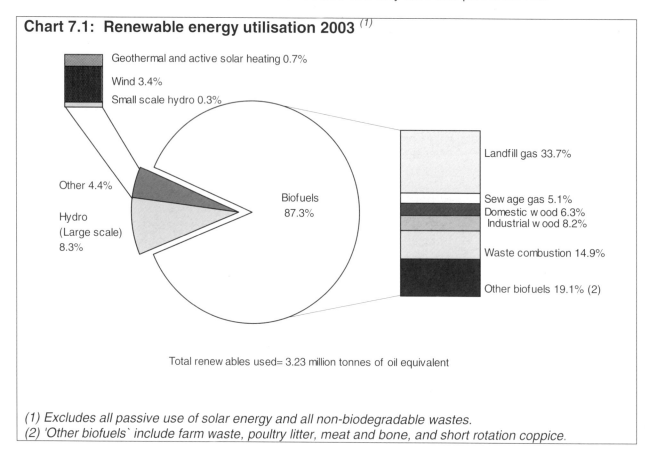

Chart 7.1: Renewable energy utilisation 2003 [1]

Geothermal and active solar heating 0.7%
Wind 3.4%
Small scale hydro 0.3%

Other 4.4%

Hydro
(Large scale)
8.3%

Biofuels
87.3%

Landfill gas 33.7%

Sewage gas 5.1%
Domestic wood 6.3%
Industrial wood 8.2%

Waste combustion 14.9%

Other biofuels 19.1% (2)

Total renewables used= 3.23 million tonnes of oil equivalent

(1) Excludes all passive use of solar energy and all non-biodegradable wastes.
(2) 'Other biofuels' include farm waste, poultry litter, meat and bone, and short rotation coppice.

7.8 The European Union's Renewables Directive (RD) (which came into force in October 2001) has a different definition of eligible renewables. The Directive's definition includes all those sources covered by this chapter except non-biodegradable wastes. FES has estimated the percentage of MSW that was non-biodegradable for all the years in the RESTATS database. For 2003 the estimate is that 37½ per cent of MSW was non-biodegradable and all of waste tyres (but see paragraph 7.65) and hospital waste. In Table 7.4 a further row gives total electricity generation on an RD basis.

7.9 In the past the main instruments for pursuing the development of renewables capacity were the Non Fossil Fuel Obligation (NFFO) Orders for England and Wales and for Northern Ireland, and the Scottish Renewable Orders (SRO). In this chapter the term "NFFO Orders" is used to refer to these instruments collectively. For projects contracted under NFFO Orders in England and Wales, details of capacity and generation were provided by the Non Fossil Purchasing Agency (NFPA). The Scottish Executive and Northern Ireland Electricity provided information on the Scottish and Northern Ireland NFFO Orders, respectively.

Renewables Targets

7.10 Thus since February 2000, the United Kingdom's renewables policy has consisted of four key strands:

- a new Renewables Obligation on all electricity suppliers in Great Britain to supply a specific proportion of electricity from eligible renewables;
- exemption of electricity from renewables[2] from the Climate Change Levy;
- an expanded support programme for new and renewable energy including capital grants and an expanded research and development programme;
- development of a regional strategic approach to planning and targets for renewables.

---

[2] *Electricity generated by hydro stations with a declared net capacity of more than 10 MW is not exempt from the Climate Change Levy.*

The aim of the Renewables Obligation (RO) is to increase the contribution of electricity from renewables in the UK so that by 2010, 10 per cent of licensed UK electricity sales should be from renewable sources eligible for the RO, and by 2015 15 per cent should be eligible.

7.11   The EU Directive proposes that Member States adopt national targets for renewables that are consistent with reaching the overall EU target of 12 per cent of energy (22.1 per cent of electricity) from renewables by 2010. The proposed UK "share" of this target is that renewables sources eligible under the RD should account for 10 per cent of UK electricity **consumption** by 2010. Thus any imported electricity certified as coming from eligible renewable sources would count towards the RD target, but any electricity generated in the UK from eligible renewable sources but exported to another country would not. The Office of Gas and Electricity Markets (OFGEM) have advised that in 2003 2,785 GWh of imported electricity were certified as Climate Change Levy exempt and therefore count as eligible renewables.

7.12   Chart 7.2 shows the growth in all sources of renewables generation since 1990 and Table 7A gives renewables shares on three different bases for the three most recent years. They show progress towards the RO and RD 10 per cent targets[3]. In 2003 the RO percentage showed continued growth. The percentage of UK electricity sales that were of electricity generated from sources eligible for the RO rose from 1.51 per cent in 2001 to 1.79 per cent in 2002 and 2.21 per cent in 2003. However, on the basis favoured by the Renewables Directive, the percentage of UK electricity consumption accounted for by RD eligible renewable sources rose from 2.85 per cent in 2001 to 3.22 per cent in 2002 and 3.35 per cent in 2003. The main reason for the large increase in the RD percentage in 2001 was the inclusion of imports of renewable sourced electricity over the interconnector with France (mainly hydro). In 2002 the further substantial increase was as a result of a consumption of electricity in the UK growing only marginally, while renewable sources increased more strongly. Generation from all renewables in the UK (on the international definition basis) accounted for 2.67 per cent of UK electricity generation in 2003 (see paragraph 7.16, below). By moving to the international definition and excluding non-biodegradable wastes the overall percentages for each of the three latest years are 0.15 per cent lower on average than on the previously published basis.

Table 7A: Percentages of electricity derived from renewable sources

	2001	2002	2003
Overall renewables percentage (revised to the international basis)	2.47	2.86	2.67
Percentage on a Renewables Obligation basis	1.51	1.79	2.21
Percentage on a Renewables Directive basis	2.85	3.22	3.35

Commodity balances for renewables in 2003 (Table 7.1), 2002 (Table 7.2) and 2001 (Table 7.3)

7.13   Nine different categories of renewable fuels are identified in the commodity balances. Some of these categories are themselves groups of renewables because a more detailed disaggregation could disclose data for individual companies. In the commodity balance tables the distinction between biodegradable and non-biodegradable wastes cannot be maintained for this reason. The largest contribution to renewables in input terms (over 87 per cent) is from biofuels, with large-scale hydro electricity production contributing the majority of the remainder as Chart 7.1 shows. Only 4½ per cent of renewable energy comes from renewable sources other than biofuels and large-scale hydro. These include solar, wind, small-scale hydro and geothermal aquifers.

7.14   79 per cent of the renewable energy produced in 2003 was transformed into electricity. This is an increase from 78 per cent in 2002 and 76 per cent in 2001. While biofuels appear to dominate the picture when fuel inputs are being measured, hydro electricity dominates when the output of electricity is being measured as Table 7.4 shows. This is because on an energy supplied basis (see Chapter 5, paragraph 5.25) hydro (and also wind and wave) inputs are assumed to be equal to the electricity produced. For landfill gas, sewage sludge, municipal solid waste and other renewables a substantial proportion of the energy content of the input is lost in the process of conversion to electricity.

---

[3] The RO target is actually 10.4 per cent of sales in the financial year 2010/11

7.15   Overall, renewable sources, excluding passive uses of solar energy, provided 1.4 per cent of the United Kingdom's total primary energy requirements in 2003. This was 0.1 percentage points higher than in 2002, which in turn was 0.2 percentage points higher than in 2001.

Capacity of, and electricity generated from renewable sources (Table 7.4)

7.16   Table 7.4 shows the capacity of, and the amounts of electricity generated from, each renewable source. Total electricity generation from renewables in 2003 amounted to 10,649 GWh, a reduction of 4 per cent on 2002. The main cause of this fall was a 33 per cent decline in output from hydro schemes caused by low rainfall and snowfall during winter 2002/3 and the summer of 2003. Only 30 per cent of generation from renewables was from hydro in 2003 compared with 43 per cent in 2003. As a result all renewable sources provided 2.67 per cent of the electricity generated in the United Kingdom in 2003, 0.19 percentage points lower than in 2002.

7.17   Electricity generated in the UK from renewable sources eligible under the Renewables Obligation in 2003 was 26 per cent greater than in 2002. This compares with growth of 18 per cent in each of the two previous years. Chart 7.2 shows the growth in the proportion of electricity produced from renewable sources. It includes the progress towards the renewables targets set under the Renewables Obligation and Renewables Directive (see paragraphs 7.10 to 7.12 above).

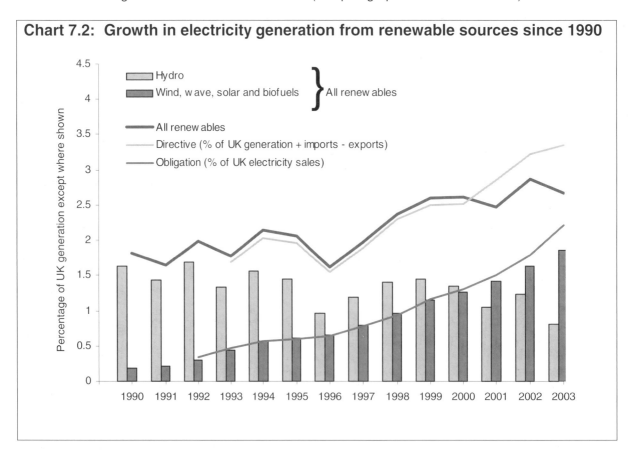

Chart 7.2: Growth in electricity generation from renewable sources since 1990

7.18   There was a 12½ per cent increase in the installed generating capacity of renewable sources in 2003, mainly as a result of a 39 per cent increase in wind capacity and a 31 per increase in the capacity fuelled by landfill gas. Large-scale hydro capacity is 3 per cent lower than it was in 2001 as some stations have been adapted to fall within the capacity limits specified by the renewables obligation. The capacity to generate from solar voltaics showed a 46 per cent increase for the second successive year.

7.19   The renewables technology that showed the biggest growth in electricity output during 2003 was the co-firing of biomass with fossil fuels (see paragraphs 7.70 and 7.71, below) with an increase of over 100 per cent. Next largest was offshore wind (also over 100 per cent) but this was from a very low base. Next highest growth was from landfill gas generation at 22½ per cent. Generation from hydro stations was 33 per cent lower for the reasons given in paragraph 7.16, above, but generation from sewage sludge digestion was also 6½ per cent lower because six sites (some quite large) that were producing in 2002 were not producing in 2003. Of these four were mothballed, one was closed and one burned natural gas in 2003.

Chart 7.3: Electrical generating capacity of renewable energy plant (excluding large-scale hydro)[1]

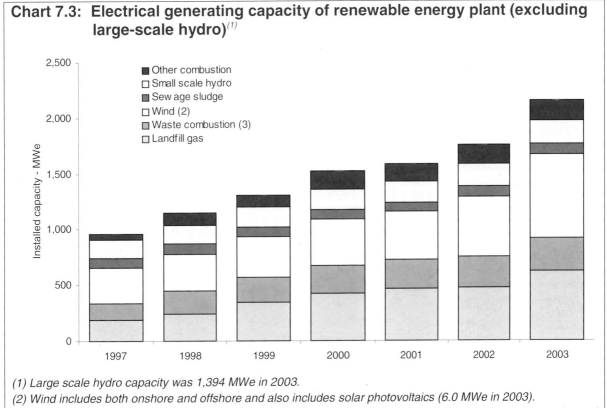

(1) Large scale hydro capacity was 1,394 MWe in 2003.
(2) Wind includes both onshore and offshore and also includes solar photovoltaics (6.0 MWe in 2003).
(3) All waste combustion plant is included because both biodegradable and non-biodegradable wastes are burned together in the same plant.

7.20　Chart 7.3 (which covers all renewables capacity except large scale hydro) illustrates the continuing increase in the electricity generation capacity from all significant renewable sources. This upward trend in the capacity of renewable sources will continue as further projects already contracted under NFFO Orders come on line and recently consented offshore windfarms and other projects come on stream.

7.21　In 2003, 55½ per cent of electricity from renewables (excluding large-scale hydro) was generated under NFFO contracts. If ex-NFFO sites (NFFO 1 and 2 in England and Wales – see paragraphs 7.23 to 7.35, below) are included the proportion increases to 72 per cent. Table 7.4, however, includes both electricity generated outside of these contracts and electricity from large-scale hydro schemes and thus reports on total electricity generation from renewables. All electricity generated from renewables is also reported within the tables of Chapter 5 of this Digest (eg Table 5.6).

7.22　Plant load factors in Table 7.4 have been calculated in terms of installed capacity and express the average hourly quantity of electricity generated as a percentage of the average capacity at the beginning and end of the year. The overall figure is heavily influenced by the availability of hydro capacity during the year, which is in turn influenced by the amount of rainfall during the preceding period. Low rainfall in the winter of 2002/2003 led to 2003 having lower hydro load factors than in the previous very dry year of 1996. Two factors have contributed to the lower load factor for wind in 2003. Firstly 110 MWe was installed late in the year and had little opportunity to contribute to generation. Secondly it is likely that the long hot summer of 2003 was not as windy as previous years but meteorological data are not yet available to substantiate this. Plant load factors for all generating plant in the UK are shown in Chapter 5, Table 5.10.

Renewable orders and operational capacity (Table 7.5)

7.23   In 1990, the first year of NFFO, projects contracted within NFFO accounted for about 34 per cent of the total capacity (excluding large-scale hydro); by 1998, this figure had risen to 86 per cent, but dropped to 50 per cent in 1999 due to the expiry of NFFO I and 2 contracts. However, in 2001 new NFFO capacity raised the proportion back to 61½ per cent with a further increase to 62½ per cent in 2002. In 2003, the NFFO capacity proportion decreased to 54½ per cent as many more new schemes and former NFFO 1 and 2 schemes applied for ROCs. 22 NFFO schemes totalling 52 MW (DNC) had begun to operate during 2003 as shown in Chart 7.4.

(a)   Non Fossil Fuel Obligation (NFFO)

7.24   The 1989 Electricity Act empowered the Secretary of State to make orders requiring the Regional Electricity Companies in England and Wales (the RECs) to secure specified amounts of electricity from renewable energy sources.

7.25   Five NFFO Orders were made, of which the first in 1990 was set for a total of 102 MW DNC. This first order resulted in contracts for 75 projects for 152 MW DNC and provided a premium price for the electricity produced which was funded from a levy on electricity sales in England and Wales. (The bulk of this levy was used to support electricity from nuclear stations.)

7.26   The second Order, made in late 1991, was set for 457 MW DNC. This resulted in 122 separate contracts   (for a total of 472 MW DNC) between the generators and the Non-Fossil Purchasing Agency (NFPA) which acted on behalf of the RECs. For landfill gas, sewage gas and waste-derived generation contracts were awarded at around 6p/kWh, while for wind-based generation a price of 11p/kWh was established. These prices reflected the limited period for the recovery of capital costs.

7.27   The third Order covers the period 1995 to 2014; this was for 627 MW DNC of contracted capacity at an average price of 4.35 p/kWh. The lower bid prices reflect the longer-term contracts, which are now available together with further developments which have led to improvements in the technologies. Taking into account factors such as the failure to gain planning permission it is estimated that about 300-400 MW DNC are likely to go forward for commissioning.

7.28   The fourth Order was announced in February 1997. Contracts have been let to 195 projects with a total DNC of 843 MW, at an average price of 3.46 p/kWh. In the fifth and largest Order, which was announced in September 1998, contracts have been let to 261 projects with a total DNC of 1,177.1 MW, at an average price of 2.71 p/kWh.

7.29   Since the expiry of the NFFO 1 and 2 contracts on 31 December 1998, these projects are no longer included in the monitoring of NFFO Orders and DTI no longer receive any status/output data on them from the NFPA. For some of these projects operational data have been obtained from other sources, while for the others estimates have been made based on output in 1998. For 2002 another source of information became available to us in the form of the Renewables Obligation data. This enabled Future Energy Solutions to identify which former NFFO 1 and 2 schemes were applying for ROCs and therefore were still running. Of the 82 NFFO 1 and 2 projects identified in this way as still live, 26 were contracted under the first order and 56 under the second order. It is appreciated that there may be some ex NFFO 1 and 2 schemes that are continuing to operate but whose output is too small to qualify for ROCs or which may need to re-furbish in order to qualify for ROCs. To that extent the estimates of NFFO capacity may be an underestimate.

7.30   As at the end of December 2003, 82 projects in the third Order were operational, with total capacities of 305 MW DNC. There were 80 schemes with a capacity of 200 MW DNC commissioned from the fourth Order projects and 76 schemes totalling 143 MW DNC from the fifth Order. Table 7.5 sets out the technologies and capacities of schemes in all five Orders.

(b)   Scottish Renewable Order (SRO)

7.31   In Scotland, the first Renewables Order was made in 1994 for approximately 76 MW DNC of new capacity and comprising 30 schemes. Four generation technology bands were covered; 12 wind, 15 hydro, two waste-to-energy and one biomass. At the end of December 2003, 19 schemes were commissioned with a capacity of 48 MW DNC.

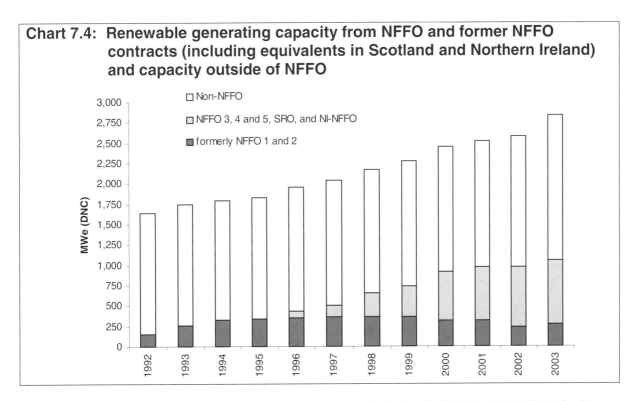

Chart 7.4: Renewable generating capacity from NFFO and former NFFO contracts (including equivalents in Scotland and Northern Ireland) and capacity outside of NFFO

Legend: □ Non-NFFO; □ NFFO 3, 4 and 5, SRO, and NI-NFFO; ■ formerly NFFO 1 and 2

7.32   A second SRO was launched in 1995 and was made in March 1997 for 114 MW DNC of new capacity comprising 26 schemes, 9 of which were waste to energy projects, 9 were hydro projects, 7 were wind projects and one was a biomass project. Under this Order, at the end of 2003 there were 13 commissioned schemes with a capacity of 50 MW DNC.

7.33   A third SRO was laid before Parliament in February 1999 for 145 MW DNC of new capacity comprising 53 schemes. Sixteen of these were waste to energy projects, 5 were hydro projects, 28 were wind projects, one was a biomass project and 3 were wave energy projects. Under this Order, at the end of 2003 there were 14 commissioned schemes with a capacity of 29 MW DNC. Table 7.5 sets out the technologies and capacities of schemes in all three Scottish Orders.

(c)   Northern Ireland Non Fossil Fuel Obligation (NI NFFO)

7.34   In Northern Ireland, a first Order was made in March 1994 for approximately 16 MW DNC comprising 20 schemes. The contracted schemes were spread throughout Northern Ireland and were divided into three technology bands. There were 6 wind schemes of around 2 MW DNC each, totalling 12.7 MW DNC; 5 sewage gas projects totalling 0.56 MW DNC; and 9 small-scale hydro schemes totalling 2.4 MW DNC. At the end of 2003, 14 schemes were commissioned with a capacity of 15 MW DNC.

7.35   A second NI Order was made in 1996 for 10 schemes, totalling 16 MW DNC. These comprised two wind schemes, two hydro schemes, two biomass, one biogas, two landfill gas and one municipal and industrial waste scheme, as shown in Table 7.5. At the end of 2003, 5 schemes were commissioned with a capacity of 3 MW DNC.

Renewable sources used to generate electricity and heat (Table 7.6)

7.36   Between 2002 and 2003 there was an increase of 11 per cent in the input of renewable sources into electricity generation. Biofuels grew by 22 per cent, and wind by 2½ per cent, but hydro use fell by a third because of the dry weather.

7.37   Compared with 5 years earlier total inputs to electricity generation have grown by 80 per cent aided by 139 per cent growth in the use of biofuels and a 47 per cent increase in the use of wind.

7.38   Table 7.6 also shows the contribution from renewables to heat generation. Here only a small share comes from geothermal and active solar heating and from various wastes, while the main contribution is from burning wood. However the use of active solar heating and of heating from biodegradable wastes have both doubled in the last five years.

Technical notes and definitions

7.39   Energy derived from renewable sources is included in the aggregate energy tables in Chapter 1 of this Digest. The main energy tables (Tables 7.1 to 7.3) present figures in the common unit of energy, the tonne of oil equivalent, which is defined in Chapter 1 paragraph 1.24. The gross calorific values and conversion factors used to convert the data from original units are given on page 205 of Annex A and inside the back cover flap. The statistical methodologies and conversion factors are in line with those used by the International Energy Agency and the Statistical Office of the European Communities. Primary electricity contributions from hydro and wind are expressed in terms of an electricity supplied model (see Chapter 5, paragraph 5.25). Electrical capacities in this chapter are now quoted as Installed capacities. However, in Chapter 5 Declared Net Capacity (DNC) of renewables is used when calculating the overall UK generating capacity. DNC takes into account the intermittent nature of the power output from some renewable sources (see paragraph 7.74, below).

7.40   The various renewable energy sources are described in the following paragraphs. This section also provides details of the quality of information provided within each renewables area, and the progress made to improve the quality of this information.

Use of existing solar energy
7.41   Nearly all buildings make use of some passive solar energy because they have windows or roof lights, which allow in natural light and provide a view of the surroundings. This existing use of passive solar energy is making a substantial contribution to the energy demand in the UK building stock. Passive solar design, in which buildings are designed to enhance solar energy use, results in additional savings in energy. A study in 1990, on behalf of the Department of Trade and Industry, estimated that this existing use saves 12.6 million tonnes of oil equivalent per year in the United Kingdom. This figure reflects an estimate of the net useful energy flow (heat and lighting) across windows and other glazing in the United Kingdom building stock. The figure is very approximate and, as in previous years, has therefore not been included in the tables in this chapter.

Active solar heating
7.42 Active solar heating employs solar collectors to heat water mainly for domestic hot water systems but also for swimming pools and other applications. Updated figures have been obtained by FES (on behalf of the Department of Trade and Industry). For 2003 an estimated 63.4 GWh for domestic hot water generation replaces gas heating; for swimming pools, an estimated 102.0 GWh generation for 2003 replaces gas (45 per cent), oil (45 per cent) or electricity (10 per cent).

Photovoltaics
7.43   Photovoltaics is the direct conversion of solar radiation into direct current electricity by the interaction of light with the electrons in a semiconductor device or cell. There has been a significant increase in capacity and generation of PV over the last year due to increased support from the Government. There is a Major Photovoltaic Demonstration Programme offering grants for small, medium and large-scale installations, which is encouraging a significant number of new projects. This was preceded by a two-phase Domestic Field Trial, which has supported the installation of approximately 200 kW in the first phase and 500 kW in the second phase, and the Large Scale Field Trial for Public Buildings, which should result in another 700-800 kW capacity. The installed capacity increased from 4.1 kW in 2002 to 6.0 kW in 2003.

Onshore wind power
7.44   A wind turbine extracts energy from the wind by means of a rotor fitted with aerodynamic-section blades using the lifting forces on the blades to turn the rotor primary shaft. This mechanical power is used to drive an electrical generator. The figures included for generation from wind turbines are based on the installed capacities, together with an average capacity factor for the United Kingdom or, where figures are available, on actual generation.

7.45   There have been a total of 302 wind projects awarded contracts under NFFO. Many of these are new projects, so this has resulted in a considerable increase in electricity generation from wind since 1990. At the end of 2002, there were 87 wind generation projects operational under NFFO. More are anticipated to be commissioned over the next 2-3 years. The figures for wind in this chapter cover all known schemes in the United Kingdom. In the five years up to 2002, wind capacity grew by a factor of 1.66, while electricity generated from wind grew by a factor of 1.88 over the same period. This is attributed to improvement in technologies together with the better siting of wind farms. This calculation cannot be extended to 2003 because the large expansion of wind capacity came at the end of the year and had little opportunity to generate in 2003.

Offshore wind power

7.46   The UK's offshore wind resource is vast, with the potential to provide more than the UK's current demand for electricity. Offshore wind speeds are higher than those onshore (typically up to 0.5m/s higher 10 km offshore) and also less turbulent. However, elevated inland sites can have higher wind speeds.

7.47   Due to the higher costs of installing each turbine offshore it is expected that, in general, the machines will be larger than their onshore counterparts (2 MW and above). This is driven by economics, with larger machine more cost effective per unit of electricity generated. The larger turbines also experience higher wind speeds, because taller towers put the rotors into the stronger winds. In addition, onshore constraints such as planning, noise effects and visual impact are likely to be reduced offshore. There are 18 sites with pre-lease agreements for offshore wind farms from Crown Estates. Scroby Sands applied for consent in 2001, the first to do so, but North Hoyle was the first to come on stream in autumn 2003.

Wave power

7.48   Waves in the oceans are created by the interaction of winds with the surface of the sea. Because of the direction of the prevailing winds and the size of the Atlantic Ocean, the United Kingdom has wave power levels, which are amongst the highest in the world. Previously (since 1985), the Department of Trade and Industry's shoreline programme has concentrated on an oscillating water column device on the Hebridean island of Islay. This 75 kW experimental prototype came on line in late 1991 and has now been decommissioned. Three wave schemes won contracts under the third SRO for a declared net capacity of 2 MW. One of these contract holders, Wavegen, has built a new 500kW scheme called the LIMPET near to the site of the prototype. This plant is now operating. The other concepts are still under development and testing and will be deployed over the next few years.

Large scale hydro

7.49   In hydro schemes the turbines that drive the electricity generators are powered by the direct action of water either from a reservoir or from the run of the river. Large-scale hydro covers plants belonging to companies with an aggregate hydro capacity of 5 MWe and over. Most of the plants are located in Scotland and Wales and mainly draw their water from high-level reservoirs with their own natural catchment areas. The schemes report their output to the Department of Trade and Industry. The coverage of these large-scale hydro figures is the same as that used in the tables in the Chapter 5 of this Digest. The data exclude pumped storage stations (see paragraph 5.49). In 2003 large-scale hydro generated 32 per cent less electricity than in 2002 because precipitation was considerably lower.

Small scale hydro

7.50   Electricity generation schemes belonging to companies with an aggregate hydro capacity below 5 MWe are classified as small scale. These are schemes being used for either domestic/farm purposes or for local sale to electricity supply companies. Data given for generation are actual figures where available, but otherwise are estimated using a typical load factor (based on NFFO schemes actual data), or the design load factor, where known. The estimated figures for 1998 and 1997 have been calculated using a load factor of 36 per cent, while those for 1996 have been calculated using a load factor of 28 per cent to reflect the reduction of generation due to the reduced rainfall. A new survey of small scale hydro sites was carried out in 1999 giving a more detailed picture of the current situation that formed the basis for estimates in 2000; a revised load factor of 38 per cent was used for 1999 and a factor of 33 per cent for 2000, 2001 and 2002 data, largely based on data provided for NFFO schemes. The load factor for 2003, however, fell to 18 per cent as a result of the reduction in precipitation that year. Small-scale hydro capacity, on the other hand, rose by 8.7 MWe compared with 2002.

Geothermal aquifers

7.51   Aquifers containing water at elevated temperatures occur in some parts of the United Kingdom at between 1,500 and 3,000 metres below the surface. This water can be pumped to the surface and used, for example, in community heating schemes. There is currently only one scheme operating in the UK at Southampton.

Biofuels

(a)   Landfill gas

7.52   Landfill gas is a methane-rich biogas formed from the decomposition of organic material in landfill. The gas can be used to fuel reciprocating engines or turbines to generate electricity or used directly in kilns and boilers. In other countries, the gas has been cleaned to pipeline quality or used as a vehicle fuel. Data on landfill gas exploitation are provided from LAMMCOS, the LAndfill gas Monitoring, Modelling and COmmunication System. This is a landfill gas database maintained by FES and containing information on all existing landfill gas exploitation schemes. Landfill gas exploitation has benefited considerably from the NFFO and this can be seen from the large rise in the amount of electricity generated since 1992. Further commissioning of landfill gas projects under NFFO will continue to increase the amount of electricity generated from this technology. Information on landfill gas was supplemented by a RESTATS survey carried out by FES in 2004 on behalf of the DTI, and covered the period up to the end of 2003. The landfill gas industry had changed in recent years with a number of mergers and takeovers. In 2003, 11 new schemes came on line under NFFO.

(b)   Sewage sludge digestion

7.53   In all sewage sludge digestion projects, some of the gas produced is used to maintain the optimum temperature for digestion. In addition, many use combined heat and power (CHP) systems. The electricity generated is either used on site or sold under the NFFO. Information from these projects was provided from the CHAPSTAT Database, which is compiled and maintained by FES on behalf of the Department of Trade and Industry (See Chapter 6).

(c)   Domestic wood combustion

7.54   Domestic wood use includes the use of logs in open fires, "AGA"-type cooker boilers and other wood burning stoves. The figure given is an approximate estimate based on a survey carried out in 1989. The Forestry Commission carried out a survey of domestic wood fuel use in 1997 but the results from this were inconclusive. As an upper limit, about 600,000 oven-dried tonnes (ODTs) were estimated to be available for domestic heating. In 2001, FES undertook a study of UK domestic wood use on behalf of DTI. A methodology was devised for surveying the three major sectors involved in wood use – the stove or boiler supplier, the wood supplier and the end user. Questionnaires were devised for all these parties and then attempts were made to contact representative samples in the various regions of the UK. From the evidence obtained via the questionnaires and telephone interviews we believe that the domestic wood burning market is growing but not in the area of wood as the primary heat source. This still remains a relatively small market and a small percentage of the wood burnt. Unfortunately, the survey was unable to provide statistically sound evidence as to the amount of wood used in the domestic sector and although it was felt that there has been a small increase in the domestic use of wood as a fuel, on the basis of the results of the approach, we could not justify modifying the current estimate for the UK. In view of the importance attached to finding out about domestic wood use, the Forestry Commission has therefore decided to undertake another study guided by the lessons learnt from the previous work. In particular they would approach the newly emerging wood cooperatives, as they are likely to be a good source if information now that they should be more well established, the National House-Building Council (NHBC) to examine new build and treating equipment suppliers, fuel suppliers and users under separate surveys. A pilot study would be undertaken to develop the correct methodology before surveying the rest of the country.

(d)   Industrial wood combustion

7.55   In 1997, the industrial wood figure (which includes sawmill residues, furniture manufacturing waste etc.) was included as a separate category for the first time. This was due to the availability of better data as a result of a survey carried out in 1996 on wood fired combustion plants above 400 kW thermal input. A follow-up survey was subsequently carried out for 2000. This survey highlighted that there were fewer sites (174) operating than in 1996 due to the imposition of more stringent emissions control.

(e)   Short rotation coppice

7.56   Short rotation willow coppice development is now becoming well established with demonstration projects underway in Northern Ireland and England. Under Northern Ireland's second Non-Fossil Fuel Renewable Energy order for electricity, two projects were live at the end of 2002.

7.57   In England, Project ARBRE in South Yorkshire was contracted under NFFO 3 to generate 10 MW of electricity of which 8 MW were to be exported to the local grid. This project ran into difficulties and was sold to new owners who are evaluating their options on taking the project forward.

(f)   Straw combustion

7.58   Straw can be burnt in high temperature boilers, designed for the efficient and controlled combustion of solid fuels and biomass to supply heat, hot water and hot air systems. There are large numbers of these small-scale batch-fed whole bale boilers. The figures given are estimates based partly on 1990 information and partly on a survey of straw-fired boilers carried out in 1993-94. A 31 MW straw fired power station near Ely, Cambridgeshire was commissioned in 2000 and has been exporting electricity since September of that year.

(g)   Waste combustion

7.59   Domestic, industrial and commercial wastes represent a significant resource for materials and energy recovery. Wastes may be combusted, as received, in purpose built incinerators or processed into a range of refuse derived fuels for both on-site and off-site utilisation. Only the non-biodegradable portion of waste is counted in renewables statistics although non-biodegradable wastes are included in this chapter as "below the line" items. The paragraphs below describe various categories of waste combustion in greater detail.

7.60   Twenty four waste-to-energy plants were in operation in 2003 burning municipal solid waste (MSW), refuse derived fuel (RDF) and general industrial waste (GIW).

7.61   **Municipal solid waste combustion:** Information was provided from the refuse incinerator operators in the United Kingdom that practice energy recovery using the RESTATS questionnaire. This included both direct combustion of unprocessed MSW and the combustion of RDF. In the latter, process waste can be partially processed to produce coarse RDF that can then be burnt in a variety of ways. By further processing the refuse, including separating off the fuel fraction, compacting, drying and densifying, it is possible to produce an RDF pellet. This pellet has around 60 per cent of the gross calorific value of British coal. The generation from MSW has been split between biodegradable sources and non-biodegradable sources using information outlined in paragraph 7.62 below. Approximately 62.5 per cent of generation from MSW was estimated to be from biodegradable sources. Non-biodegradable municipal solid waste is no longer included in the overall renewables percentage now that the international definition of renewables has been adopted (see paragraph 7.1). However, such wastes are still shown in the tables accompanying this chapter as 'below the line' items.

7.62   There has been an ongoing programme of waste analysis in the UK for many years; such analyses may be carried out to an accuracy of $\pm$ 1 per cent. Such studies are guided by the use of ACORN (A Classification of Residential Neighbourhoods) socio-economic profiles which are used to select sample areas for the analysis of household collected waste and is based on the premise that households of similar socio-economic characteristics are likely to have similar behavioural, purchasing and lifestyle characteristics; this will be reflected in the quantity and composition of waste that those households produce. The large and recently completed study in Wales showed that the only category in domestic waste to show a statistically significant seasonal variation was garden waste; as garden waste is a small percentage (certainly when compared to food and kitchen waste), the effect on the operation of biomass-to-energy plants should be almost unnoticed. Although this study was carried out for Wales, there is virtually no regional variation to be seen any more so it is likely that these figures will become the UK standard. Recent work has shown that UK domestic waste has a biodegradable content of 67.5 per cent $\pm$ 1 per cent his accounts for about 62.5 per cent of the energy generated from its combustion. Municipal Solid Waste (MSW) comprises of domestic waste plus other feedstocks, such as, general industrial waste, building demolition waste and tree clippings from civil amenities. This has the net effect of reducing the percentage composition of the biodegradable content to 61 per cent $\pm$ 1 per cent. Because the combustion properties of some of the other biodegradable materials added is similar to that of domestic waste, this has virtually no effect on the percentage of the energy generated from the biodegradables component, which remains at about 62.5 per cent. This is a reduction from the 66 per cent that was used in previous editions of this Digest as these were based on historic waste analysis data.

7.63 **General industrial waste combustion:** Certain wastes produced by industry and commerce can be used as a source of energy for industrial processes or space heating. These wastes include general waste from factories such as paper, cardboard, wood and plastics.

7.64 A survey conducted in 2001 has highlighted that although there are 6 waste-to-energy plants burning GIW, these are all MSW facilities. As no sites are solely burning GIW for heat or electricity generation, this feedstock is being handled under the MSW category.

7.65 **Specialised waste combustion:** Specialised wastes arise as a result of a particular activity or process. Materials in this category include scrap tyres, hospital wastes, poultry litter, meal and bone and farm waste digestion. The large tyre incineration plant with energy recovery did not generate in 2003. Although part of waste tyre combustion is of biodegradable waste, because there is no agreed method of calculating the small biodegradable content, all of the generation from waste tyres has been included under non-biodegradable wastes in this chapter (see paragraph 7.62, above).

7.66 Information on hospital waste incineration was supplemented this year by a RESTATS survey, carried out by FES in 2004 on behalf of DTI, and covered a period up to the end of 2003. The survey confirmed whether the older sites were still operating, and identified any new operating facilities. Information on both their thermal and electrical outputs between 2000 and 2003 were gathered where data were available. There were no major changes, as the sector appeared to have stabilised since the introduction of the new emission legislation. There may, however, be future changes in due to the appearance of new technologies, such as microwave treatment, and increased segregation of clinical waste.

7.67 One poultry litter combustion project started generating electricity in 1992; a second began in 1993. Both of these are NFFO projects. In addition, a small-scale CHP scheme began generating towards the end of 1990 however this has now closed due to new emissions regulations. A further NFFO scheme started generating in 1998, and during 2000 an SRO scheme began to generate. Over the most recent 4 years one of the earlier poultry litter projects was fuelled mainly by meat and bone. A new poultry litter scheme became fully operational in 2001.

7.68 Information on farm waste digestion in the United Kingdom is based on a survey carried out during 1991-1992 with a follow-up study in 1996. There was a farm digestion project generating electricity under the NFFO; its output was included in the commodity balances but is has now ceased to operate. In 2003, however, a large centralised anaerobic digestion scheme (Holsworthy) generating electricity under NFFO 5 came on-line. With the exception of this scheme, data collected from the 1996 survey were used to derive estimates for 1997 through to 2003. It is planned to carry out a survey of farm waste digestion in 2004.

(h)   Co-firing of biomass with fossil fuels

7.69 Co-firing of biomass fuel in fossil fuel power stations is not a new idea. Technically it has been proven in power stations worldwide, although, until recently, it was not practised in the UK. The biomass fuel is usually fed by means of the existing stoking mechanism as a partial substitute for the fossil fuel. The combustion system may cope with up to a 25 per cent substitution without any major changes to the boiler design and airflows, but fuel preparation and transport systems may be the limiting feature at percentages much lower than this.

7.70 Since 2002, co-firing of biomass with fossil fuels has been eligible under the RO, the first time that any renewable energy initiative has included co-firing. As the purpose of this was to enable markets and supply chains for biomass to develop, and not to support coal fired power stations, the following limits were placed on co-firing:
- only electricity generated before 1 April 2011 would be eligible;
- from 1 April 2006 at least 75 per cent of the biomass must consist of energy crops.

7.71   However, the scheme has now been extended to allow longer for an energy crop market to develop, through establishing biomass operations at co-fired stations. The key changes are as follows:

- fossil fuel stations are allowed to convert to biomass without refurbishment;
- any biomass can be co-fired until 31 March 2009 with no minimum percentage of energy crops;
- 25 per cent of co-fired biomass must be energy crops from 1 April 2009 until 31 March 2010;
- 50 per cent of co-fired biomass must be energy crops from 1 April 2010 until 31 March 2011;
- 75 per cent of co-fired biomass must be energy crops from 1 April 2011 until 31 March 2016. Co-firing ceases to be eligible for ROCs after this date.

To balance the above changes and reduce the risk of flooding the ROC market with co-firing ROCs, thereby affecting ROC prices and investor confidence adversely, it is proposed that the 25 per cent cap from 1 April 2006 on an individual supplier should be changed to:

- 10 per cent from 1 April 2006 until 31 March 2011;
- 5 per cent from 1 April 2011 until 31 March 2016.

Combined Heat and Power

7.72   A Combined Heat and Power (CHP) plant is an installation where there is a simultaneous generation of usable heat and power (usually electricity) in a single process. Some CHP installations are fuelled either wholly or partially by renewable sources of energy. The main renewable sources that are used for CHP are biofuels particularly sewage gas.

7.73   Chapter 6 of this Digest summarises information on the contribution made by CHP to the United Kingdom's energy requirements in 1999 to 2003 using the results of annual studies undertaken to identify all CHP schemes. Included in Tables 6.1 to 6.9 of that chapter is information on the contribution of renewable sources to CHP generation in each year from 1999 to 2003. Corresponding data for 1996 to 1998 are available on the DTI web site. The information contained in those tables is therefore a subset of the data contained within the tables presented in this chapter.

Capacity and load factor

7.74   The electrical capacities are given in Table 7.4 as installed capacities ie the maximum continuous rating of the generating sets in the stations. In Chapter 5 DNC (Declared Net Capacity) is used, ie the maximum continuous rating of the generating sets in the stations, less the power consumed by the plant itself, and reduced by a specified factor to take into account the intermittent nature of the energy source e.g. 0.43 for wind and 0.33 for shoreline wave. DNC represents the nominal maximum capability of a generating set to supply electricity to consumers. For electrical capacities of generation using renewables in DNC terms see Table 7.1.1 on the DTI web site.

7.75   Plant load factors in this chapter have been calculated in terms of installed capacity (ie the maximum continuous rating of the generating sets in the stations) and express the average hourly quantity of electricity generated as a percentage of the average capacity at the beginning and end of the year.

Contact :   *Steve Dagnall, Future Energy Solutions*
steve.dagnall@aeat.co.uk
0870 190 6092

Mike Janes, DTI, Statistician
mike.janes@dti.gsi.gov.uk
020-7215 5186

7.1 Commodity balances 2003
Renewables and waste

Thousand tonnes of oil equivalent

	Wood waste	Wood	Poultry litter, meat and bone, straw, farm waste and SRC(3)	Sewage gas	Landfill gas
Supply					
Production	266	204	504	165	1,088
Other sources	-	-	-	-	-
Imports	-	-	110	-	-
Exports	-	-	-	-	-
Marine bunkers	-	-	-	-	-
Stock change (1)	-	-	-	-	-
Transfers	-	-	-	-	-
Total supply	266	204	614	165	1,088
Statistical difference (2)	-	-	-	-	-
Total demand	266	204	614	165	1,088
Transformation	59	-	542	113	1,075
Electricity generation	-	-	542	113	1,075
Major power producers	-	-	292	-	-
Autogenerators	-	-	250	113	1,075
Heat generation	59	-	-	-	-
Petroleum refineries	-	-	-	-	-
Coke manufacture	-	-	-	-	-
Blast furnaces	-	-	-	-	-
Patent fuel manufacture	-	-	-	-	-
Other	-	-	-	-	-
Energy industry use	-	-	-	-	-
Electricity generation	-	-	-	-	-
Oil and gas extraction	-	-	-	-	-
Petroleum refineries	-	-	-	-	-
Coal extraction	-	-	-	-	-
Coke manufacture	-	-	-	-	-
Blast furnaces	-	-	-	-	-
Patent fuel manufacture	-	-	-	-	-
Pumped storage	-	-	-	-	-
Other	-	-	-	-	-
Losses	-	-	-	-	-
Final consumption	207	204	72	53	14
Industry	207	-	-	-	14
Unclassified	207	-	-	-	14
Iron and steel	-	-	-	-	-
Non-ferrous metals	-	-	-	-	-
Mineral products	-	-	-	-	-
Chemicals	-	-	-	-	-
Mechanical engineering, etc	-	-	-	-	-
Electrical engineering, etc	-	-	-	-	-
Vehicles	-	-	-	-	-
Food, beverages, etc	-	-	-	-	-
Textiles, leather, etc	-	-	-	-	-
Paper, printing, etc	-	-	-	-	-
Other industries	-	-	-	-	-
Construction	-	-	-	-	-
Transport	-	-	-	-	-
Air	-	-	-	-	-
Rail	-	-	-	-	-
Road	-	-	-	-	-
National navigation	-	-	-	-	-
Pipelines	-	-	-	-	-
Other	-	204	72	53	-
Domestic	-	204	-	-	-
Public administration	-	-	-	53	-
Commercial	-	-	-	-	-
Agriculture	-	-	72	-	-
Miscellaneous	-	-	-	-	-
Non energy use	-	-	-	-	-

(1) Stock fall (+), stock rise (-).
(2) Total supply minus total demand.
(3) SRC is short rotation coppice.

(4) Municipal solid waste, general industrial waste and hospital waste.
(5) The amount of shoreline wave included is less than 0.1 ktoe.

7.1 Commodity balances 2003 (continued)

Renewables and waste

Thousand tonnes of oil equivalent

Waste(4) and tyres	Geothermal and active solar heat	Hydro	Wind and wave (5)	Total renewables	
					Supply
819	21	278	111	3,454	Production
-	-	-	-	-	Other sources
-	-	-	-	110	Imports
-	-	-	-	-	Exports
-	-	-	-	-	Marine bunkers
-	-	-	-	-	Stock change (1)
-	-	-	-	-	Transfers
819	21	278	111	3,565	**Total supply**
-	-	-	-	-	**Statistical difference** (2)
819	21	278	111	3,565	**Total demand**
720	-	278	111	2,896	**Transformation**
720		278	111	2,837	Electricity generation
89	-	221	-	602	Major power producers
630	-	57	111	2,235	Autogenerators
-	-	-	-	59	Heat generation
-	-	-	-	-	Petroleum refineries
-	-	-	-	-	Coke manufacture
-	-	-	-	-	Blast furnaces
-	-	-	-	-	Patent fuel manufacture
-	-	-	-	-	Other
-	-	-	-	-	**Energy industry use**
-	-	-	-	-	Electricity generation
-	-	-	-	-	Oil and gas extraction
-	-	-	-	-	Petroleum refineries
-	-	-	-	-	Coal extraction
-	-	-	-	-	Coke manufacture
-	-	-	-	-	Blast furnaces
-	-	-	-	-	Patent fuel manufacture
-	-	-	-	-	Pumped storage
-	-	-	-	-	Other
-	-	-	-	-	**Losses**
99	21	-	-	669	**Final consumption**
6	-	-	-	226	**Industry**
6	-	-	-	226	Unclassified
-	-	-	-	-	Iron and steel
-	-	-	-	-	Non-ferrous metals
-	-	-	-	-	Mineral products
-	-	-	-	-	Chemicals
-	-	-	-	-	Mechanical engineering, etc
-	-	-	-	-	Electrical engineering, etc
-	-	-	-	-	Vehicles
-	-	-	-	-	Food, beverages, etc
-	-	-	-	-	Textiles, leather, etc
-	-	-	-	-	Paper, printing, etc
-	-	-	-	-	Other industries
-	-	-	-	-	Construction
-	-	-	-	-	**Transport**
-	-	-	-	-	Air
-	-	-	-	-	Rail
-	-	-	-	-	Road
-	-	-	-	-	National navigation
-	-	-	-	-	Pipelines
93	21	-	-	443	**Other**
23	21	-	-	248	Domestic
51	-	-	-	104	Public administration
-	-	-	-	-	Commercial
-	-	-	-	72	Agriculture
19	-	-	-	19	Miscellaneous
-	-	-	-	-	**Non energy use**

7.2 Commodity balances 2002

Renewables and waste

	Wood waste	Wood	Poultry litter, meat and bone, straw, farm waste and SRC(3)	Sewage gas	Landfill gas
Supply					
Production	266	204	440r	174r	892
Other sources	-	-	-	-	-
Imports	-	-	-	-	-
Exports	-	-	-	-	-
Marine bunkers	-	-	-	-	-
Stock change (1)	-	-	-	-	-
Transfers	-	-	-	-	-
Total supply	266	204	440r	174r	892
Statistical difference (2)	-	-	-	-	-
Total demand	266	204	440	174	892
Transformation	63r	-	368r	121r	879
Electricity generation	-	-	368r	121r	879
Major power producers	-	-	184r	-	-
Autogenerators	-	-	184r	121r	879
Heat generation	63r	-	-	-	-
Petroleum refineries	-	-	-	-	-
Coke manufacture	-	-	-	-	-
Blast furnaces	-	-	-	-	-
Patent fuel manufacture	-	-	-	-	-
Other	-	-	-	-	-
Energy industry use	-	-	-	-	-
Electricity generation	-	-	-	-	-
Oil and gas extraction	-	-	-	-	-
Petroleum refineries	-	-	-	-	-
Coal extraction	-	-	-	-	-
Coke manufacture	-	-	-	-	-
Blast furnaces	-	-	-	-	-
Patent fuel manufacture	-	-	-	-	-
Pumped storage	-	-	-	-	-
Other	-	-	-	-	-
Losses	-	-	-	-	-
Final consumption	203r	204	72	53	14
Industry	203r	-	-	-	14
Unclassified	203r	-	-	-	14
Iron and steel	-	-	-	-	-
Non-ferrous metals	-	-	-	-	-
Mineral products	-	-	-	-	-
Chemicals	-	-	-	-	-
Mechanical engineering, etc	-	-	-	-	-
Electrical engineering, etc	-	-	-	-	-
Vehicles	-	-	-	-	-
Food, beverages, etc	-	-	-	-	-
Textiles, leather, etc	-	-	-	-	-
Paper, printing, etc	-	-	-	-	-
Other industries	-	-	-	-	-
Construction	-	-	-	-	-
Transport	-	-	-	-	-
Air	-	-	-	-	-
Rail	-	-	-	-	-
Road	-	-	-	-	-
National navigation	-	-	-	-	-
Pipelines	-	-	-	-	-
Other	-	204	72	53	-
Domestic	-	204	-	-	-
Public administration	-	-	-	53	-
Commercial	-	-	-	-	-
Agriculture	-	-	72	-	-
Miscellaneous	-	-	-	-	-
Non energy use	-	-	-	-	-

(1) Stock fall (+), stock rise (-).
(2) Total supply minus total demand.
(3) SRC is short rotation coppice.
(4) Municipal solid waste, general industrial waste and hospital waste.
(5) The amount of shoreline wave included is less than 0.1 ktoe.

7.2 Commodity balances 2002 (continued)

Renewables and waste

Thousand tonnes of oil equivalent

Waste(4) and tyres	Geothermal and active solar heat	Hydro	Wind and wave (5)	Total renewables	
					Supply
797r	17	412	108	3,310r	Production
-	-	-	-	-	Other sources
-	-	-	-	-	Imports
-	-	-	-	-	Exports
-	-	-	-	-	Marine bunkers
-	-	-	-	-	Stock change (1)
-	-	-	-	-	Transfers
797r	17	412	108	3,310r	**Total supply**
-	-	-	-	-	**Statistical difference** (2)
797r	17	412	108	3,310r	**Total demand**
706r	-	412	108	2,656r	**Transformation**
706r	-	412	108	2,593r	Electricity generation
90r	-	338	-	612r	Major power producers
616r	-	74	108	1,981r	Autogenerators
-	-	-	-	63r	Heat generation
-	-	-	-	-	Petroleum refineries
-	-	-	-	-	Coke manufacture
-	-	-	-	-	Blast furnaces
-	-	-	-	-	Patent fuel manufacture
-	-	-	-	-	Other
-	-	-	-	-	**Energy industry use**
-	-	-	-	-	Electricity generation
-	-	-	-	-	Oil and gas extraction
-	-	-	-	-	Petroleum refineries
-	-	-	-	-	Coal extraction
-	-	-	-	-	Coke manufacture
-	-	-	-	-	Blast furnaces
-	-	-	-	-	Patent fuel manufacture
-	-	-	-	-	Pumped storage
-	-	-	-	-	Other
-	-	-	-	-	**Losses**
91	17	-	-	654r	**Final consumption**
6	-	-	-	222r	**Industry**
6	-	-	-	222r	Unclassified
-	-	-	-	-	Iron and steel
-	-	-	-	-	Non-ferrous metals
-	-	-	-	-	Mineral products
-	-	-	-	-	Chemicals
-	-	-	-	-	Mechanical engineering, etc
-	-	-	-	-	Electrical engineering, etc
-	-	-	-	-	Vehicles
-	-	-	-	-	Food, beverages, etc
-	-	-	-	-	Textiles, leather, etc
-	-	-	-	-	Paper, printing, etc
-	-	-	-	-	Other industries
-	-	-	-	-	Construction
-	-	-	-	-	**Transport**
-	-	-	-	-	Air
-	-	-	-	-	Rail
-	-	-	-	-	Road
-	-	-	-	-	National navigation
-	-	-	-	-	Pipelines
85	17	-	-	432	**Other**
23	17	-	-	244	Domestic
43	-	-	-	97	Public administration
-	-	-	-	-	Commercial
-	-	-	-	72	Agriculture
19	-	-	-	20	Miscellaneous
-	-	-	-	-	**Non energy use**

7.3 Commodity balances 2001

Renewables and waste

	Wood waste	Wood	Poultry litter, meat and bone, straw, farm waste and SRC(3)	Sewage gas	Landfill gas
Supply					
Production	265	204	352	168	836
Other sources	-	-	-	-	-
Imports	-	-	-	-	-
Exports	-	-	-	-	-
Marine bunkers	-	-	-	-	-
Stock change (1)	-	-	-	-	-
Transfers	-	-	-	-	-
Total supply	265	204	352	168	836
Statistical difference (2)	-	-	-	-	-
Total demand	265	204	352	168	836
Transformation	71	-	280	119	822
Electricity generation	-	-	280	119	822
Major power producers	-	-	166	-	-
Autogenerators	-	-	114	119	822
Heat generation	71	-	-	-	-
Petroleum refineries	-	-	-	-	-
Coke manufacture	-	-	-	-	-
Blast furnaces	-	-	-	-	-
Patent fuel manufacture	-	-	-	-	-
Other	-	-	-	-	-
Energy industry use	-	-	-	-	-
Electricity generation	-	-	-	-	-
Oil and gas extraction	-	-	-	-	-
Petroleum refineries	-	-	-	-	-
Coal extraction	-	-	-	-	-
Coke manufacture	-	-	-	-	-
Blast furnaces	-	-	-	-	-
Patent fuel manufacture	-	-	-	-	-
Pumped storage	-	-	-	-	-
Other	-	-	-	-	-
Losses	-	-	-	-	-
Final consumption	194	204	72	49	14
Industry	194	-	-	-	14
Unclassified	194	-	-	-	14
Iron and steel	-	-	-	-	-
Non-ferrous metals	-	-	-	-	-
Mineral products	-	-	-	-	-
Chemicals	-	-	-	-	-
Mechanical engineering, etc	-	-	-	-	-
Electrical engineering, etc	-	-	-	-	-
Vehicles	-	-	-	-	-
Food, beverages, etc	-	-	-	-	-
Textiles, leather, etc	-	-	-	-	-
Paper, printing, etc	-	-	-	-	-
Other industries	-	-	-	-	-
Construction	-	-	-	-	-
Transport	-	-	-	-	-
Air	-	-	-	-	-
Rail	-	-	-	-	-
Road	-	-	-	-	-
National navigation	-	-	-	-	-
Pipelines	-	-	-	-	-
Other	-	204	72	49	-
Domestic	-	204	-	-	-
Public administration	-	-	-	49	-
Commercial	-	-	-	-	-
Agriculture	-	-	72	-	-
Miscellaneous	-	-	-	-	-
Non energy use	-	-	-	-	-

(1) Stock fall (+), stock rise (-).
(2) Total supply minus total demand.
(3) SRC is short rotation coppice.
(4) Municipal solid waste, general industrial waste and hospital waste.
(5) The amount of shoreline wave included is less than 0.1 ktoe.

7.3 Commodity balances 2001 (continued)

Renewables and waste

Thousand tonnes of oil equivalent

Waste(4) and tyres	Geothermal and active solar heat	Hydro	Wind and wave (5)	Total renewables	
					Supply
737r	14	349	83	3,008r	Production
-	-	-	-	-	Other sources
-	-	-	-	-	Imports
-	-	-	-	-	Exports
-	-	-	-	-	Marine bunkers
-	-	-	-	-	Stock change (1)
-	-	-	-	-	Transfers
737r	14	349	83	3,008r	**Total supply**
-	-	-	-	-	**Statistical difference** (2)
737r	14	349	83	3,008r	**Total demand**
653r	-	349	83	2,377r	**Transformation**
653r	-	349	83	2,306r	Electricity generation
88r	-	276	-	530	Major power producers
565r	-	72	83	1,776r	Autogenerators
-	-	-	-	71	Heat generation
-	-	-	-	-	Petroleum refineries
-	-	-	-	-	Coke manufacture
-	-	-	-	-	Blast furnaces
-	-	-	-	-	Patent fuel manufacture
-	-	-	-	-	Other
-	-	-	-	-	**Energy industry use**
-	-	-	-	-	Electricity generation
-	-	-	-	-	Oil and gas extraction
-	-	-	-	-	Petroleum refineries
-	-	-	-	-	Coal extraction
-	-	-	-	-	Coke manufacture
-	-	-	-	-	Blast furnaces
-	-	-	-	-	Patent fuel manufacture
-	-	-	-	-	Pumped storage
-	-	-	-	-	Other
-	-	-	-	-	**Losses**
84	14	-	-	631	**Final consumption**
6	-	-	-	214	**Industry**
6	-	-	-	214	Unclassified
-	-	-	-	-	Iron and steel
-	-	-	-	-	Non-ferrous metals
-	-	-	-	-	Mineral products
-	-	-	-	-	Chemicals
-	-	-	-	-	Mechanical engineering, etc
-	-	-	-	-	Electrical engineering, etc
-	-	-	-	-	Vehicles
-	-	-	-	-	Food, beverages, etc
-	-	-	-	-	Textiles, leather, etc
-	-	-	-	-	Paper, printing, etc
-	-	-	-	-	Other industries
-	-	-	-	-	Construction
-	-	-	-	-	**Transport**
-	-	-	-	-	Air
-	-	-	-	-	Rail
-	-	-	-	-	Road
-	-	-	-	-	National navigation
-	-	-	-	-	Pipelines
77	14	-	-	417	**Other**
24	14	-	-	242	Domestic
43	-	-	-	92	Public administration
-	-	-	-	-	Commercial
-	-	-	-	72	Agriculture
10	-	-	-	10	Miscellaneous
-	-	-	-	-	**Non energy use**

7.4 Capacity of, and electricity generated from, renewable sources

	1999	2000	2001	2002	2003
Installed Capacity (MWe) *(1)*					
Wind:					
Onshore	357.0	408.0	423.5	530.6	678.4
Offshore	-	3.8	3.8	3.8	63.8
Shoreline wave	-	0.5	0.5	0.5	0.5
Solar photovoltaics	1.2	2.0	2.8	4.1	6.0
Hydro:					
Small scale	176.7	183.6	188.7	194.2	202.9
Large scale *(2)*	1,413.0	1,419.0	1,440.0	1,396.0r	1,394.0
Biofuels and wastes:					
Landfill gas	343.3	425.1	464.8	472.9	619.1
Sewage sludge digestion	91.3	85.3	85.0	96.0	100.6
Municipal solid waste combustion	229.6	253.2	260.0	278.9	298.8
Other *(3)*	108.0	157.0	157.0	176.5r	183.9
Total biofuels and wastes	772.2	920.6	966.8	1,024.3r	1,202.4
Total	**2,720.2**	**2,937.4**	**3,026.0**	**3,153.6r**	**3,548.0**
Co-firing *(4)*	-	-	-	..	92.4
Generation (GWh)					
Wind:					
Onshore *(5)*	850	945	960	1,251	1,276
Offshore *(6)*	-	1	5	5	10
Solar photovoltaics	1	1	2	3	3
Hydro:					
Small scale *(5)*	207	214	210	204	115
Large scale *(2)*	5,128	4,871	3,845	4,584	3,113
Biofuels:					
Landfill gas	1,703	2,188	2,507	2,679	3,276
Sewage sludge digestion	410	367	363	368r	343
Municipal solid waste combustion *(7)*	856	840	880r	907r	965
Co-firing with fossil fuels	-	-	-	286	602
Other *(8)*	426r	401r	743r	807r	947
Total biofuels	3,395r	3,796r	4,493r	5,047r	6,133
Total generation *(9)*	**9,581**	**9,828**	**9,516**	**11,093**	**10,649**
Total renewables generation on an obligation basis *(10)*	**3,597r**	**4,117r**	**4,851r**	**5,722r**	**7,186**
Total renewables generation on a directive basis *(10)*	**9,581r**	**9,828r**	**11,256r**	**12,761r**	**13,434**
Non-biodegradable wastes *(11)*	592	553	562	578	585
Load factors (per cent) *(12)*					
Onshore wind	28.2	28.2	26.4	29.9	24.1
Hydro	38.4	36.4	28.7	34.0r	23.1
Biofuels	54.6r	51.2r	54.3r	57.9r	62.9
Total (including wastes)	**44.0**	**41.9**	**38.6**	**43.1r**	**38.3**

(1) Capacity on a DNC basis is shown in Long Term Trends Table 7.1.1 available on the DTI web site - see paragraph 7.74.
(2) Excluding pumped storage stations. Capacities are as at the end of December.
(3) Includes the use of farm waste digestion, waste tyres, poultry litter, meat and bone, straw combustion, and short rotation coppice.
(4) This is the proportion of fossil fuelled capacity used for co-firing of renewables based on the proportion of generation accounted for by the renewable source.
(5) Actual generation figures are given where available, but otherwise are estimated using a typical load factor or the design load factor, where known.
(6) In 2000 and subsequent years includes less than 0.05 GWh of electricity from shoreline wave.
(7) Biodegradable part only.
(8) Includes the use of farm waste digestion, poultry litter combustion, meat and bone combustion, straw and short rotation coppice.
(9) International definition now used (see paragraph 7.1) so figures are lower than in previous Digests
(10) See paragraphs 7.7 and 7.8 for definitions.
(11) Non-biodegradable part of municipal solid waste plus waste tyres, hosptal waste and general industrial waste.
(12) Load factors are calculated based on installed capacity at the beginning and the end of the year - see paragraph 7.75.

7.5 Renewable orders and operational capacity

Technology band	Contracted projects		Live projects operational at 31 December 2003 (1)	
	Number	Capacity MW	Number	Capacity MW
England and Wales				
NFFO - 1 (1990)				
Hydro	26	11.85	9	7.63
Landfill gas	25	35.50	17	29.32
Municipal and industrial waste	4	40.63	4	40.63
Other	4	45.48	2	25.38
Sewage gas	7	6.45	6	5.98
Wind	9	12.21	2	5.81
Total (2)	**75**	**152.11**	**40**	**114.74**
NFFO - 2 (late 1991)				
Hydro	12	10.86	2	2.78
Landfill gas	28	48.45	26	46.39
Municipal and industrial waste	10	271.48	2	31.50
Other	4	30.15	-	-
Sewage gas	19	26.86	17	18.39
Wind	49	84.43	21	52.20
Total (2)	**122**	**472.23**	**68**	**151.26**
NFFO - 3 (1995)				
Energy crops and agricultural and forestry waste - gasification	3	19.06		
Energy crops and agricultural and forestry waste - other	6	103.81	2	69.50
Hydro	15	14.48	8	11.74
Landfill gas	42	82.07	42	82.07
Municipal and industrial waste	20	241.87	7	89.12
Wind - large	31	145.92	10	41.02
Wind - small	24	19.71	13	11.86
Total	**141**	**626.90**	**82**	**305.31**
NFFO - 4 (1997)				
Hydro	31	13.22	9	2.49
Landfill gas	70	173.68	57	146.00
Municipal and industrial waste - CHP	10	115.29	4	33.48
Municipal and industrial waste - fluidised bed combustion	6	125.93		
Wind - large	48	330.36	4	12.97
Wind - small	17	10.33	5	3.27
Anaerobic digestion of agricultural waste	6	6.58	1	1.43
Energy crops and forestry waste gasification	7	67.34		
Total	**195**	**842.72**	**80**	**199.64**
NFFO - 5 (1998)				
Hydro	22	8.87	3	0.64
Landfill gas	141	313.73	67	137.26
Municipal and industrial waste	22	415.75		
Municipal and industrial waste - CHP	7	69.97		
Wind - large	33	340.16		
Wind - small	36	28.67	6	4.85
Total	**261**	**1,177.15**	**76**	**142.75**
NFFO Total	**794**	**3,271.11**	**346**	**913.70**

(1) Sites that have closed and sites that are not currently using renewables as fuel have been excluded.

(2) See footnote 2, overleaf.

This table continues on the next page.

7.5 Renewable orders and operational capacity (continued)

		Contracted projects		Live projects operational at 31 December 2003 *(1)*	
	Technology band	Number	Capacity MW	Number	Capacity MW
Scotland					
SRO - 1 (1994)	Biomass	1	9.80	1	9.80
	Hydro	15	17.25	9	8.81
	Waste to Energy	2	3.78	2	3.78
	Wind	12	45.60	7	25.13
	Total	**30**	**76.43**	**19**	**47.52**
SRO - 2 (1997)	Biomass	1	2.00		
	Hydro	9	12.36	2	1.46
	Waste to Energy	9	56.05	6	17.65
	Wind	7	43.63	5	31.29
	Total	**26**	**114.04**	**13**	**50.40**
SRO - 3 (1999)	Biomass	1	12.90		
	Hydro	5	3.90		
	Waste to Energy	16	49.11	7	16.04
	Wave	3	2.00	1	0.20
	Wind - large	11	63.43	1	8.29
	Wind - small	17	14.06	5	4.28
	Total	**53**	**145.40**	**14**	**28.81**
SRO Total		**109**	**335.87**	**46**	**126.73**
Northern Ireland					
NI NFFO - 1 (1994)	Hydro	9	2.37	8	2.33
	Sewage gas	5	0.56		
	Wind	6	12.66	6	12.66
	Total	**20**	**15.60**	**14**	**14.99**
NI NFFO - 2 (1996)	Biogas	1	0.25		
	Biomass	2	0.30	2	0.30
	Hydro	2	0.25	1	0.08
	Landfill gas	2	6.25		
	Municipal and industrial waste	1	6.65		
	Wind	2	2.57	2	2.57
	Total	**10**	**16.27**	**5**	**2.95**
NI NFFO Total		**30**	**31.87**	**19**	**17.94**
All NFFO and equivalents		**933**	**3,638.85**	**411**	**1,058.37**

(1) Sites that have closed and sites that are not currently using renewables as fuel have been excluded.

(2) The NFPA NFFO database has reported that at the end of December 2003 442 sites totalling 1,146.29 MW had gone live under NFFO, but this includes all NFFO-1 and NFFO-2 sites for England and Wales, some of which have closed or are not currently using renewables as fuels. The following table compares the totals for live projects, above, with the overall NFFO total:

	Number	MW
All live NFFO and equivalents	411	1,058.37
NFFO-1 no longer classed as live and operational	26	42.71
NFFO-2 no longer classed as live and operational	24	45.21
All NFFO and equivalents	461	1,146.29

7.6 Renewable sources used to generate electricity and heat[(1)(2)]

				Thousand tonnes of oil equivalent	
	1999	2000	2001	2002	2003
Used to generate electricity (3)					
Wind:					
Onshore	73.1	81.3	82.6	107.6	109.7
Offshore	-	0.1	0.4	0.4	0.9
Solar photovoltaics	0.1	0.1	0.2	0.2	0.3
Hydro:					
Small scale	17.8	18.4	18.1	17.5	9.9
Large scale (4)	441.0	418.8	330.7	394.2	267.7
Biofuels:					
Landfill gas	558.4	717.6	822.2	878.5	1,074.5
Sewage sludge digestion	134.6	120.4	119.0	120.6r	112.5
Municipal solid waste combustion (5)	345.0	350.1	387.1r	420.2r	445.8
Co-firing with fossil fuels	-	-	-	94.0	197.3
Other (6)	123.0r	143.9r	245.6r	273.6r	344.6
Total biofuels	1,161.0	1,332.0	1,573.9	1,786.8	2,174.8
Total	**1,693.0r**	**1,850.7r**	**2,005.8r**	**2,306.7**	**2,563.1**
Non-biodegradable wastes (7)	272.5	253.3	266.2	286.1	273.7
Used to generate heat					
Active solar heating	9.4	11.1	13.2	16.1	19.8
Biofuels :					
Landfill gas	13.6	13.6	13.6	13.6	13.6
Sewage sludge digestion	54.2	48.3	49.4	53.4	52.5
Wood combustion - domestic	204.2	204.2	204.2	204.2	204.2
Wood combustion - industrial	367.7	298.6	264.6	265.6	265.6
Straw combustion, farm waste digestion and short rotation coppice	72.2	72.2	72.2	72.2	72.2
Municipal solid waste combustion (5)	20.2r	25.6r	29.0r	33.6r	33.6
Total biofuels	732.1r	662.4r	632.9r	642.6r	641.7
Geothermal aquifers	0.8	0.8	0.8	0.8	0.8
Total	**742.3r**	**674.2r**	**647.0r**	**659.5r**	**662.3**
Non-biodegradable wastes (7)	49.3	52.3	54.5	57.2	65.5
Total use of renewable sources and wastes					
Solar heating and photovoltaics	9.4r	11.2	13.4	16.3	20.0
Onshore and offshore wind	73.1	81.3	83.0	108.0	110.5
Hydro	458.8	437.3	348.7	411.7	277.5
Biofuels	1,893.1r	1,994.3r	2,206.9r	2,429.4r	2,816.5
Geothermal aquifers	0.8	0.8	0.8	0.8	0.8
Total	**2,435.3r**	**2,524.9r**	**2,652.8r**	**2,966.3r**	**3,225.4**
Non-biodegradable wastes (7)	321.8	305.6	320.7	343.4	339.2
All renewables and wastes (8)	**2,757.1**	**2,830.5**	**2,973.5**	**3,309.6r**	**3,564.7**

(1) Includes some waste of fossil fuel origin.

(2) See paragraphs 7.39 to 7.75 for technical notes and definitions of the categories used in this table.

(3) For wind, solar PV and hydro, the figures represent the energy content of the electricity supplied but for biofuels the figures represent the energy content of the fuel used.

(4) Excluding pumped storage stations.

(5) Biodegradable part only.

(6) Includes electricity from farm waste digestion, poultry litter combustion, meat and bone combustion, straw and short rotation coppice.

(7) Non-biodegradable part of municipal solid waste plus waste tyres, hospital waste, and general industrial waste.

(8) The figures in this row correspond to the total demand and total supply figures in Tables 7.1, 7.2 and 7.3.

Digest of United Kingdom Energy Statistics
2004

Annexes

Annex A: Energy and commodity balances, conversion factors and calorific values

Annex B: Glossary

Annex C: Further sources

Annex D: Major events in the Energy Industry, 2002-2004

Department of Trade and Industry

Annex A
Energy and commodity balances, conversion factors and calorific values

Balance principles

A.1   This Annex outlines the principles behind the balance presentation of energy statistics. It covers these in general terms. Fuel specific details are given in the appropriate chapters of this publication.

A.2   Balances are divided into two types, each of which performs a different function.

a) *commodity balance* – a balance for each energy commodity that uses the units usually associated with that commodity. By using a single column of figures, it shows the flow of the commodity from its sources of supply through to its final use. Commodity balances are presented in the individual fuel chapters of this publication.

b) *energy balance* - presents the commodity balances in a common unit and places them alongside one another in a manner that shows the dependence of the supply of one commodity on another. This is useful as some commodities are manufactured from others. The layout of the energy balance also differs slightly from the commodity balance. The energy balance format is used in Chapter 1.

A.3   Energy commodities can be either primary or secondary. Primary energy commodities are drawn (extracted or captured) from natural reserves or flows, whereas secondary commodities are produced from primary energy commodities. Crude oil and coal are examples of primary commodities, whilst petrol and coke are secondary commodities manufactured from them. For balance purposes, electricity may be considered to be both primary electricity (for example, hydro, wind) or secondary (produced from steam turbines using steam from the combustion of fuels).

A.4   Both commodity and energy balances show the flow of the commodity from its production, extraction or import through to its final use.

A.5   A simplified model of the commodity flow underlying the balance structure is given in Chart A.1. It illustrates how primary commodities may be used directly and/or be transformed into secondary commodities. The secondary fuels then enter final consumption or may also be transformed into another energy commodity (for example, electricity produced from fuel oil). To keep the diagram simple these "second generation" flows have not been shown.

A.6   The arrows at the top of the chart represent flows to and from the "pools" of primary and secondary commodities, from imports and exports and, in the case of the primary pool, extraction from reserves (eg the production of coal, gas and crude oil).

Commodity balances (Tables 2.1 to 2.6, 3.1 to 3.6, 4.1, 5.1, and 7.1 to 7.3)

A.7   A commodity balance comprises a supply section and a demand section. The supply section gives available sources of supply (ie exports are subtracted). The demand section is divided into a transformation section, a section showing uses in the energy industries (other than for transformation) and a section covering uses by final consumers for energy or non-energy purposes. Final consumption for energy purposes is divided into use by sector of economic activity. The section breakdowns are described below.

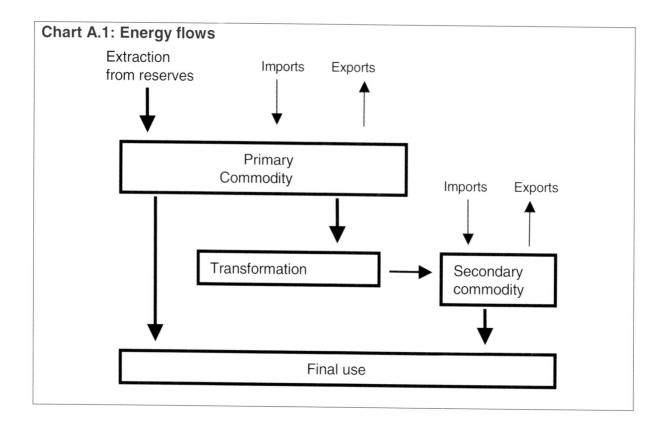

Chart A.1: Energy flows

Extraction from reserves → Primary Commodity

Imports → Primary Commodity

Exports ← Primary Commodity

Primary Commodity → Transformation

Transformation → Secondary commodity

Imports → Secondary commodity

Exports ← Secondary commodity

Primary Commodity → Final use

Secondary commodity → Final use

Supply

Production

A.8   Production, within the commodity balance, covers indigenous production (extraction or capture of primary commodities) and generation or manufacture of secondary commodities. Production is always gross, that is, it includes the quantities used during the extraction or manufacturing process.

Other sources

A.9   Production from other sources covers sources of supply that do not represent "new" supply. These may be recycled products, recovered fuels (slurry or waste coal), or electricity from pumped storage plants. The production of these quantities will have been reported in an earlier accounting period or have already been reported in the current period of account. Exceptionally, the *Other sources* row in the commodity balances for ethane, propane and butane is used to receive transfers of these hydrocarbons from gas stabilisation plants at North Sea terminals. In this manner, the supplies of primary ethane, propane and butane from the North Sea are combined with the production of these gases in refineries, so that the disposals may be presented together in the balances.

Imports and exports

A.10   The figures for imports and exports relate to energy commodities moving into or out of the United Kingdom as part of transactions involving United Kingdom companies. Exported commodities are produced in the United Kingdom and imported commodities are for use within the United Kingdom (although some may be re-exported before or after transformation). The figures thus exclude commodities either exported from or imported into HM Customs bonded areas or warehouses. These areas, although part of the United Kingdom, are regarded as being outside of the normal United Kingdom's customs boundary, and so goods entering into or leaving them are not counted as part of the statistics on trade used in the balances.

A.11   Similarly, commodities that only pass through the United Kingdom on their way to a final destination in another country are also excluded. However, for gas these transit flows are included because it is difficult to identify this quantity separately, without detailed knowledge of the contract information covering the trade. This means that for gas, there is some over statement of the level of imports and exports, but the net flows are correct.

A.12 The convention in these balances is that exports are shown with a negative sign.

Marine bunkers
A.13 These are deliveries of fuels (usually fuel oil or gas oil) to ships of any flag (including the United Kingdom) for consumption during the voyage to other countries. Marine bunkers are treated rather like exports and shown with a negative sign.

Stock changes
A.14 Additions to (- sign) and withdrawals from stocks (+ sign) held by producers and transformation industries correspond to withdrawals from and additions to supply, respectively.

Transfers
A.15 There are several reasons why quantities may be transferred from one commodity balance to another:
- a commodity may no longer meet the original specification and be reclassified;
- the name of the commodity may change through a change in use;
- to show quantities returned to supply from consumers. These may be by-products of the use of commodities as raw materials rather than fuels.

A.16 A quantity transferred from a balance is shown with a negative sign to represent a withdrawal from supply and with a positive sign in the receiving commodity balance representing an addition to its supply.

Total supply
A.17 The total supply available for national use is obtained by summing the flows above this entry in the balance.

Total demand
A.18 The various figures for the disposals and/or consumption of the commodities are summed to provide a measure of the demand for them. The main categories or sectors of demand are described in paragraphs A.32 to A.42.

Statistical difference
A.19 Any excess of supply over demand is shown as a statistical difference. A negative figure indicates that demand exceeds supply. Statistical differences arise when figures are gathered from a variety of independent sources and reflect differences in timing, in definition of coverage of the activity, or in commodity definition. Differences also arise for methodological reasons in the measurement of the flow of the commodity eg if there are differences between the volumes recorded by the gas producing companies and the gas transporting companies. A non-zero statistical difference is normal and, provided that it is not too large, is preferable to a statistical difference of zero as this suggests that a data provider has adjusted a figure to balance the account.

Transformation
A.20 The transformation sector of the balance covers those processes and activities that transform the original primary (and sometimes secondary) commodity into a form which is better suited for specific uses than the original form. Most of the transformation activities correspond to particular energy industries whose main business is to manufacture the product associated with them. Certain activities involving transformation take place to make products that are only partly used for energy needs (coke oven coke) or are by-products of other manufacturing processes (coke oven and blast furnace gases). However, as these products and by-products are then used, at least in part, for their energy content they are included in the balance system.

A.21 The figures given under the activity headings of this sector represent the quantities used for transformation. The production of the secondary commodities will be shown in the *Production* row of the corresponding commodity balances.

Electricity generation
A.22   The quantities of fuels burned for the generation of electricity are shown in their commodity balances under this heading. The activity is divided into two parts, covering the major power producers (for whom the main business is the generation of electricity for sale) and autogenerators (whose main business is not electricity generation but who produce electricity for their own needs and may also sell surplus quantities). The amounts of fuels shown in the balance represent the quantities consumed for the gross generation of electricity. Where a generator uses combined heat and power plant, the figures include only the part of the fuel use corresponding to the electricity generated.

A.23   In relation to autogenerators' data, the figures for quantities of fuel used for electricity generation appear under the appropriate fuel headings in the *Transformation* sector heading for *Autogenerators,* whilst the electricity generated appears in the *Electricity* column under *Production.* A breakdown of the information according to the branch of industry in which the generation occurs is not shown in the balance but is given in Chapter 1, Table 1.9. The figures for energy commodities consumed by the industry branches shown under final consumption include all use of electricity, but exclude the fuels combusted by the industry branches to generate the electricity.

Heat generation
A.24   The quantities of fuel burned to generate heat that is sold under the provision of a contract to a third party are shown in their commodity balances under this heading. It includes heat that is generated and sold by combined heat and power plants and by community heating schemes (also called district heating).

Petroleum refineries
A.25   Crude oil, natural gas liquids and other oils needed by refineries for the manufacture of finished petroleum products are shown under this heading.

Coke manufacture and blast furnaces
A.26   Quantities of coal for coke ovens and all fuels used within blast furnaces are shown under this heading. The consumption of fuels for heating coke ovens and the blast air for blast furnaces are shown under "Energy industry use".

Patent fuel manufacture
A.27   The coals and other solid fuels used for the manufacture of solid patent fuels are reported under this heading.

Other
A.28   Any minor transformation activities not specified elsewhere are captured under this heading.

Energy industry use
A.29   Consumption by both extraction and transformation industries to support the transformation process (but not for transformation itself) are included here according to the energy industry concerned. Typical examples are the consumption of electricity in power plants (eg for lighting, compressors and cooling systems) and the use of extracted gases on oil and gas platforms for compressors, pumps and other uses. The headings in this sector are identical to those used in the transformation sector with the exception of *Pumped storage.* In this case, the electricity used to pump the water to the reservoir is reported.

Losses
A.30   This heading covers the intrinsic losses that occur during the transmission and distribution of electricity and gas (including manufactured gases). Other metering and accounting differences for gas and electricity are within the statistical difference, as are undeclared losses in other commodities.

Final consumption
A.31   *Final consumption* covers both final energy consumption (by different consuming sectors) and the use of energy commodities for non-energy purposes, that is *Non energy use.* Final consumption occurs when the commodities used are not for transformation into secondary commodities. The energy concerned disappears from the account after use. Any fuel used for electricity generation by

final consumers is identified and reported separately within the transformation sector. When an enterprise generates electricity, the figure for final consumption of the industrial sector to which the enterprise belongs includes its use of the electricity it generates itself (as well as supplies of electricity it purchases from others) but does not include the fuel used to generate that electricity.

A.32   The classification of consumers according to their main business follows, as far as practicable, the *Standard Industrial Classification (SIC2003).* The qualifications to, and constraints on, the classification are described in the technical notes to Chapter 1, paragraphs 1.24 to 1.58. Table 1E in Chapter 1 shows the breakdown of final consumers used, and how this corresponds to the SIC2003.

Industry

A.33   Two sectors of industry (iron and steel and chemicals) require special mention because the activities they undertake fall across the transformation, final consumption and non-energy classifications used for the balances. Also, the data permitting an accurate allocation of fuel use within each of these major divisions are not readily available.

Iron and steel

A.34   The iron and steel industry is a heavy energy user for transformation and final consumption activities. Figures shown under final consumption for this industry branch reflect the amounts that remain after quantities used for transformation and energy sector own use have been subtracted from the industry's total energy requirements. Use of fuels for transformation by the industry may be identified within the transformation sector of the commodity balances.

A.35   The amounts of coal used for coke manufacture by the iron and steel industry are in the transformation sector of the coal balance. Included in this figure is the amount of coal used for coke manufacture by the companies outside of the iron and steel industry, ie solid fuel manufacturers. The corresponding production of coke and coke oven gas may be found in the commodity balances for these products. The use of coke in blast furnaces is shown in the commodity balance for coke, and the gases produced from blast furnaces and the associated basic oxygen steel furnaces are shown in the production row of the commodity balance for blast furnace gas.

A.36   Fuels used for electricity generation by the industry are included in the figures for electricity generation by autogenerators and are not distinguishable as being used by the iron and steel sector in the balances. Electricity generation and fuel used for this by broad industry group are given in Table 1.9.

A.37   Fuels used to support coke manufacture and blast furnace gas production are included in the quantities shown under *Energy industry use.* These gases and other fuels do not enter coke ovens or blast furnaces, but are used to heat the ovens and the blast air supplied to furnaces.

Chemicals

A.38   The petro-chemical industry uses hydrocarbon fuels (mostly oil products and gases) as feedstock for the manufacture of its products. Distinguishing the energy use of delivered fuels from their non-energy use is complicated by the absence of detailed information. The procedures adopted to estimate the use are described in paragraphs A.41 and A.42 under *Non energy use.*

Transport

A.39   Figures under this heading are almost entirely quantities used strictly for transport purposes. However, the figures recorded against road transport usually include some fuel that is actually consumed in some "off-road" activities. Similarly, figures for railway fuels include some amounts of burning oil not used directly for transport purposes. Transport sector use of electricity includes all electricity used in industries classified to SIC2003 Groups 60 to 63. Fuels supplied to cargo and passenger ships undertaking international voyages are reported as *Marine bunkers* (see paragraph A.13). Supplies to fishing vessels are included under "agriculture".

Other sectors

A.40   The classification of all consumers groups under this heading, except *domestic*, follows *SIC1992* and is described in Table 1E in Chapter 1. The consistency of the classification across different commodities cannot be guaranteed because the figures reported are dependent on what the data suppliers can provide.

Non energy use

A.41　The non energy use of fuels may be divided into two types. They may be used directly for their physical properties eg lubricants or bitumen used for road surfaces, or by the petro-chemical industry as raw materials for the manufacture of goods such as plastics. In their use by the petro-chemical industry, relatively little combustion of the fuels takes place and the carbon and/or hydrogen they contain are largely transferred into the finished product. However, in some cases heat from the manufacturing process or from combustion of by-products may be used. Data for this energy use are rarely available. Depending on the feedstock, non energy consumption is either estimated or taken to be the deliveries to the chemicals sector.

A.42　Both types of non energy use are shown under the *Non energy use* heading at the foot of the balances.

The energy balance (Tables 1.1 to 1.3)

Principles

A.43　The energy balance conveniently presents:

- an overall view of the United Kingdom's energy supplies;
- the relative importance of each energy commodity;
- dependence on imports;
- the contribution of our own fossil and renewable resources;
- the interdependence of commodities on one another.

A.44　The energy balance is constructed directly from the commodity balances by expressing the data in a common unit, placing them beside one another and adding appropriate totals. Heat sold is also included as a fuel. However, some rearrangement of the commodity balance format is required to show transformation of primary into secondary commodities in an easily understood manner.

A.45　Energy units are widely used as the common unit, and the current practice for the United Kingdom and the international organisations which prepare balances is to use the tonne of oil equivalent or a larger multiple of this unit, commonly thousands. One tonne of oil equivalent is defined as 10^7 kilocalories (41.868 gigajoules). The tonne of oil equivalent is another unit of energy like the gigajoule, kilocalorie or kilowatt hour, rather than a physical quantity. It has been chosen as it is easier to visualise than the other units. Due to the natural variations in heating value of primary fuels such as crude oil, it is rare that one tonne of oil has an energy content equivalent to one tonne of oil equivalent, however it is generally within a few per cent of the heating value of a tonne of oil equivalent. The energy figures are calculated from the natural units of the commodity balances by multiplying by factors representing the calorific (heating) value of the fuel. The gross calorific values of fuels are used for this purpose. When the natural unit of the commodity is already an energy unit (electricity in kilowatt hours, for example) the factors are just constants, converting one energy unit to another.

A.46　Most of the underlying definitions and ideas of commodity balances can be taken directly over into the energy balance. However, production of secondary commodities and, in particular, electricity are treated differently and need some explanation. The components of the energy balance are described below, drawing out the differences of treatment compared with the commodity balances.

Primary supply

A.47　Within the energy balance, the production row covers only extraction of primary fuels and the generation of primary energy (hydro, nuclear, wind). Note the change of row heading from *Production* in the commodity balances to *Indigenous production* in the energy balance. Production of secondary fuels and secondary electricity are shown in the transformation sector and not in the indigenous production row at the top of the balance.

A.48　For fossil fuels, indigenous production represents the marketable quantity extracted from the reserves. Indigenous production of *Primary electricity* comprises hydro-electricity, wind and nuclear energy. The energy value for hydro-electricity is taken to be the energy content of the electricity produced from the hydro power plant and not the energy available in the water driving the turbines. A similar approach is adopted for electricity from wind generators. The electricity is regarded as the primary energy form because there are currently no other uses of the energy resource "upstream" of the generation. The energy value attached to nuclear electricity is discussed in paragraph A.52.

A.49 The other elements of the supply part of the balance are identical to those in the commodity balances. In particular, the sign convention is identical, so that figures for exports and international marine bunkers carry negative signs. A stock build carries a negative sign to denote it as a withdrawal from supply whilst a stock draw carries a positive sign to show it as an addition to supply.

A.50 The *Primary supply* is the sum of the figures above it in the table, taking account of the signs, and expresses the national requirement for primary energy commodities from all sources and foreign supplies of secondary commodities. It is an indicator of the use of indigenous resources and external energy supplies. Both the amount and mixture of fuels in final consumption of energy commodities in the United Kingdom will differ from the primary supply. The "mix" of commodities in final consumption will be much more dependent on the manufacture of secondary commodities, in particular electricity.

Transformation

A.51 Within an energy balance the presentation of the inputs to and outputs from transformation activities requires special mention, as it is carried out using a compact format. The transformation sector also plays a key role in moving primary electricity from its own column in the balance into the electricity column, so that it can be combined with electricity from fossil fuelled power stations and the total disposals shown.

A.52 Indigenous production of primary electricity comprises nuclear electricity, hydro electricity and electricity from wind generation. Nuclear electricity is obtained by passing steam from nuclear reactors through conventional steam turbine sets. The heat in the steam is considered to be the primary energy available and its value is calculated from the electricity generated using the average thermal efficiency of nuclear stations, currently 38.05 in the United Kingdom. The electrical energy from hydro and wind is transferred from the *Primary electricity* column to the *Electricity* column using the *transfers* row because electricity is the form of primary energy and no transformation takes place. However, because the form of the nuclear energy is the steam from the nuclear reactors, the energy it contains is shown entering electricity generation and the corresponding electricity produced is included with all electricity generation in the figure, in the same row, under the *Electricity* column.

A.53 Quantities of fuels entering transformation activities (fuels into electricity generation and heat generation, crude oil into petroleum product manufacture (refineries), or coal into coke ovens) are shown with a negative sign to represent the input and the resulting production is shown as a positive number.

A.54 For electricity generated by Major power producers, the inputs are shown in the *Major power producers* row of the *coal, manufactured fuel, primary oils, petroleum products, gas, renewables* and *primary electricity* columns. The total energy input to electricity generation is the sum of the values in these first seven columns. The *Electricity* column shows total electricity generated from these inputs and the transformation loss is the sum of these two figures, given in the *Total* column.

A.55 Within the transformation sector, the negative figures in the *Total* column represent the losses in the various transformation activities. This is a convenient consequence of the sign convention chosen for the inputs and outputs from transformation. Any positive figures represent a transformation gain and, as such, are an indication of incorrect data.

A.56 In the energy balance, the columns containing the input commodities for electricity generation, heat generation and oil refining are separate from the columns for the outputs. However, for the transformation activities involving solid fuels this is only partly the case. Coal used for the manufacture of coke is shown in the coke manufacture row of the transformation section in the coal column, but the related coke and coke oven gas production are shown combined in the *Manufactured fuels* column. Similarly, the input of coke to blast furnaces and the resulting production of blast furnace gas are not identifiable and have been combined in the *Manufactured fuels* column in the *Blast furnace* row. As a result, only the net loss from blast furnace transformation activity appears in the column.

A.57   The share of each commodity or commodity group in primary supply can be calculated from the table. This table also shows the demand for primary as well as foreign supplies. Shares of primary supplies may be taken from the *Primary supply* row of the balance.   Shares of fuels in final consumption may be calculated from the final consumption row.

Energy industry use and final consumption
A.58   The figures for final consumption and energy industry use follow, in general, the principles and definitions described under commodity balances in paragraphs A.29 to A.42.

Standard conversion factors

1 tonne of oil equivalent (toe)	$= 10^7$ kilocalories
	= 396.83 therms
	= 41.868 GJ
	= 11,630 kWh
100,000 British thermal units (Btu)	= 1 therm

The following prefixes are used for multiples of joules, watts and watt hours:

kilo (k)	= 1,000	or 10^3
mega (M)	= 1,000,000	or 10^6
giga (G)	= 1,000,000,000	or 10^9
tera (T)	= 1,000,000,000,000	or 10^{12}
peta (P)	= 1,000,000,000,000,000	or 10^{15}

WEIGHT

1 kilogramme (kg)	= 2.2046 pounds (lb)
1 pound (lb)	= 0.4536 kg
1 tonne (t)	= 1,000kg
	= 0.9842 long ton
	= 1.102 short ton (sh tn)
1 Statute or long ton	= 2,240 lb
	= 1.016 t
	= 1.102 sh tn

VOLUME

1 cubic metre (cu m)	-
1 cubic foot (cu ft)	= 0.02832 cu m
1 litre	= 0.22 Imperial gallons (UK gall)
1 UK gallon	= 8 UK pints
	= 1.201 US gallons
	= 4.54609 litres
1 barrel	= 159.0 litres
	= 34.97 UK gal
	= 42 US gal

LENGTH

| 1 mile | = 1.6093 kilometres |
| 1 kilometre (km) | = 0.62137 miles |

TEMPERATURE

1 scale degree Celsius (C) = 1.8 scale degrees Fahrenheit (F)

For conversion of temperatures: $^{\circ}C = 5/9\ (^{\circ}F\ -32)$; $^{\circ}F = 9/5\ ^{\circ}C\ +32$

Average conversion factors for petroleum

	Imperial gallons per tonne	Litres per tonne		Imperial gallons per tonne	Litres per tonne
Crude oil:			Gas/diesel oil:		
Indigenous	264	1,199	Gas oil	261	1,187
Imported	260	1,181	Marine diesel oil	255	1,157
Average of refining throughput	262	1,192			
			Fuel oil:		
Ethane	601	2,730	All grades	227	1,031
Propane	435	1,975	Light fuel oil:		
Butane	377	1,715	1% or less sulphur	231	1,048
Naphtha (l.d.f.)	304	1,382	>1% sulphur	231	1,048
			Medium fuel oil:		
Aviation gasoline	307	1,397	1% or less sulphur	238	1,083
			>1% sulphur	225	1,025
Motor spirit:			Heavy fuel oil:		
All grades	300	1,362	1% or less sulphur	220	1,002
Unleaded Super	299	1,361	>1% sulphur	222	1,009
Premium	299	1,357			
Ultra low sulphur petrol	300	1,362			
Lead replacement petrol	299	1,361	Lubricating oils:		
			White	251	1,142
Middle distillate feedstock	205	930	Greases	252	1,147
Kerosene:			Other	248	1,127
Aviation turbine fuel	275	1,251	Bitumen	214	974
Burning oil	275	1,248	Petroleum coke	185	843
			Petroleum waxes	271	1,231
DERV fuel: all	265	1,203	Industrial spirit	274	1,247
0.005% or less sulphur	265	1,203	White spirit	282	1,282
>0.005% sulphur	261	1,187			

Note: The above conversion factors, which for refined products have been compiled by the UK Petroleum Industry Association, apply to the year 2003, and are only approximate for other years.

A.1 Estimated average gross calorific values of fuels

GJ per tonne | GJ per tonne

	GJ per tonne		GJ per tonne
Coal:		**Renewable sources:**	
All consumers (weighted average) *(1)*	26.9	Domestic wood *(2)*	10.0
Power stations *(1)*	26.1	Industrial wood *(3)*	11.9
Coke ovens *(1)*	30.5	Straw	15.0
Low temperature carbonisation plants		Poultry litter	8.8
and manufactured fuel plants	31.0	Meat and bone	18.6
Collieries	30.1	General industrial waste	16.0
Agriculture	28.0	Hospital waste	14.0
Iron and steel	30.4	Municipal solid waste *(4)*	9.5
Other industries (weighted average)	26.8	Refuse derived waste *(4)*	18.5
Non-ferrous metals	25.3	Short rotation coppice *(5)*	10.6
Food, beverages and tobacco	30.5	Tyres	32.0
Chemicals	27.8		
Textiles, clothing, leather etc.	29.9	**Petroleum:**	
Pulp, paper, printing etc.	28.8	Crude oil (weighted average)	45.7
Mineral products	27.9	Petroleum products (weighted average)	45.9
Engineering (mechanical and		Ethane	50.7
electrical engineering and			
vehicles)	30.6	Butane and propane (LPG)	49.4
Other industries	28.3	Light distillate feedstock for gasworks	47.2
		Aviation spirit and wide cut gasoline	47.3
		Aviation turbine fuel	46.2
Domestic		Motor spirit	47.1
House coal	31.0	Burning oil	46.2
Anthracite and dry steam coal	33.8	Gas/diesel oil (DERV)	45.6
Other consumers	30.0	Fuel oil	43.6
Imported coal (weighted average)	27.6	Power station oil	43.6
Exports (weighted average)	31.6	Non-fuel products (notional value)	43.2

MJ per cubic metre

	GJ per tonne		MJ per cubic metre
Coke (including low temperature		Natural gas *(6)*	39.6
carbonisation cokes)	29.8	Coke oven gas	18.0
Coke breeze	24.8	Blast furnace gas	3.0
Other manufactured solid fuel	31.1	Landfill gas	38.6
		Sewage gas	38.6

(1) Applicable to UK consumption - based on calorific value for home produced coal plus imports and, for "All consumers" net of exports.

(2) Based on a 50 per cent moisture content.

(3) Average figure covering a range of possible feedstock.

(4) Average figure based on survey returns.

(5) On an "as received" basis. On a "dry" basis 18.6 GJ per tonne.

(6) The gross calorific value of natural gas can also be expressed as 10.992 kWh per cubic metre. This value represents the average calorific value seen for gas when extracted. At this point it contains not just methane, but also some other hydrocarbon gases (ethane, butane, propane). These gases are removed before the gas enters the National Transmission System for sale to final consumers. As such, this calorific value will differ from that readers will see quoted on their gas bills.

Note: The above estimated average gross calorific values apply only to the year 2003. For calorific values of fuels in earlier years see Table A.2 and previous issues of this Digest. See the notes in Chapter 1, paragraph 1.52 regarding net calorific values. The calorific values for coal other than imported coal are based on estimates provided by the main coal producers, but with some exceptions as noted on Table A.2. The calorific values for petroleum products have been calculated using the method described in Chapter 1, paragraph 1.27. The calorific values for coke oven gas and blast furnace gas are provided by the Iron and Steel Statistics Bureau (ISSB).

Data reported in this Digest in 'thousand tonnes of oil equivalent' have been prepared on the basis of 1 tonne of oil equivalent having an energy content of 41.868 gigajoules (GJ), (1 GJ = 9.478 therms) - see notes in Chapter 1, paragraphs 1.24 to 1.26.

A.2 Estimated average gross calorific values of fuels, 1980, 1990 and 1999 to 2003

GJ per tonne (gross)

	1980	1990	1999	2000	2001	2002	2003
Coal							
All consumers *(1)(2)*	25.6	25.5	26.2	26.2	26.1	26.2r	26.1
All consumers - home produced plus imports minus exports *(1)*	..	..	27.0	27.0	26.9	26.9	26.9
Power stations *(2)*	23.8	24.8	25.5	25.6	25.4	25.6r	25.5
Power stations - home produced plus imports *(1)*	..	..	25.9	26.0	26.1	26.1	26.1
Coke ovens *(2)*	30.5	30.2	31.5	31.2	31.5	31.3	31.4
Coke ovens - home produced plus imports *(1)*	..	..	30.5	30.4	30.5	30.5	30.5
Low temperature carbonisation plants and manufactured fuel plants	19.1	29.2	30.1	30.3	30.3	30.5	31.0
Collieries	27.0	28.6	29.3	29.6	29.8	29.7	30.1
Agriculture	30.1	28.9	28.9	29.2	29.0	28.5	28.0
Iron and steel industry *(3)*	29.1	28.9	30.7	30.7	29.4r	30.4	30.4
Other industries *(1)*	27.1	27.8	26.7	26.7	26.6	26.5	26.8
Non-ferrous metals	..	23.1	25.1	25.1	24.9	25.0	25.3
Food, beverages and tobacco	28.6	28.1	29.1	29.5	29.3	30.0	30.5
Chemicals	25.8	27.3	27.2	28.7	27.1	27.4r	27.8
Textiles, clothing, leather & footwear	27.5	27.7	28.0	30.4	30.0	29.9	29.9
Pulp, paper, printing, etc.	26.5	27.9	27.7	28.7	28.8	28.9	28.8
Mineral products *(4)*	..	28.2	26.7	27.0	27.0	27.0	27.9
Engineering *(5)*	27.7	28.3	29.3	29.3	29.3	30.7	30.6
Other industry *(6)*	28.4	28.5	29.1	30.2	30.5	28.4	28.3
Unclassified	..	27.1	..	..	..	..	..
Domestic							
House coal	30.1	30.2	30.9	30.9	30.9	31.1	31.0
Anthracite and dry steam coal	33.3	33.6	33.5	33.6	33.9	33.9	33.8
Other consumers	27.5	27.5	25.3	29.2	29.2	30.1	29.6
Imported coal *(1)*	..	28.3	28.2	28.0	27.6	27.6	27.6
of which Steam coal	..	..	26.8	26.6	26.7	26.5	26.7
Coking coal	..	..	30.4	30.4	30.4	30.4	30.4
Anthracite	..	..	31.2	31.2	31.1	30.4r	30.1
Exports *(1)*	..	29.0	31.7	32.0	32.1	31.7	31.6
of which Steam coal	..	..	32.1	31.0	30.7	30.0	29.9
Anthracite	..	..	31.5	32.6	32.7	32.6	32.3
Coke *(7)*	28.1	28.1	29.8	29.8	29.8	29.8	29.8
Coke breeze	24.4	24.8	24.8	24.8	24.8	24.8	24.8
Other manufactured solid fuels *(1)*	27.6	27.6	30.9	30.8	30.6	30.9	31.1
Petroleum							
Crude oil *(1)*	45.2	45.6	45.7	45.7	45.7	45.7	45.7
Liquified petroleum gas	49.6	49.4	49.4	49.4	49.4	49.4	49.4
Ethane	52.3	50.6	50.7	50.7	50.7	50.7	50.7
LDF for gasworks/Naphtha	47.8	47.9	47.7	47.7	47.6	47.6	47.2
Aviation spirit and wide-cut gasoline (AVGAS & AVTAG)	47.2	47.3	47.3	47.3	47.3	47.3	47.3
Aviation turbine fuel (AVTUR)	46.4	46.2	46.2	46.2	46.2	46.2	46.2
Motor spirit	47.0	47.0	47.1	47.0	47.1	47.1	47.1
Burning oil	46.5	46.2	46.2	46.2	46.2	46.2	46.2
Vaporising oil	45.9	45.9	..	..	..	..	..
Gas/diesel oil (including DERV)	45.5	45.4	45.6	45.6	45.6	45.6	45.6
Fuel oil	42.8	43.2	43.2	43.1	43.5	43.4	43.6
Power station oil	42.8	43.2	43.2	43.1	43.5	43.4	43.6
Non-fuel products (notional value)	42.2	43.2	43.4	43.8	42.8	42.7	43.2
Petroleum coke	..	39.5	35.8	35.8	35.8	35.8	35.8
Orimulsion *(8)*	..	29.7	..	..	..	..	..

(1) Weighted averages.
(2) Home produced coal only.
(3) From 2001 onwards almost entirely sourced from imports.
(4) Based on information provided by the British Cement Industry Association; almost all coal used by this sector in the latest 4 years was imported.
(5) Mechanical engineering and metal products, electrical and instrument engineering and vehicle manufacture.
(6) Includes construction.
(7) Since 1995 the source of these figures has been the ISSB.
(8) Orimulsion use ceased in 1997.

Annex B
Glossary

Advanced gas-cooled reactor (AGR) A type of nuclear reactor cooled by carbon dioxide gas.

Anthracite Within this publication, anthracite is coal classified as such by UK coal producers and importers of coal. Typically it has a high heat content making it particularly suitable for certain industrial processes and for use as a domestic fuel.

Anthropogenic Produced by human activities.

Associated Gas Natural gas found in association with crude oil in a reservoir, either dissolved in the oil or as a cap above the oil.

Autogeneration Generation of electricity by companies whose main business is not electricity generation, the electricity being produced mainly for that company's own use.

Aviation spirit A light hydrocarbon oil product used to power piston-engined aircraft power units.

Aviation turbine fuel The main aviation fuel used for powering aviation gas-turbine power units (jet aircraft engine).

Benzole A colourless liquid, flammable, aromatic hydrocarbon by-product of the iron and steel making process. It is used as a solvent in the manufacture of styrenes and phenols but is also used as a motor fuel.

Biogas Energy produced from the anaerobic digestion of sewage and industrial waste.

Bitumen The residue left after the production of lubricating oil distillates and vacuum gas oil for upgrading plant feedstock. Used mainly for road making and construction purposes.

Blast furnace gas Mainly produced and consumed within the iron and steel industry. Obtained as a by-product of iron making in a blast furnace, it is recovered on leaving the furnace and used partly within the plant and partly in other steel industry processes or in power plants equipped to burn it. A similar gas is obtained when steel is made in basic oxygen steel converters; this gas is recovered and used in the same way.

Breeze Breeze can generally be described as coke screened below 19 mm (¾ inch) with no fines removed, but the screen size may vary in different areas and to meet the requirements of particular markets.

BNFL British Nuclear Fuels plc.

Burning oil A refined petroleum product, with a volatility in between that of motor spirit and gas diesel oil primarily used for heating and lighting.

Butane Hydrocarbon (C_4H_{10}), gaseous at normal temperature, but generally stored and transported as a liquid. Used as a component in Motor Spirit to improve combustion, and for cooking and heating (see LPG).

Calorific values (CVs)	The energy content of a fuel can be measured as the heat released on complete combustion. The SI (Système International - see note below) derived unit of energy and heat is the Joule. This is the energy per unit volume of the fuel and is often measured in GJ per tonne. The energy content can be expressed as an upper (or gross) value and a lower (or net) value. The difference between the two values is due to the release of energy from the condensation of water in the products of combustion. Gross calorific values are used throughout this publication.
CO_2	Carbon dioxide. Carbon dioxide contributes about 60 per cent of the potential global warming effect of man-made emissions of greenhouse gases. Although this gas is naturally emitted by living organisms, these emissions are offset by the uptake of carbon dioxide by plants during photosynthesis; they therefore tend to have no net effect on atmospheric concentrations. The burning of fossil fuels, however, releases carbon dioxide fixed by plants many millions of years ago, and thus increases its concentration in the atmosphere.
Co-firing	The burning of biomass products in fossil fuel power stations
Coke oven coke	The solid product obtained from carbonisation of coal, principally coking coal, at high temperature, it is low in moisture and volatile matter. Used mainly in iron and steel industry.
Coke oven gas	Gas produced as a by-product of solid fuel carbonisation and gasification at coke ovens, but not from low temperature carbonisation plants. Synthetic coke oven gas is mainly natural gas which is mixed with smaller amounts of blast furnace and basic oxygen steel furnace gas to produce a gas with almost the same quantities as coke oven gas.
Coking coal	Within this publication, coking coal is coal sold by producers for use in coke ovens and similar carbonising processes. The definition is not therefore determined by the calorific value or caking qualities of each batch of coal sold, although calorific values tend to be higher than for steam coal. Not all coals form cokes. For a coal to coke it must exhibit softening and agglomeration properties, ie the end product must be a coherent solid.
Colliery methane	Methane released from coal seams in deep mines which is piped to the surface and consumed at the colliery or transmitted by pipeline to consumers.
Combined cycle gas Turbine (CCGT)	Combined cycle gas turbine power stations combine gas turbines and steam turbines which are connected to one or more electrical generators in the same plant. The gas turbine (usually fuelled by natural gas or oil) produces mechanical power (to drive the generator) and heat in the form of hot exhaust gases. These gases are fed to a boiler, where steam is raised at pressure to drive a conventional steam turbine, which is also connected, to an electrical generator.
Combined Heat and Power (CHP)	CHP is the simultaneous generation of usable heat and power (usually electricity) in a single process. The term CHP is synonymous with cogeneration and total energy, which are terms often used in the United States or other Member States of the European Community. The basic elements of a CHP plant comprise one or more prime movers driving electrical generators, where the steam or hot water generated in the process is utilised via suitable heat recovery equipment for use either in industrial processes, or in community heating and space heating. For further information see Chapter 6 paragraph 6.31.

Conventional thermal power stations	These are stations which generate electricity by burning fossil fuels to produce heat to convert water into steam, which then powers steam turbines.
Cracking/conversion	A refining process using combinations of temperature, pressure and in some cases a catalyst to produce petroleum products by changing the composition of a fraction of petroleum, either by splitting existing longer carbon chain or combining shorter carbon chain components of crude oil or other refinery feedstock's. Cracking allows refiners to selectively increase the yield of specific fractions from any given input petroleum mix depending on their requirements in terms of output products.
Crude oil	A mineral oil consisting of a mixture of hydrocarbons of natural origins, yellow to black in colour, of variable density and viscosity.
DERV	Diesel engined road vehicle fuel used in internal combustion engines that are compression-ignited (see gas diesel oil).
Distillation	A process of separation of the various components of crude oil and refinery feedstocks using the different temperatures of evaporation and condensation of the different components of the mix received at the refineries.
DNC	Declared net capacity and capability are used to measure the maximum power available from generating stations at a point in time. See Chapter 5 paragraphs 5.50 and 5.51 and Chapter 7 paragraph 7.73 for a fuller definition.
Downstream	Used in oil and gas processes to cover the part of the industry after the production of the oil and gas. For example, it covers refining, supply and trading, marketing and exporting.
Embedded Generation	Embedded generation is electricity generation by plant which has been connected to the distribution networks of the public electricity distributors rather than directly to the National Grid Company's transmission systems. Typically they are either smaller stations located on industrial sites, or combined heat and power plant, or renewable energy plant such as wind farms, or refuse burner generators. The category also includes some domestic generators such as those with electric solar panels. For a description of the current structure of the electricity industry in the UK see paragraphs 5.3 to 5.8 of Chapter 5.
Energy use	Energy use of fuel mainly comprises use for lighting, heating or cooling, motive power and power for appliances. See also non-energy use.
ESA	European System of National and Regional Accounts. An integrated system of economic accounts which is the European version of the System of National Accounts (SNA).
EESs	The Energy Efficiency Commitment (formerly known as Energy Efficiency Standards of Performance) is an obligation placed on all energy suppliers to offer help and advice to their customers to improve the energy efficiency of their homes.
Ethane	A light hydrocarbon gas (C_2H_6) in natural gas and refinery gas streams (see LPG).

EU-ETS	European Union Emissions Trading Scheme. This is due to commence on 1st January 2005 and involves the trading of emissions allowances as means of reducing emissions by a fixed amount.
EUROSTAT	Statistical Office of the European Communities (SOEC).
Exports	For some parts of the energy industry, statistics on trade in energy related products can be derived from two separate sources. Firstly, figures can be reported by companies as part of systems for collecting data on specific parts of the energy industry (eg as part of the system for recording the production and disposals of oil from the UK continental shelf). Secondly, figures are also available from the general systems that exist for monitoring trade in all types of products operated by HM Customs & Excise.
Feedstock	In the refining industry, a product or a combination of products derived from crude oil, destined for further processing other than blending. It is distinguished from use as a chemical feedstock etc. See non-energy use.
Final energy Consumption	Energy consumption by final user – ie which is not being used for transformation into other forms of energy.
Fossil fuels	Coal, natural gas and fuels derived from crude oil (for example petrol and diesel) are called fossil fuels because they have been formed over long periods of time from ancient organic matter.
Fuel oils	The heavy oils from the refining process; used as fuel in furnaces and boilers of power stations, industry, in domestic and industrial heating, ships, locomotives, metallurgic operations, and industrial power plants etc.
Fuel oil - Light	Fuel oil made up of heavier straight-run or cracked distillates and used in commercial or industrial burner installations not equipped with pre-heating facilities.
Fuel oil - Medium	Other fuel oils, sometimes referred to as bunker fuels, which generally require pre-heating before being burned, but in certain climatic conditions do not require pre-heating.
Fuel oil - Heavy	Other heavier grade fuel oils which in all situations require some form of pre-heating before being burned.
Fuel poverty	The common definition of a fuel poor household is one needing to spend in excess of 10 per cent of household income to achieve a satisfactory heating regime (21°C in the living room and 18°C in the other occupied rooms).
Gas Diesel Oil	The medium oil from the refinery process; used as a fuel in diesel engines (ie internal combustion engines that are compression-ignited), burned in central heating systems and used as a feedstock for the chemical industry.
GDP	Gross Domestic Product.
GDP deflator	An index of the ratio of GDP at current prices to GDP at constant prices. It provides a measure of general price inflation within the whole economy.

Gigajoule (GJ)	A unit of energy equal to 10^9 joules (see note on joules below).

Gigajoule (GJ) A unit of energy equal to 10^9 joules (see note on joules below).

Gigawatt (GW) A unit of electrical power, equal to 10^9 watts.

Gigawatt hour (GWh) Unit of electrical energy, equal to 0.0036 TJ. A 1 GW power station running for one hour produces 1 GWh of electrical energy.

Heat sold Heat (or steam) that is produced and sold under the provision of a contract. Heat sold is derived from heat generated by Combined Heat and Power (CHP) plants and from community heating schemes without CHP plants.

HMCE HM Customs and Excise.

Imports See the first paragraph of the entry for exports above. Before the 1997 edition of the Digest, the term "arrivals" was used to distinguish figures derived from the former source from those import figures derived from the systems operated by HM Customs & Excise. To make it clearer for users, a single term is now being used for both these sources of figures (the term imports) as this more clearly states what the figures relate to, which is goods entering the UK.

International Energy Agency (IEA) The IEA is an autonomous body located in Paris which was established in November 1974 within the framework of the Organisation for Economic Co-operation and Development (OECD) to implement an international energy programme.

Indigenous production For oil this includes production from the UK Continental Shelf both onshore and offshore.

Industrial spirit Refined petroleum fractions with boiling ranges up to 200°C dependent on the use to which they are put – eg seed extraction, rubber solvents, perfume etc.

Joules A joule is a generic unit of energy in the conventional SI system (see note on SI below). It is equal to the energy dissipated by an electrical current of 1 ampere driven by 1 volt for 1 second; it is also equal to twice the energy of motion in a mass of 1 kilogram moving at 1 metre per second.

Landfill gas The methane-rich biogas formed from the decomposition of organic material in landfill.

LDF Light distillate feedstock.

Liquefied petroleum Gas (LPG) Gas usually propane or butane, derived from oil and put under pressure so that it is in liquid form. Often used to power portable cooking stoves or heaters and to fuel some types of vehicle, eg some specially adapted road vehicles, forklift trucks.

Lead Replacement Petrol (LRP) An alternative to Leaded Petrol containing a different additive to lead (in the UK usually potassium based) to perform the lubrication functions of lead additives in reducing engine wear.

Lubricating oils Refined heavy distillates obtained from the vacuum distillation of petroleum residues. Includes liquid and solid hydrocarbons sold by the lubricating oil trade, either alone or blended with fixed oils, metallic soaps and other organic and/or inorganic bodies.

Magnox	A type of gas-cooled nuclear fission reactor developed in the UK, so called because of the magnesium alloy used to clad the uranium fuel.
Major power producers	Companies whose prime purpose is the generation of electricity (paragraph 5.46 of Chapter 5 gives a full list of major power producers).
Motor spirit	Blended light petroleum product used as a fuel in spark-ignition internal combustion engines (other than aircraft engines).
Natural gas	Natural gas is a mixture of naturally occurring gases found either in isolation, or associated with crude oil, in underground reservoirs. The main component is methane; ethane, propane, butane, hydrogen sulphide and carbon dioxide may also be present, but these are mostly removed at or near the well head in gas processing plants.
Naphtha	(Light distillate feedstock) – Petroleum distillate boiling predominantly below 200°C.
Natural gas - compressed	Natural gas that has been compressed to reduce the volume it occupies to make it easier to transport other than in pipelines. Whilst other petroleum gases can be compressed such that they move into liquid form, the volatility of natural gas is such that liquefaction cannot be achieved without very high pressures and low temperatures being used. As such, the compressed form is usually used as a "half-way house".
Natural gas liquids (NGLs)	A mixture of liquids derived from natural gas and crude oil during the production process, including propane, butane, ethane and gasoline components (pentanes plus).
NETA	New Electricity Trading Arrangements - In England and Wales these arrangements replaced "the pool" from 27 March 2001. The arrangements are based on bi-lateral trading between generators, suppliers, traders and customers and are designed to be more efficient, and provide more market choice.
Non-energy use	Includes fuel used for chemical feedstock, solvents, lubricants, and road making material.
NFFO	Non Fossil Fuel Obligation. The 1989 Electricity Act empowers the Secretary of State to make orders requiring the Regional Electricity Companies in England and Wales to secure specified amounts of electricity from renewable sources.
NO_X	Nitrogen oxides. A number of nitrogen compounds including nitrogen dioxide are formed in combustion processes when nitrogen in the air or the fuel combines with oxygen. These compounds can add to the natural acidity of rainfall.
OFGEM	The regulatory office for gas and electricity markets.
Orimulsion	An emulsion of bitumen in water that can be used as a fuel in some power stations.
ONS	Office for National Statistics.
OTS	Overseas Trade Statistics of the United Kingdom.
Patent fuel	A composition fuel manufactured from coal fines by shaping with the addition of a binding agent (typically pitch). The term manufactured solid fuel is also used.

Petrochemical feedstock	All petroleum products intended for use in the manufacture of petroleum chemicals. This includes middle distillate feedstock of which there are several grades depending on viscosity. The boiling point ranges between 200 C and 400 C.
Petroleum cokes	Carbonaceous material derived from hydrocarbon oils, uses for which include metallurgical electrode manufacture and in the manufacture of cement.
Petroleum wax	Includes paraffin wax, which is a white crystalline hydrocarbon material of low oil content normally obtained during the refining of lubricating oil distillate, paraffin scale, slack wax, microcrystalline wax and wax emulsions.
Photovoltaics	The direct conversion of solar radiation into electricity by the interaction of light with the electrons in a semiconductor device or cell.
Plant capacity	The maximum power available from a power station at a point in time (see also paragraph 5.50 of Chapter 5).
Plant loads, demands and efficiency	Measures of how intensively and efficiently power stations are being used. These terms are defined in paragraphs 5.52 and 5.53 of Chapter 5.
PPRS	Petroleum production reporting system. Licensees operating in the UK Continental Shelf are required to make monthly returns on their production of hydrocarbons (oil and gas) to the DTI. This information is recorded in the PPRS, which is used to report flows, stocks and uses of hydrocarbon from the well-head through to final disposal from a pipeline or terminal (see paragraphs F.29 to F.31 of Annex F on DTI's energy statistics website).
Process oils	Partially processed feedstocks which require further processing before being classified as a finished product suitable for sale. They can also be used as a reaction medium in the production process.
Primary fuels	Fuels obtained directly from natural sources, eg coal, oil and natural gas.
Primary electricity	Electricity obtained other than from fossil fuel sources, eg nuclear, hydro and other non-thermal renewables. Imports of electricity are also included.
Propane	Hydrocarbon containing three carbon atoms (C_3H_8), gaseous at normal temperature, but generally stored and transported under pressure as a liquid.
PWR	Pressurised water reactor. A nuclear fission reactor cooled by ordinary water kept from boiling by containment under high pressure.
Reforming	Processes by which the molecular structure of different fractions of petroleum can be modified. It usually involves some form of catalyst, most often platinum, and allows the conversion of lower grades of petroleum product into higher grades, improving their octane rating. It is a generic term for processes such as cracking, cyclization, dehydrogenation and isomerisation. These processes generally led to the production of hydrogen as a by-product, which can be used in the refineries in some desulphurization procedures.

Refinery fuel	Petroleum products produced by the refining process that are used as fuel at refineries.
Renewable energy sources	Renewable energy includes solar power, wind, wave and tide, and hydroelectricity. Solid renewable energy sources consist of wood, straw, short rotation coppice, other biomass and the biodegradable fraction of wastes. Gaseous renewables consist of landfill gas and sewage gas. Non-biodegradable wastes are not counted as a renewables source but appear in the Renewable sources of energy chapter of this Digest for completeness.
Reserves	With oil and gas these relate to the quantities identified as being present in underground cavities. The actual amounts that can be recovered depend on the level of technology available and existing economic situations. These continually change; hence the level of the UK's reserves can change quite independently of whether or not new reserves have been identified.
SI (Système International)	Refers to the agreed conventions for the measurement of physical quantities.
SIC	Standard Industrial Classification in the UK. Last revised in 2003 and known as SIC(2003), replaced previous classifications SIC(92), SIC(80) and SIC(68). SIC(92) was compatible with European Union classification NACE Rev1 (Nomenclature générale des activités économiques dans les Communautés européennes as revised in October 1990) and similarly SIC(2003) is consistent with NACE Rev1.1 which came into effect in January 2003. Classification systems need to be periodically revised because over time new products, processes and industries emerge.
Secondary fuels	Fuels derived from natural primary sources of energy. For example electricity generated from burning coal, gas or oil is a secondary fuel, as are coke and coke oven gas.
Steam coal	Within this publication, steam coal is coal classified as such by UK coal producers and by importers of coal. It tends to be coal having lower calorific values; the type of coal that is typically used for steam raising.
SO$_2$	Sulphur Dioxide. Sulphur dioxide is a gas produced by the combustion of sulphur-containing fuels such as coal and oil.
Synthetic coke oven gas	Mainly a natural gas, which is mixed with smaller amounts of blast furnace, and BOS (basic oxygen steel furnace) gas to produce a gas with almost the same quantities as coke oven gas.
Temperature correction	The temperature corrected series of total inland fuel consumption indicates what annual consumption might have been if the average temperature during the year had been the same as the average for the years 1961 to 1990.
Thermal Sources of Electricity	These include coal, oil, natural gas, nuclear, landfill gas, sewage gas, municipal solid waste, farm waste, tyres, poultry litter, short rotation coppice, straw, coke oven gas, blast furnace gas, and waste products from chemical processes.
Tonne of oil equivalent (toe)	A common unit of measurement which enables different fuels to be compared and aggregated. (See Chapter 1 paragraphs 1.24 to 1.25 for further information and Annex A page 197 for conversion factors).

Tars	Viscous materials usually derived from the destructive distillation of coal which are by-products of the coke and iron making processes.
Therm	A common unit of measurement similar to a tonne of oil equivalent which enables different fuels to be compared and aggregated. (see Annex A.)
Thermal efficiency	The thermal efficiency of a power station is the efficiency with which heat energy contained in fuel is converted into electrical energy. It is calculated for fossil fuel burning stations by expressing electricity supplied as a percentage of the total energy content of the fuel consumed (based on average gross calorific values). For nuclear stations it is calculated using the quantity of heat released as a result of fission of the nuclear fuel inside the reactor.
UKCS	United Kingdom Continental Shelf.
UKPIA	UK Petroleum Industry Association. The trade association for the UK petroleum industry.
Ultra low sulphur Diesel (ULSD)	A grade of diesel fuel which has a much lower sulphur content (less than 0.005 per cent or 50 parts per million) and of a slightly higher volatility than ordinary diesel fuels. As a result it produces fewer emissions when burned. As such it enjoys a lower rate of excise duty in the UK than ordinary diesel (by 3 pence per litre) to promote its use. Virtually 100 per cent of sales of DERV fuel in the UK are ULSD.
Ultra low sulphur Petrol (ULSP)	A grade of motor spirit with a similar level of sulphur to ULSD (less than 0.005 per cent or 50 parts per million). In the March 2000 Budget it was announced that a lower rate of excise duty than ordinary petrol for this fuel would be introduced during 2000, which was increased to 3 pence per litre in the March 2001 Budget. It has quickly replaced ordinary premium grade unleaded petrol in the UK market place.
Upstream	A term to cover the activities related to the exploration, production and delivery to a terminal or other facility of oil or gas for export or onward shipment within the UK.
VAT	Value added tax.
Watt (W)	The conventional unit to measure a rate of flow of energy. One watt amounts to 1 joule per second.
White spirit	A highly refined distillate with a boiling range of about 150°C to 200°C used as a paint solvent and for dry cleaning purposes etc.

Annex C
Further sources of United Kingdom energy publications

Some of the publications listed below give shorter term statistics, some provide further information about energy production and consumption in the United Kingdom and in other countries, and others provide more detail on a country or fuel industry basis. The list also covers recent publications on energy issues and policy, including statistical information, produced or commissioned by the DTI. The list is not exhaustive and the titles of publications and publishers may alter. Unless otherwise stated, all titles are available from

DTI Publications Orderline
Web: www.dti.gov.uk/publications
Phone: 0870 150 2500
Address: ADMAIL, 528, London, SW1W 0YT
Email: publications@dti.gsi.gov.uk

and can also be found on the DTI Web site at www.dti.gov.uk/energy/inform/ .

Department of Trade and Industry publications on energy

Energy Statistics
Monthly, quarterly and annual statistics on production and consumption of overall energy and individual fuels in the United Kingdom together with energy prices is available in MS Excel format on the Internet at www.dti.gov.uk/energy/inform/energy_stats/ .

Energy Trends
Quarterly publication. Covers all major aspects of energy. Provides a comprehensive picture of energy production and use. Contains analysis of data and articles covering energy issues. Available on subscription, with Quarterly Energy Prices publication, from EMU3-SID2, Department of Trade and Industry, Bay 232, 1 Victoria Street, London, SW1H 0ET, tel. 020-7215 2697/2698. Single copies are available from the DTI Publications Orderline at the address given at the start of this Annex, price £5.

Quarterly Energy Prices
Quarterly publication. From June 2001 replaced energy prices information formerly available in the monthly publication Energy Trends and the annual Digest of UK Energy Statistics. Contains tables, charts and commentary covering energy prices to domestic and industrial consumers for all the major fuels as well as presenting comparisons of fuel prices in the European Union and G7 countries. Available on subscription, with Energy Trends publication, from EMU3-SID2, Department of Trade and Industry, Bay 232, 1 Victoria Street, London, SW1H 0ET, tel. 020-7215 2697/2698. Single copies are available from the DTI Publications Orderline at the address given at the start of this Annex, price £7.

Energy Sector Indicators 2004
Energy Sector Indicators for 2004 was published on 26 April 2004 as a supplement to the First Annual Report on the Energy White Paper (see below). The content is designed to show the extent to which secure, diverse and sustainable supplies of energy to UK Businesses and consumers at competitive prices are ensured. As well as the four key indicators used in the Report, and 27 supporting indicators there is the full range of background indicators that have been published in the corresponding booklet for earlier years. Energy Sector Indicators 2004 is available on the DTI web site at:
www.dti.gov.uk/energy/inform/energy_indicators/index.shtml
and in hard copy (free of charge) from DTI Publications Orderline.

UK Energy in Brief

This booklet summarises the latest statistics on energy production, consumption and prices in the United Kingdom. The figures are taken from "Digest of UK Energy Statistics". Available free from EMU3-SID2, Department of Trade and Industry, Bay 232, 1 Victoria Street, London, SW1H 0ET, tel. 020-7215 2697/2698 and from the DTI Publications Orderline

Development of the Oil and Gas Resources of the United Kingdom

Publication of Development of UK Oil and Gas Resources, commonly known as the "Brown Book", ended with the 2001 edition. That edition, as well as more up-to-date information on the UK offshore industry, is available via DTI's Oil and Gas website: www.og.dti.gov.uk .

Industrial Energy Markets: Energy markets in UK manufacturing industry 1973 to 1993 - Energy Paper 64

Using tables of data drawn from the 1989 Purchases Inquiry conducted by the Office for National Statistics, the report, which updates one produced in 1989, sets out the implications for the trends in industrial energy consumption over the period from 1973 to 1993. Available from The Stationery Office, tel 0870 600 5522 and can be ordered through Government Bookshops. Not available on the Internet.

Energy Consumption in the UK

Energy Consumption in the United Kingdom brings together statistics from a variety of sources to produce a comprehensive review of energy consumption in the UK since the 1970s. This booklet describes the key trends in energy consumption in the UK since 1970 with a particular focus on trends since 1990. The information is presented in five sections covering firstly overall energy consumption, then energy consumption in the transport, domestic, industrial and service sectors. It includes an analysis of the factors driving the changes in energy consumption, the impact of increasing activity, increased efficiency, and structural change in the economy, while detailed tables can be found on the Internet at www.dti.gov.uk/energy/inform/energy_consumption/ecuk.pdf .

Energy Projections for the UK:- Energy Paper 68

Energy Paper 68 presents the results of an exercise to update the Government's projections of future UK energy demand and related emissions of carbon and sulphur dioxides to 2020. It builds on work issued as a working paper in March 2000 and its projections underpin the Climate Change Programme launched by the DETR in November 2000. The paper contributes to policy development and assessment of the UK's efforts to meet its national and international greenhouse gases targets. Available from The Stationery Office, tel 0870 600 5522.

Energy Paper 68 Update

To support the analysis underlying the introduction of the European Union Emissions Trading Scheme, notably the National Allocation Plan (NAP), DTI have updated its energy and emissions projections, last published in Energy Paper 68 (see above). A working paper showing revised energy projections has been published on the DTI website. It is available at:
www.dti.gov.uk/energy/sepn/euets.shtml#uep . Updated energy projections have informed the NAP which was submitted to the European Commission in April 2004.

Social Effects of Energy Liberalisation: The UK Experience

This paper reviews the impact of liberalisation of the energy markets, and the effects on the fuel industries, the consumer and the environment. Available free from EMU3-SID2, Department of Trade and Industry, Bay 232, 1 Victoria Street, London, SW1H 0ET, tel. 020-7215 2697/2698.

Energy Liberalisation Indicators in Europe: A preliminary report of a study carried out by OXERA for the Governments of the UK and the Netherlands.

This paper presents preliminary results from a study carried out by OXERA on behalf of the Governments of the UK and the Netherlands. The study develops a set of indicators, within a hierarchical structure, for monitoring the development of competition in gas and electricity markets across Europe. The study mainly concentrates on the electricity market and presents some preliminary results for a subset of European countries including the UK and Netherlands. Available free from EMU3-SID2, Department of Trade and Industry, Bay 232, 1 Victoria Street, London, SW1H 0ET, tel. 020-7215 2697/2698.

Energy Liberalisation Indicators in Europe: A consultation paper based on a study carried out by OXERA for the Governments of the UK and the Netherlands.

This consultation paper sets out the methodology used and presents results for a subset of European countries including the UK and the Netherlands. Available free from EMU3-SID2, Department of Trade and Industry, Bay 232, 1 Victoria Street, London SW1H 0ET, tel. 020-7215 2697/2698.

Social, Environmental and Security of Supply Policies in a Competitive Energy Market: A Review of Delivery Mechanisms in the United Kingdom, Summary Paper

This paper outlines the UK experience so far in using competitive energy markets to deliver social, environmental and security of supply policies. It highlights the benefits that have emerged from this approach and sets out the instruments the Government has used to enhance policy delivery. Available free from EMU3-SID2, Department of Trade and Industry, Bay 232, 1 Victoria Street, London, SW1H 0ET, tel. 020-7215 2697/2698.

The UK Fuel Poverty Strategy: November 2001

Produced by the Department of Trade and Industry and the Department for Environment, Food and Rural Affairs (Defra). The strategy sets out the Government's objectives, policies and targets for alleviating fuel poverty in the UK over the next 10 years. Available free from Department of Trade and Industry Publications Orderline.

The UK Fuel Poverty Strategy, 1st and 2nd Annual Progress Reports

Produced by the Department of Trade and Industry and Defra in association with the Devolved Administrations. These reports set out what progress has been made on tackling fuel poverty following the publication of the UK Fuel Poverty Strategy in November 2001. They were accompanied by detailed annexes published on the DTI web site. One of these accompanying the second report was an update of the 19 Fuel Poverty Indicators as developed by the Fuel Poverty Monitoring and Technical Group. Also published with the second report was a consultation document detailing proposed amendments to the methodology by which fuel poverty figures for England are calculated. The web references for these documents are:
www.dti.gov.uk/energy/consumers/fuel_poverty/index.shtml
and
www.dti.gov.uk/energy/consumers/fuel_poverty/fuel_strategy.shtml .
The reports are also available free from Department of Trade and Industry Publications Orderline.

Energy– Its impact on the environment and society

This booklet outlines the environmental and social impacts of energy production and use. It includes information on carbon dioxide and other emissions, the environmental consequences of energy production and supply activities and an analysis of the drivers of energy demand. It also covers the evolution and impact of competition in the energy market, quality of service and fuel poverty. Available free from EMU3-SID2, Department of Trade and Industry, Bay 232, 1 Victoria Street, London SW1H 0ET, tel. 020-7215 2697/2698 and from the DTI Publications Orderline.

Energy White Paper and 1st Annual Report

The Government's Energy White Paper, "Our energy future - creating a low carbon economy", was published by the Secretary of State for Trade and Industry on 24 February 2003. The report addresses the challenges facing energy, by setting out a long-term strategic vision for energy policy. It is the product of extensive consultative and analytical work and has over 6,500 contributions. The White Paper is available on the DTI web site at www.dti.gov.uk/energy/whitepaper/index.shtml and in hard copy from The Stationery Office or through Government Bookshops.

The first annual report, published in April 2004, reviews progress over the last 12 months and the way ahead. It is available on the DTI web site at:
www.dti.gov.uk/energy/sepn/firstannualreport.shtml

Other publications including energy information

General
Basic Statistics of the Community (annual); *Statistical Office of the European Communities*
Digest of Welsh Statistics (annual); *Welsh Office* (available from ESS Division, Welsh Office, Cathays Park, Cardiff)
Eurostatistics - Data for Short Term Analysis; *Statistical Office of the European Communities*
Monthly Digest of Statistics; *Office for National Statistics*
Northern Ireland Annual Abstract of Statistics (annual); *Department of Finance and Personnel,* (available from the Policy & Planning Unit, Department of Finance & Personnel, Stormont, Belfast BT4 3SW)
Overseas Trade Statistics of the United Kingdom; *H.M. Customs & Excise*
  - Business Monitor MM20 (monthly) (extra-EU trade only)
  - Business Monitor MM20A (monthly) (intra and extraEU
  - trade data, relatively limited level of production detail)
  - Business Monitor MQ20 (quarterly) (intra-EU trade only)
  - Business Monitor MA20 (annual) (intra- and extra-EU trade);
Purchases Inquiry 1989, 1994-1998; Office *for National Statistics*
Rapid Reports - energy and industry (ad hoc); *Statistical Office of the European Communities*
Regional Trends (annual); *Office for National Statistics*
Scottish Abstract of Statistics (annual); *Scottish Office*
United Kingdom Minerals Yearbook (annual); *British Geological Survey* (available from the British Geological Survey, Keyworth, Nottingham, NG12 5GG)
Yearbook of Regional Statistics (annual); *Statistical Office of the European Communities*

Energy
Annual Bulletin of General Energy Statistics for Europe; *United Nations Economic Commission for Europe*
BP Statistical Review of World Energy (annual); (available from The Editor, BP Statistical Review, The British Petroleum Company plc, Corporate Communications Services, Britannic House, 1 Finsbury Circus, London EC2M 7BA)
Energy - Monthly Statistics; *Statistical Office of the European Communities*
Energy Balances of OECD Countries (annual); *OECD International Energy Agency*
Energy Statistics and Balances of OECD Countries (annual); *OECD International Energy Agency*
Energy Statistics and Balances of Non-OECD Countries (annual); *OECD International Energy Agency*

Energy - Yearly Statistics; *Statistical Office of the European Communities*
UN Energy Statistics Yearbook (annual); *United Nations Statistical Office*

Coal
Annual Bulletin of Coal Statistics for Europe; *United Nations Economic Commission for Europe*
Annual Reports and Accounts of The Coal Authority and the private coal companies; (*apply to the Headquarters of the company concerned)*
Coal Information (annual); *OECD International Energy Agency*

Oil and gas
Annual Bulletin of Gas Statistics for Europe; *United Nations Economic Commission for Europe*
BP Review of World Gas (annual); (*available from British Petroleum Company plc, Corporate Communications Services, Britannic House, 1 Finsbury Circus, London EC2M 7BA)*
Annual Reports and Accounts of National Grid Transco, Centrica and other independent gas supply companies; (contact *the Headquarters of the company concerned directly)*
Oil and Gas Information (annual); *OECD International Energy Agency*
Quarterly Oil Statistics and Energy Balances; *OECD International Energy Agency*
UK Petroleum Industry Statistics Consumption and Refinery Production (annual and quarterly); *Institute of Petroleum (available from IP, 61 New Cavendish Street, London W1M 8AR)*

Electricity
Annual Bulletin of Electric Energy Statistics for Europe; *United Nations Economic Commission for Europe*

Annual Reports and Accounts of the Electricity Supply Companies, Distributed Companies and Generators; (*apply to the Headquarters of the company concerned*)
Annual Report of the Office of Electricity Regulation; OFGEM
Electricity Supply in OECD Countries; *OECD International Energy Agency*
National Grid Company - Seven Year Statement - (annual) *National Grid Transco - For further details telephone 01203 423065*
Operation of Nuclear Power Stations (annual); *Statistical Office of the European Communities*
Electricity Information (annual); *OECD International Energy Agency*

Prices
Energy Prices (annual); *Statistical Office of the European Communities* (summarises price information published in the European Commissions Weekly Oil Price, and half-yearly Statistics in Focus on Gas Prices and Electricity Prices)
Energy Prices and Taxes (quarterly); *OECD International Energy Agency*
Electricity prices (annual); *Eurostat*
Gas prices (annual); *Eurostat*

Environment
Digest of Environmental Statistics (Annual); *Department of the Environment, Food and Rural Affairs (Defra).*
Indicators of Sustainable Development for the United Kingdom; *Department of the Environment, Food and Rural Affairs (Defra)*
Quality of life counts, Indicators for a strategy for sustainable development for the United Kingdom: a baseline assessment; *Department of the Environment, Food and Rural Affairs (Defra)*
Environment Statistics (annual); *Eurostat*
UK Environment (adhoc/one-off release); *Department of the Environment, Food and Rural Affairs (Defra)*

Renewables
New and Renewable Energy, Prospects for the 21st Century. A series of consultation papers reports on the outcome of the review conducted by the Government and the possible ways forward in implementing the Government's new drive for renewables. Available on the DTI website and via the DTI Publications Orderline, publications@dti.gsi.gov.uk

Fuel Poverty
English House Condition Survey – 1996 Energy Report:- Produced by the Department of Environment, Food and Rural Affairs. This report presents the detailed findings of the 1996 English House Condition Survey (EHCS) on the energy efficiency and thermal performance of the stock, energy action by occupants and landlords and the potential for future energy and carbon savings.

Useful energy related websites

The DTI website can be found at www.dti.gov.uk, the energy information and statistics website is at www.dti.gov.uk/energy/inform/index.shtml

Other Government websites

Central Office of Information	www.nds.coi.gov.uk
Customs and Excise	www.hmce.gov.uk
Department for Environment, Food and Rural Affairs	www.defra.gov.uk
HM Government Online	www.direct.gov.uk/
Department for Transport	www.dft.gov.uk
National Statistics	www.statistics.gov.uk
Northern Ireland Departments	www.northernireland.gov.uk
Office of the Deputy Prime Minister	www.odpm.gov.uk
Ofgem	www.ofgem.gov.uk
Scottish Executive	www.scotland.gov.uk
Scottish Parliament	www.scottish.parliament.uk
The National Assembly for Wales	www.wales.gov.uk
UK Parliament	www.parliament.uk

Other useful energy related websites

Association of Electricity Producers	www.aepuk.com
BP	www.bp.com/home.do
British Wind Energy Association	www.bwea.com
Building Research Establishment	www.bre.co.uk
Coal Authority	www.coal.gov.uk/
Energywatch	www.energywatch.org.uk/
Energy Networks Association	www.energynetworks.org
Europa (European Union Online)	www.europa.eu.int/
Eurostat	www.europa.eu.int/comm/eurostat/
Future Energy Solutions	www.future-energy-solutions.com
Institute of Energy	www.dti.gov.uk/JEMU
Institute of Petroleum	www.petroleum.co.uk
Interconnector (UK) Ltd	www.interconnector.com
International Energy Agency	www.iea.org
Iron and Steel Statistics Bureau	www.issb.co.uk
National Grid Transco	www.ngtgroup.com
NETCEN (Air quality estimates)	www.airquality.co.uk
The Stationery Office	www.the-stationery-office.co.uk/
UK Offshore Operators Association (UKOOA)	www.ukooa.co.uk
UK Petroleum Industry Association	www.ukpia.com
United Nations Statistics Division	unstats.un.org/unsd/default.htm
US Department of Energy	www.energy.gov
US Energy Information Administration	www.eia.doe.gov

Annex D
Major events in the Energy Industry

2004

Sustainable Energy Policy

DTI published the first annual report on implementation of the Energy White Paper on 26 April as part of a series of documents, all of which contribute to creating a low-carbon economy. These included the Government's Energy Efficiency Implementation Plan (DEFRA), the Combined Heat and Power strategy (DEFRA), and a consultation paper about biofuels (DFT). A range of statistical indicators to monitor progress towards the goals of the White Paper was also published in the booklet "UK Energy Sector Indicators". The annual report describes a wide range of achievements over the last 12 months: a "good start" to a 50-year programme to meet ambitious goals. More information, including the UK energy sector indicators and an annex on achievements in the English regions, is at

www.dti.gov.uk/energy/sepn/firstannualreport.shtml.

Energy Bill

The Energy Bill completed all its stages in the House of Lords on schedule by 20 April and was on track to receive Royal Assent by July.

Fuel Poverty

On 26 April 2004, the Government published its second annual progress report on the UK Fuel Poverty strategy, which is available on the Internet at: www.dti.gov.uk/energy/consumers/fuel_poverty/index.shtml . The report showed continuing good progress: the number of UK households in fuel poverty was down from around 5½ million in 1996 to around 2¼ million in 2002. A number of detailed annexes to the report (published on the internet only), provide various other indicators of progress in related areas, and present a number of proposals for improvements to the methodology used to produce figures for fuel poverty for England.

The independent Fuel Poverty Advisory Group published its second report in February 2004. The Group made several recommendations, the key ones of which were:

- There should be a measurable joint Public Service Agreement between DTI and DEFRA covering fuel poverty;
- Current programmes will not be sufficient to meet the Government target for England by 2010; they need to be increased by at least 50 per cent. The Government should set out its own estimates;
- There should be better integration of Warm Front and the Energy Efficiency Commitment when these are revised in 2005;
- There should be Government funding for extension of the gas network, to tackle fuel poverty;
- Government Departments should more proactively address fuel poverty, and co-ordinate their activity better.

Emissions Trading

The EU Emissions Trading Scheme (EU-ETS) will start in January 2005. Up to 2000 UK installations, which collectively emit about half of the economy's carbon dioxide emissions will participate. The UK's National Allocation Plant (NAP), setting out how it is intended to implement the scheme, was submitted to the European Commission on 30 April. A consultation document was issued alongside this in early May. The NAPs submitted by Member States will be subject to review by other member states and by the Commission. Final approval of NAPs by the Commission is due in October 2004.

Coal

Hatfield colliery closed in January 2004. Wistow mine closed in May 2004 as part of the run down of the Selby complex.

Oil and gas

US oil firm Apache announced plans to spend around £137 million in 2004 on various projects in the Forties field in the North Sea. This included drilling more than 20 wells to gain a "substantial" increase in production. Forties - acquired from BP for around £400 million in January 2003 - currently produces around 50,000 barrels of oil per day (as of May 2004).

The 22nd Offshore and 12th Onshore Oil and Gas Licensing Rounds were announced on 4 March. The 22nd Round makes available the largest number of offshore blocks since the 2nd Round in 1965. As well as continuing to include options for "promote" licences and traditional licences, the Round offers a further new form of licence, the "frontier" licence, for blocks in the Atlantic Margin, West of the Shetland Islands. Applications were due in on 3 and 4 June.

Electricity

The findings of the investigation by DTI's Engineering Inspectorate into the major power failures in London on 28 August 2003 and in Birmingham on 5 September 2003 were communicated to the respective electricity companies in January. Inspectors worked closely with the companies to ensure their recommendations were taken forward.

Nuclear

The Secretary of State announced on 5 January that British Energy (BE) had completed the sale of its interest in its US joint venture, Amergen, in December. All amounts outstanding under the Government's loan facility to BE have been paid off, but facility remained available to BE up to a maximum of £200 million.

2003

Sustainable Energy Policy

The Sustainable Energy Policy Network (SEPN) website was launched in June 2003. SEPN represents a new way of working for government, ensuring the right communications and links are made across and beyond government to deliver the White Paper. The website makes public which officials are responsible for progressing these objectives.

Royal Assent for the Brian White Sustainable Energy Act was announced on Thursday 30 October. The Act implements the DTI Energy White Paper commitment to provide statutory backing to regulatory impact assessments, including environmental impact assessments, undertaken by Ofgem for all significant new policies. It also provides the legal basis for accessing surplus funds from the Non-Fossil Fuels Obligation held by Ofgem.

Energy White Paper

On 24 February 2003 the Government published its Energy White Paper "Our energy future – creating a low carbon economy". The White Paper set out a new energy policy, designed to deal with the three major challenges that confront the UK's energy system: the challenge of climate change, the challenge of declining indigenous energy supplies, and the need to keep the UK's energy infrastructure up to date with changing technologies and needs.

To address these challenges, the White Paper set four new goals for energy policy: to put the United Kingdom on a path to cut carbon dioxide emissions by some 60 per cent by about 2050, with real progress by 2020; to maintain the reliability of energy supplies; to promote competitive energy markets in the UK and beyond, helping to raise the rate of sustainable economic growth and improve UK productivity; and to ensure that every home is adequately and affordably heated.

For the first time, the environment was put at the heart of Government's energy policy, causing energy efficiency and renewables to feature prominently in the White Paper, as the main ways of delivering carbon cuts. A new Europe-wide emissions trading scheme to be introduced in 2005 will create a powerful incentive to producers and consumers to use less energy and to switch to lower or zero-carbon forms of electricity.

Energy Bill

The Energy Bill was designed to establish the Nuclear Decommissioning Agency, create the GB-wide electricity market, "BETTA", and develop the legal framework necessary to approve offshore renewable energy developments. Stephen Timms, the Energy Minister, presented the draft Bill to the Legislative Programme Committee on 18 November. The LP Committee cleared the Bill and it was introduced in the House of Lords on 27 November, immediately after the Queens Speech, and had a second reading on 11 December.

Energy Markets

On 17 June, Stephen Timms wrote to companies involved in BETTA to confirm that the BETTA system would go-live in April 2005. A consultation on transmission charging in the GB-wide electricity trading regime under BETTA was published in August.

Proposals to complete the liberalisation of the electricity and gas markets across the EU were adopted on 15 June. The DTI played a leading role in the Energy Council in ensuring the measures will produce a competitive and open market by 2007.

Fuel Poverty

On 4 March 2003, the Government published its first annual progress report on the UK Fuel poverty strategy:
www.dti.gov.uk/energy/consumers/fuel_poverty/index.shtml.
The Fuel Poverty Advisory Group also reported on this date for the first time. Their report is also available at the web address given above.

Renewables Obligation

It was announced in December that the Renewables Obligation, governing how much energy suppliers must provide from Green energy sources, is to be extended from 2011/12 to 2015/16. This is expected to lead to the development of enough renewable energy to power 3 million homes. A number of other changes to the Obligation were also announced in 2003: co-firing (ie of biomass and conventional fuels) will be extended to give more time for an energy crop market to develop, small generators will be able to earn Renewable Obligation Certificates (ROCs) by accumulating their output over a year and the conversion of fossil fuelled generating stations to pure biomass, without the need for refurbishment, will be allowed.

Energy Efficiency

In the 2003 Budget in April the Government noted that economic growth and social progress must be balanced with action to protect and improve the environment. One of the main areas in which the Government confirmed that it would be undertaking further consultation was on specific measures to encourage household energy efficiency, following on from an earlier consultation on the use of economic instruments to promote energy efficiency in the domestic sector.

Coal

Clipstone colliery closed in April and in June Betwys colliery announced closure. Output from the Selby complex began to decline prior to its proposed closure by June 2004.

Coal Investment Aid, with a budget of £60m was launched in June. It is intended to create or safeguard jobs in socially and economically disadvantaged areas by encouraging coal producers to enter into commercially realistic projects that maintain access to coal reserves.

The Coal Health Claims Unit has worked to accelerate the rate at which payments are made to claimants. A redeveloped coalclaims.com website launched. The Department also began making general damages offers on posthumous Vibration White Finger cases where no medical evidence is available.

Oil and Gas

In February 2003, to encourage a wider range of bids for offshore oil and gas exploration licences, the DTI enhanced the licensing system to include a new "promote" licence in the 21st Offshore Licensing Round. This new type of licence, offered at a 10th of the price of a traditional licence for the first 2 years of its term, is aimed at attracting smaller newcomers wishing to find oil and gas. Its introduction led to a good response in the 21st Round and an increase in licence applications. More information can be found on the Oil and Gas website: www.og.dti.gov.uk .

On 31 July Energy Minister Stephen Timms announced the results of the 21st Offshore Round, offering 88 new North Sea licences. The licences went to 62 companies, 27 being new entrants to the area. The awards underlined the success of the new "Promote" licences, mentioned above.

In October 2003, the Energy Minister met with his Norwegian counterpart to sign an agreement on key principles that will be incorporated in a new Framework Treaty covering future cross-border oil and gas co-operation between the two countries. The Agreement opens the way for the construction of a large gas pipeline (Langeled) from Norwegian offshore infrastructure capable of delivering up to 20 per cent of the UK's current gas requirements from Winter 2006/7 and clarifies the regulatory regime that would apply to a range to future cross-border projects.

In November, Mr Timms gave approval to the giant Buzzard oil field. With an estimated 500 million barrels of oil to be recovered, and overall investment of £1.35 billion – the largest in the UK North Sea in the last decade, and equivalent to around a third of the industry total annual expenditure, Buzzard will make a significant contribution to the UK's oil production and to the economy.

Power cuts

On 14 August, a large area of the North East USA, including New York, and of Eastern Canada suffered cascading power cuts. Some 60 million people were affected within a matter of minutes as the system operators lost control of the networks, causing an uncontrolled series of power cuts.

On 28 August a power failure occurred affecting large parts of South London and parts of Kent. National Grid Transco redirected supplies via another circuit but at this time a separate fault occurred causing loss of supply to 410,000 customers. Power was restored to all customers in the space of 40 minutes.

Following power failures in London and the West Midlands, Stephen Timms asked the Engineering Inspectorate to carry out a detailed investigation of these faults, including a review of power supply arrangements for London Underground and Network Rail. In parallel with this, the EI worked on a joint investigation with Ofgem into these incidents. The findings of the investigation by the Engineering Inspectorate were communicated to the respective electricity companies in January and inspectors worked closely with the companies to ensure their recommendations were taken forward.

Electricity

In January 2003, Powergen announced the closure at the end of March of two already partly mothballed coal-fired power stations that it had acquired from TXU in October 2002, namely Drakelow and High Marnham. It said it would also mothball two 675 MW oil-fired units at Grain and one 450 MW gas fired unit at Killingholme, the three of which had already earmarked for mothballing in the previous autumn but had kept running to provide electricity for the former TXU customers it had acquired. In the event Powergen re-instated 650 MW of capacity at Grain in the autumn of 2003 and made available part of Killingholme's 600 MW capacity for winter 2003/04. International power also re-instated 250 MW at Deeside for winter 2003/04, and RWE Innogy leased Fifoots Point power station from its administrators to operate over the winter.

In May 2003, Centrica completed the acquisition of Lakeland Power's Roosecote Power Station (229 MW), which had suspended operations in November 2002. Centrica also purchased Barry Power station (250 MW) from AES in July. Scottish and Southern Energy bought the distribution network operator, Midland Electricity from Aquila Networks in July and also acquired 100 per cent of Medway power station (688 MW) in October

Nuclear

At the end of March 2003 BNFL's Calder Hall nuclear power station closed.

An agreement was signed in June allowing UK companies to start nuclear clean-up work to start in North West Russia.

British Energy announced on 1 October that it had formally agreed with creditors the terms of its proposed restructuring announced on 28 November 2002. The company requested the increase in its Government loan because the costs of unplanned outages and increases in the required levels of trading collateral, have had an adverse impact on liquidity. In response the Secretary of State announced a temporary increase in the credit facility available to British Energy from £200m to £275m which would revert to £200m by 22 February 2004 at the latest.

During 2003 HMG and BNFL conducted a joint strategy review of the company. The review conclusions were announced in a written statement to the House of Commons on 11 December 2003. One of the key conclusions of the review was that a new BNFL parent company would be established in April 2005, the principal focus of which will be clean-up activities at UK sites. At the same time, a new group of subsidiary companies will be established which will have initial responsibility for managing clean-up and operations at BNFL's UK sites under transitional arrangements to be agreed with the Nuclear Decommissioning Authority (NDA).

On 24 June 2003, the DTI published the draft Nuclear Sites and Radioactive Substances Bill. The draft Bill set out provisions to establish the Nuclear Decommissioning Authority (NDA), as foreshadowed in the July 2002 White Paper, *Managing the Nuclear Legacy: A strategy for action*. The draft Bill was subject to a period of public consultation which ended on 1 September 2003. Revised provisions to establish the NDA were included in the Energy Bill, which was introduced to the House of Lords on 27 November.

Renewables

Two rounds of Offshore Licensing took place in 2003, which brought forwards a large number of proposals. Capital grants of £59 million were given to six of the first round offshore wind projects, with a total capacity of around 530 MW. The awards made in the second Round, which cover15 wind farm projects, will provide enough electricity for more than one in six households (4 million homes). The projects are in three strategic areas (Thames Estuary, Greater Wash and North West) with generation due to begin 2007-08. North Hoyle – the UK's first major offshore windfarm – began generating electricity. £10m of DTI capital grants has supported the project, which is due to be completed early next year. The 30 turbines will provide renewable energy for up to 50,000 homes.

2002

Climate Change levy

In the Chancellor's 2002 Budget statement he strengthened the existing policy to support business energy efficiency by announcing proposals to:

- Freeze the climate change levy rates;

- Give complete exemption from the climate change levy to electricity generated by good quality combined heat and power (CHP) or from coalmine methane. Implementations of these exemptions are subject to EU state aids approval;
- Add heat pumps, radiant, warm air and solar heaters, energy-efficient refrigeration equipment and compressor equipment to the list of energy-saving technologies, which can benefit from enhanced capital allowances against tax. This provision is also to be extended to equipment for leasing.

Emissions Trading Scheme

The Government's emissions trading scheme was launched on 2 April 2002. Thirty-four organisations successfully bid to join the scheme for permits in an auction for permits held on 11 –12 March 2002.

Energy Efficiency

The Energy Efficiency Commitment is an obligation (expressed as a total energy saving in TWh) placed by the Government on gas and electricity suppliers to encourage and assist their customers to make energy savings through measures such as cavity wall insulation, loft insulation, boiler replacement and energy saving light bulbs. Suppliers make a contribution to the cost of the measure at a level that will induce the customer to take it up.

The scheme, began on 1 April, and will run from 2002 to 2005. The overall target on all suppliers has been set at a level that is expected to lead to estimated ongoing annual energy savings for consumers of around £275 million by 2005, as well as annual reductions in carbon emissions of around 0.4 million tonnes by 2005. It is estimated that the scheme will cost energy suppliers around £3.60 per customer, per fuel, each year. The scheme focuses help on the fuel poor and companies will be required to seek at least 50 per cent of their target fuel savings from disadvantaged customers.

Fuel Poverty

The Fuel Poverty Advisory Group, which had been announced in the November 2001 UK Fuel Poverty Strategy, met for the first time in March 2002. The Group is an Advisory Non-Departmental Public Body sponsored by DEFRA/DTI. Its primary task is to report on the progress of delivery of the Government's Fuel Poverty Strategy and to propose and implement improvements to regional or local mechanisms for its delivery.

The Group consist of a chairman and senior representatives from organisations such as the energy industry, charities and consumer bodies. These members would be representative ex officio members rather than individuals, who should be able to take a broad and impartial view.

In March 2002, the Department for Transport, Local Government and the Regions published revised guidance on the decent home standard and how social landlords can quantify the extent of non-decent housing within their stock to help them better deal with the problem. A decent home is one that meets the following criteria:

- is above the current statutory minimum standard for housing;
- is in a reasonable state of repair;
- has reasonably modern facilities and services;
- provides a reasonable degree of thermal comfort.

The Scottish Executive issued its draft Fuel Poverty Statement in March 2002, inviting comments on the way the Executive plans to tackle fuel poverty in Scotland.

Again in March, Ofgem published its second annual report on its Social Action Plan setting out progress towards Ofgem's aim to ensure competition benefits all customers and to develop polices to help the fuel poor.

Coal

Longannet colliery owned by the Scottish Coal Company Ltd ceased operation and went into liquidation in March 2002. Price of Wales Colliery closed in August 2002.

Oil and Gas

PILOT "Progressing Partnership" Work Group was launched in March 2002. Within PILOT, the joint Government/Industry oil and gas task force, a new initiative for progressing partnership was born. Looking at common behavioural and supply chain barriers, the Group's aim was to address issues inhibiting recovery of Britain's oil and gas reserves. This led to a number of new initiatives, including getting "fallow" assets into the hands of those companies best placed to exploit them, and streamlining commercial agreements, to allow for swifter transfer of licence interests in offshore acreage. More information can be found at: www.og.dti.gov.uk or www.pilottaskforce.co.uk .

Gas and Electricity

In October, TXU Europe agreed to sell its UK assets, including 5.3 million electricity and gas customers and 2.9GW of capacity to Powergen for £1.37 billion. The sale made Powergen the second largest supplier of retail energy behind Centrica.

Electricity

London Electricity acquired the distribution business of Eastern Electricity and the distribution and retail businesses of Seeboard.

In March 2002 Fifoots Point coal fired power station owned by AES went into receivership followed by Lakeland Power's Roosecote station in November 2002 and Westfield's Fife Power in December 2002

Power stations mothballed during 2002 included: one unit at Deeside (International Power); one unit at Killingholme (Powergen); and two units at Grain (Powergen).

Nuclear Power: British Energy

Following a sudden deterioration in its financial situation, the private sector nuclear electricity generator, British Energy (BE) approached the Government in early September 2002 seeking immediate financial support and discussions about longer term restructuring. The company owns eight nuclear power stations and generates about 20 per cent of Britain's electricity. In accordance with the Government's overriding priorities of nuclear safety and the security of electricity supplies, it provided short-term financial support to, and entered into discussions with, BE.

BE announced a proposed restructuring plan on 28 November, and the Government is taking financial responsibility for BE's historic spent fuel liabilities, and underwriting new arrangements announced by the company to fund decommissioning and other nuclear liabilities.

Nuclear

Bradwell power station owned by BNFL Magnox ceased production after 40 years of service.

On 4 July 2002, the Government published proposals for radically altering existing arrangements for managing publicly-funded nuclear clean up in its White Paper, *Managing the Nuclear Legacy: A strategy for action*. The cornerstone of the new policy involved the establishment of a Nuclear Decommissioning Authority (NDA) to ensure the safe, secure, cost-effective and environmentally friendly decommissioning and clean up of the twenty nuclear sites currently operated by BNFL and UKAEA. To this end, it will develop a UK-wide strategy for dealing with the nuclear 'legacy'. Public consultation on the White Paper ended on 14 October. Detailed provisions to establish the NDA were later published in the draft Nuclear Sites and Radioactive Substances Bill on 24 June 2003.

CHP

In the 2002 Budget it was announced that all CHP generated electricity would be exempt from the Climate Change Levy (CCL). This is a key measure that is likely to help set the sector on course to meet the Government's target of at least 10,000MWe of CHP capacity by 2010. Previously, only CHP electricity used on site or sold direct to other users had qualified for CCL exemption. In addition leased assets became be eligible for Enhanced Capital Allowances (ECAs).

In May 2002, Defra published for consultation the draft CHP Strategy that describes the full range of measures thought sufficient to for the Government's target of at least 10,000 MWe of Good Quality CHP to be met by 2010. It included market incentives, guidance and information, financial assistance and legislative action to support growth of the CHP industry. The consultation ran between 15 May and 7 August. A summary document was published on the Defra website in November. The final Strategy will be published in 2003.

Micro CHP

In the 2002 Budget it was announced that domestic micro CHP installed under the Warm Front Team will attract the reduced rate of VAT. Micro CHP is a new technology that we expect to make a significant contribution to domestic energy efficiency in the future. Reducing VAT on the cost of installation will help to give this new technology a useful kick-start.

Renewables

On 1 April 2002, the Government introduced an obligation on all licensed electricity suppliers that required them to supply a specified proportion of their electricity from eligible renewable sources. That proportion will rise in stages from 3 per cent in the 2002 year to 10 per cent by 2010.

During the year the first two offshore windfarms were approved and construction began at Scroby Sands and North Hoyle.

For major events in earlier years see the DTI web site version of this annex at:
www.dti.gov.uk/energy/inform/dukes2004/04annexd.pdf